3/18

Understanding Multivariable Calculus:
Problems, Solutions, and Tips

Bruce H. Edwards, Ph.D.

THE
GREAT
COURSES®

PUBLISHED BY:

THE GREAT COURSES
Corporate Headquarters
4840 Westfields Boulevard, Suite 500
Chantilly, Virginia 20151-2299
Phone: 1-800-832-2412
Fax: 703-378-3819
www.thegreatcourses.com

MIX
Paper from
responsible sources
FSC® C011935

FSC
www.fsc.org

Bruce H. Edwards, Ph.D.

Professor of Mathematics
University of Florida

Professor Bruce H. Edwards has been a Professor of Mathematics at the University of Florida since 1976. He received his B.S. in Mathematics from Stanford University in 1968 and his Ph.D. in Mathematics from Dartmouth College in 1976. From 1968 to 1972, he was a Peace Corps volunteer in Colombia, where he taught mathematics (in Spanish) at Universidad Pedagógica y Tecnológica de Colombia.

Professor Edwards's early research interests were in the broad area of pure mathematics called algebra. His dissertation in quadratic forms was titled "Induction Techniques and Periodicity in Clifford Algebras." Beginning in 1978, Professor Edwards became interested in applied mathematics while working summers for NASA at the Langley Research Center in Virginia. This work led to his research in numerical analysis and the solution of differential equations. During his sabbatical year, 1984 to 1985, he worked on two-point boundary value problems with Professor Leo Xanthis at the Polytechnic of Central London. Professor Edwards's current research is focused on the algorithm called CORDIC that is used in computers and graphing calculators for calculating function values.

Professor Edwards has coauthored a number of mathematics textbooks with Professor Ron Larson of Penn State Erie, The Behrend College. Together, they have published leading texts in calculus, applied calculus, linear algebra, finite mathematics, algebra, trigonometry, and precalculus.

Over the years, Professor Edwards has received many teaching awards at the University of Florida. He was named Teacher of the Year in the College of Liberal Arts and Sciences in 1979, 1981, and 1990. In addition, he was named the College of Liberal Arts and Sciences Student Council Teacher of the Year and the University of Florida Honors Program Teacher of the Year in 1990. He also served as the Distinguished Alumni Professor for the UF Alumni Association from 1991 to 1993. The winners of this two-year award are selected by graduates of the university. The Florida Section of the Mathematical Association of America awarded Professor Edwards the Distinguished Service Award in 1995 for his work in mathematics education for the state of Florida. His textbooks have been honored with various awards from the Text and Academic Authors Association.

Professor Edwards has taught a wide range of mathematics courses at the University of Florida, from first-year calculus to graduate-level classes in algebra and numerical analysis. He particularly enjoys teaching calculus to freshmen because of the beauty of the subject and the enthusiasm of the students.

Professor Edwards has been a frequent speaker at both research conferences and meetings of the National Council of Teachers of Mathematics. He has spoken on issues relating to the Advanced Placement calculus examination, especially on the use of graphing calculators.

Professor Edwards has taught four other Great Courses:

- *Mathematics Describing the Real World: Precalculus and Trigonometry*;

- *Understanding Calculus: Problems, Solutions, and Tips*;

- *Understanding Calculus II: Problems, Solutions, and Tips*; and

- *Prove It: The Art of Mathematical Argument.* ∎

Table of Contents

INTRODUCTION

Professor Biography i
Course Scope 1

LESSON GUIDES

LESSON 1
A Visual Introduction to 3-D Calculus 3

LESSON 2
Functions of Several Variables 7

LESSON 3
Limits, Continuity, and Partial Derivatives 11

LESSON 4
Partial Derivatives—One Variable at a Time 15

LESSON 5
Total Differentials and Chain Rules 19

LESSON 6
Extrema of Functions of Two Variables 22

LESSON 7
Applications to Optimization Problems 26

LESSON 8
Linear Models and Least Squares Regression 29

LESSON 9
Vectors and the Dot Product in Space 32

LESSON 10
The Cross Product of Two Vectors in Space 36

LESSON 11
Lines and Planes in Space 40

LESSON 12
Curved Surfaces in Space 44

LESSON 13
Vector-Valued Functions in Space 48

LESSON 14
Kepler's Laws—The Calculus of Orbits 52

LESSON 15
Directional Derivatives and Gradients 55

Table of Contents

LESSON 16
Tangent Planes and Normal Vectors to a Surface..58

LESSON 17
Lagrange Multipliers—Constrained Optimization 61

LESSON 18
Applications of Lagrange Multipliers..64

LESSON 19
Iterated Integrals and Area in the Plane 67

LESSON 20
Double Integrals and Volume 71

LESSON 21
Double Integrals in Polar Coordinates..75

LESSON 22
Centers of Mass for Variable Density 79

LESSON 23
Surface Area of a Solid...83

LESSON 24
Triple Integrals and Applications...87

LESSON 25
Triple Integrals in Cylindrical Coordinates 91

LESSON 26
Triple Integrals in Spherical Coordinates..95

LESSON 27
Vector Fields—Velocity, Gravity, Electricity 99

LESSON 28
Curl, Divergence, Line Integrals 104

LESSON 29
More Line Integrals and Work by a Force Field... 108

LESSON 30
Fundamental Theorem of Line Integrals..112

LESSON 31
Green's Theorem—Boundaries and Regions...117

LESSON 32
Applications of Green's Theorem 122

LESSON 33
Parametric Surfaces in Space.. 126

Table of Contents

LESSON 34
Surface Integrals and Flux Integrals... 130

LESSON 35
Divergence Theorem—Boundaries and Solids 136

LESSON 36
Stokes's Theorem and Maxwell's Equations 140

SUPPLEMENTAL MATERIAL

Solutions.. 144
Glossary 193
Summary of Differentiation Formulas... 214
Summary of Integration Formulas 216
Quadric Surfaces... 218
Bibliography.. 221

Understanding Multivariable Calculus: Problems, Solutions, and Tips

Scope:

The goal of this course is to complete your understanding and appreciation of calculus by seeing how calculus is extended to three dimensions. Many of the ideas of elementary calculus in the plane generalize naturally to space, whereas other concepts will be brand new. Most concepts will be introduced using illustrative examples, and you will see how multivariable calculus plays a fundamental role in all of science and engineering. You will also gain a new appreciation for the achievements of higher mathematics.

You will begin by seeing how functions of a single variable are generalized to functions of two (or more) variables. In particular, the graphs of such functions are surfaces in space. After a brief look at limits, you will generalize elementary derivatives to partial derivatives. You will learn how to generalize the differential to total differentials, work with a more general chain rule, and find extrema for functions of more than one variable. This leads to optimization applications and linear modeling of data.

You will then study vectors in space, a natural extension of vectors in the plane. Lines and planes are studied in depth, as well as other surfaces in space. You will use vector-valued functions to understand Kepler's laws and prove one of them using calculus.

Your study then takes you to the world of multivariable integration, which is far more powerful than its single-variable counterpart. You will see how to define and use double and triple integrals, which have applications to volume, surface area, mass, and far more. You will study additional kinds of integrals that become possible in space: line integrals and surface integrals (including integrals for flux through a surface), defined using vector fields.

One of the recurring themes throughout these lessons is the fundamental theorem of calculus. Recall from elementary calculus how the fundamental theorem relates integration and differentiation:

$$\int_a^b F'(x)\,dx = F(b) - F(a).$$

This theorem will appear in other forms in multivariable calculus, including in the famous fundamental theorem of line integrals, which allows you to integrate over a piecewise smooth curve to make sense of such topics as gravitation and conservation of energy.

Line integrals (which can be used with any curvy line and might therefore be better called "curve integrals") combine with double, triple, and surface integrals to form three of the crowning theorems in all of calculus, each of which generalizes the ability of the fundamental theorem of calculus to extract maximum information from relatively limited inputs, in far more powerful ways. These are Green's theorem (which relates the double integral of a region to a line integral around the corresponding boundary), the divergence theorem (which relates the triple integral of a solid to the surface integral over the surface of that solid), and Stokes's theorem (which relates the surface integral over a surface to the line integral over the boundary of a surface). Stokes was a colleague and friend of James Clerk Maxwell at Cambridge University, and the course concludes by touching on mathematical connections between our capstone generalizations of the fundamental theorem of calculus and Maxwell's famous equations of electromagnetism.

This course presents essentially the same topics as a typical university-level, third-semester calculus course. The material is based on the 10th edition of the bestselling textbook *Calculus* by Ron Larson and Bruce H. Edwards (Brooks/Cole, 2014). However, any standard calculus textbook can be used for reference and support throughout the course.

The study of multivariable calculus has surprisingly few prerequisites. For a high school student who has completed the equivalent of the Advanced Placement Calculus AB and Calculus BC courses, this course is a very logical next step. And although some university programs teach multivariable calculus only after linear algebra and/or differential equations, no such preparation is assumed or needed for this course. Indeed, a good grasp of precalculus and first-semester calculus is often the only essential preparation.

That's because calculus II and multivariable calculus start from a shared foundation but proceed in substantially different directions. For example, while *Understanding Calculus II: Problems, Solutions, and Tips*, a natural predecessor for this course, does introduce some topics in preparation for multivariable calculus—conics, vectors, parametric equations, polar coordinates, and vector-valued functions—the bulk of that course is concerned with topics such as infinite series that are important for higher forms of mathematical analysis but are not featured in multivariable calculus. Moreover, in this course, any preparatory topics from calculus II are briefly reintroduced—but in terms of three dimensions—making the two courses even more distinct and self-contained.

Graphing calculators and computers are playing an increasing role in the mathematics classroom. Without a doubt, graphing technology can enhance the understanding of calculus, so some instances where graphing calculators are used to verify and confirm calculus results have been included. For the video lessons, many of the graphs of surfaces were produced using *Mathematica* software—a more limited online version of which can even be explored on your own, at little or no cost, using the website Wolfram|Alpha (www.wolframalpha.com).

By the end of this course, you will have covered all the important theoretical ideas and theorems of a three-semester university calculus sequence, without dwelling on their technical proofs. You will be prepared for courses in engineering, physics, and other subjects that use calculus.

Students are encouraged to use all course materials to their maximum benefit, including the video lessons, which you can review as many times as you wish; the individual lesson summaries and accompanying problems in the workbook; and the supporting materials in the back of the workbook, including the solutions to all problems and various review items. ■

A Visual Introduction to 3-D Calculus
Lesson 1

Topics

- Introduction to multivariable calculus.

- Generalizing elementary calculus to three dimensions.

- The three-dimensional coordinate system.

- Distance and midpoint formulas.

- Introduction to functions of two variables.

Definitions and Theorems

- In the **three-dimensional coordinate system**, points are represented by ordered triples, (x, y, z). For example, the origin is $(0, 0, 0)$.

- The **distance** between the points (x_1, y_1, z_1) and (x_2, y_2, z_2) is given by the formula

$$d = \sqrt{(x_2 - x_1)^2 + (y_2 - y_1)^2 + (z_2 - z_1)^2}.$$

- A **sphere** with center (x_0, y_0, z_0) and radius r is the set of all points (x, y, z) such that the distance between (x, y, z) and (x_0, y_0, z_0) is r. That is,

$$d = \sqrt{(x - x_0)^2 + (y - y_0)^2 + (z - z_0)^2} = r.$$

This simplifies to the equation of a sphere, $(x - x_0)^2 + (y - y_0)^2 + (z - z_0)^2 = r^2$.

- The **midpoint** between the points (x_1, y_1, z_1) and (x_2, y_2, z_2) is given by the formula

$$\left(\frac{x_1 + x_2}{2}, \frac{y_1 + y_2}{2}, \frac{z_1 + z_2}{2} \right).$$

- If $z = f(x, y)$ is a **function of two variables**, then x and y are called the **independent** variables, and z is the **dependent** variable.

Summary

Welcome to *Understanding Multivariable Calculus: Problems, Solution, and Tips*. In our first lesson, we show how many of the fundamental ideas of elementary calculus can be extended to multivariable calculus. That is, we look at how calculus in the two-dimensional plane is generalized to three-dimensional space. After these introductory remarks, we develop the three-dimensional coordinate system as well as the distance and midpoint formulas. We end the lesson with a brief look at functions of two variables.

Elementary Calculus Compared to Multivariable Calculus

In these lessons, we will see how elementary calculus, the calculus of two dimensions, can be extended to multivariable calculus, the calculus of three dimensions, or space. Let's briefly note some of the ideas we will develop.

You know about the xy–coordinate system, in which points are represented by ordered pairs, (x, y). You will learn how to represent points in space as ordered triples, (x, y, z).

You know about functions of a single variable, such as $f(x) = \sin x$. You will learn about functions of two (or more) variables, $z = f(x, y)$, such as $z = x^2 + y^2$.

You know about the graph of a function of a single variable (see **Figure 1.1**). You will learn to graph functions of two variables in space (see **Figure 1.2**).

You know about derivatives of functions of a single variable, such as the derivative $\frac{d}{dx}[\sin x] = \cos x$. You will learn about partial derivatives of functions of two or more variables, $\frac{\partial f}{\partial x}$, $\frac{\partial f}{\partial y}$.

You know about integrals in elementary calculus, $\int f(x)\,dx$ and $\int_a^b f(x)\,dx$. You will learn about double integrals, $\int_a^b \int_c^d f(x, y)\,dy\,dx$; triple integrals; line integrals; and more.

You know about the fundamental theorem of calculus: If F is an antiderivative of f, then $\int_a^b f(x)\,dx = F(b) - F(a)$. You will learn about many generalizations of this theorem, including Green's theorem, the divergence theorem, and Stokes's theorem.

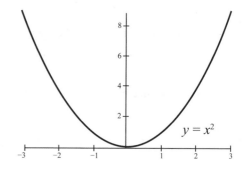

$y = x^2$

Figure 1.1

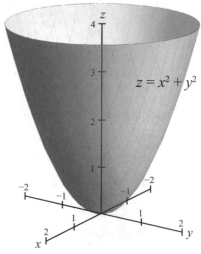

$z = x^2 + y^2$

Figure 1.2

You know about vectors in the plane, $\mathbf{v} = \langle v_1, v_2 \rangle$. You will learn about vectors in space, $\mathbf{v} = \langle v_1, v_2, v_3 \rangle$.

You know about vector-valued functions in the plane, such as $\mathbf{r}(t) = \cos t \mathbf{i} + \sin t \mathbf{j}$. You will learn about vector-valued functions in space, such as the helix given by $\mathbf{r}(t) = \cos t \mathbf{i} + \sin t \mathbf{j} + t \mathbf{k}$.

You know about finding maximum and minimum values of functions in elementary calculus. You will learn more advanced optimization techniques for functions of two variables.

Example 1

Find the distance between the points $(2, -1, 3)$ and $(1, 0, -2)$.

Solution

Using the distance formula, we have

$$d = \sqrt{(1-2)^2 + (0+1)^2 + (-2-3)^2} = \sqrt{1+1+25} = \sqrt{27} = 3\sqrt{3}.$$

Example 2

Find the equation of the sphere having $(4, -2, 3)$ and $(0, 4, -3)$ as endpoints of a diameter.

Solution

The center of the sphere is the midpoint, $\left(\dfrac{4+0}{2}, \dfrac{-2+4}{2}, \dfrac{3-3}{2} \right) = (2, 1, 0)$.

By the distance formula, the radius is

$$r = \sqrt{(0-2)^2 + (4-1)^2 + (-3-0)^2} = \sqrt{4+9+9} = \sqrt{22}.$$

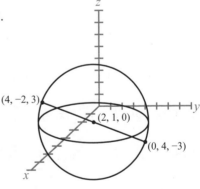

The equation of the sphere is $(x-2)^2 + (y-1)^2 + (z-0)^2 = \left(\sqrt{22} \right)^2$, which simplifies to $(x-2)^2 + (y-1)^2 + z^2 = 22$. (See **Figure 1.3**.)

Figure 1.3

Example 3

For the function of two variables $z = f(x, y) = x^2 + xy$, we have $f(0, 0) = 0$ and $f(2, 1) = 2^2 + 2(1) = 6$.

Study Tips

- We will use a right-handed coordinate system in space. That is, if the x-axis is your right hand and the y-axis is your left hand, then the z-axis points upward.

5

- The formulas for distance, midpoint, and sphere are immediate generalizations for the familiar formulas for distance, midpoint, and circle in elementary calculus.

- Given (x, y) in the domain of a function f of two variables, the value in the range is $z = f(x, y)$.

Pitfall

- Just as in elementary calculus, you cannot divide by zero or take square roots of negative numbers. For instance, if $f(x, y) = \sqrt{y} + \dfrac{1}{x + y}$, then $f(0, -2)$ and $f(3, -3)$ are undefined.

Problems

1. Calculate the derivative of the function $f(x) = \ln 2x + e^{3x}$.

2. Calculate the integral $\displaystyle\int_0^{\pi/2} \cos x\, dx$.

3. Determine the vector with initial point $P(1, 2)$ and terminal point $Q(-4, 0)$.

4. Eliminate the parameter to demonstrate that the graph of the vector-value function $\mathbf{r}(t) = 3\cos t\mathbf{i} + 3\sin t\mathbf{j}$ is a circle.

5. Find the critical numbers and relative extrema of the function $f(x) = 2x^3 + 3x^2 - 12x$.

6. Find the distance between the points $(1, -2, 4)$ and $(6, -2, -2)$.

7. Find the midpoint of the line segment joining the points $(4, 0, -6)$ and $(8, 8, 20)$.

8. Find the equation of the sphere with center $(0, 2, 5)$ and radius 2.

9. Calculate $f(1, 3)$ if $f(x, y) = \ln y + e^{x+y}$.

10. Calculate $g(\pi, 0)$ if $g(x, y) = 3\cos(x + y) - \sin(x - y)$.

Functions of Several Variables
Lesson 2

Topics

- Functions of two or more independent variables.

- Graphs of functions of two variables.

- Traces.

- Level curves and level surfaces.

- Applications of functions of two variables.

Definitions and Theorems

- Let D be a set of ordered pairs of real numbers. If to each ordered pair (x, y) in D there corresponds a unique real number $z = f(x, y)$, then f is called a **function of** x and y. The set D is the **domain** of f, and the corresponding set of values $f(x, y)$ is the **range** of f.

- The **graph** of a function of two variables $z = f(x, y)$ consists of all points (x, y, z) such that $z = f(x, y)$.

- A **trace** is the intersection of a surface with a plane.

- Let $z = f(x, y)$ and c be a constant. A **level curve** or **contour line** is the set of all points in the plane satisfying $f(x, y) = c$.

Summary

In this lesson, we continue our study of functions of two or more independent variables. We will formally define functions of two variables, including their domains and ranges. We will see that it is easy to combine such functions and also extend these ideas to functions of three or more variables. Perhaps the most important and interesting theme of this lesson is the graph of a function of two variables. To this end, we look at traces and level curves for functions of two variables. Typical applications of level curves are topographic maps. Finally, we will set up an application involving the minimal cost of construction of a box.

Example 1

Find the domain of the function $f(x, y) = \sqrt{4 - x^2 - y^2}$.

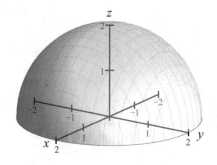

Figure 2.1

Solution

The expression inside the radical must be nonnegative, so the domain consists of all ordered pairs satisfying $4 - x^2 - y^2 \geq 0$.

So, we have $D = \{(x, y) : x^2 + y^2 \leq 4\}$.

The domain is a circle of radius 2. Notice that the graph of the function is a hemisphere of radius 2 centered at the origin, $x^2 + y^2 + z^2 = 4$, $0 \leq z \leq 2$. (See **Figure 2.1**.)

Example 2

Find the largest possible value of the function of two variables
$z = f(x, y) = 2x + 4y - x^2 - y^2$.

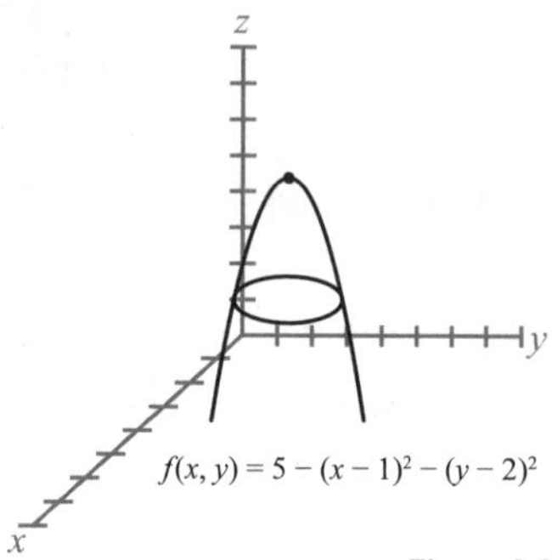

Solution

By completing the square, we see that $z = f(x, y) = 5 - (x - 1)^2 - (y - 2)^2$.

$$f(x, y) = 5 - (x - 1)^2 - (y - 2)^2$$

Figure 2.2

Therefore, the largest possible value is 5, which is obtained when $x = 1$ and $y = 2$. Notice that there is no smallest value. (See **Figure 2.2**.)

Example 3

Let $f(x, y) = \sqrt{16 - 4x^2 - y^2}$. Describe the level curve for $c = 0$. (See **Figure 2.3**.)

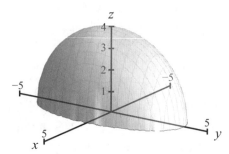

Figure 2.3

Solution

Setting $f(x, y) = c$, we have $\sqrt{16 - 4x^2 - y^2} = 0$.

This simplifies to the ellipse $16 - 4x^2 - y^2 = 0 \Rightarrow \dfrac{x^2}{4} + \dfrac{y^2}{16} = 1$.

In the figure (see **Figure 2.4**), we have drawn this ellipse, along with some other level curves.

Example 4

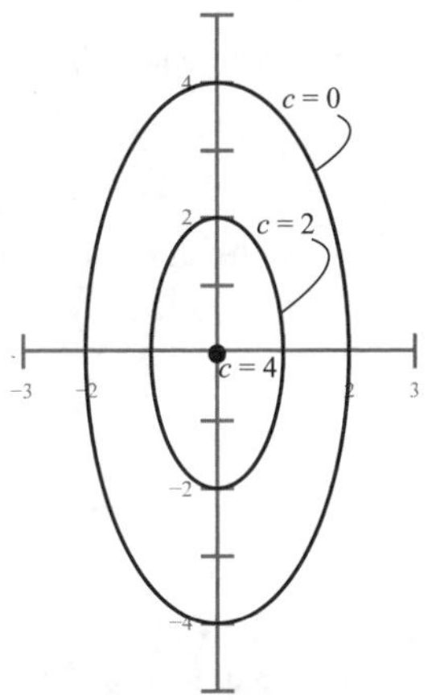

A rectangular box with an open top has a length of x feet, a width of y feet, and a height of z feet (see **Figure 2.5**). It costs \$3 per square foot to build the base and \$2 per square foot to build the sides. Write the cost C of constructing the box as a function of x, y, and z.

Solution

The cost depends on the cost of the base and the four sides.

$$C = 3.00xy + 2(2.00yz) + 2(2.00)(xz) = 3xy + 4yz + 4xz.$$

Later in this course, we will determine the minimum cost of the box, given a fixed volume.

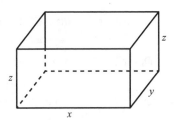

Figure 2.4

Study Tips

- If $z = f(x, y)$, then x and y are called the **independent** variables, and z is the **dependent** variable.

Figure 2.5

- In general, the range of a function of two variables is more difficult to determine than the domain. Often, a graph can help determine the range.

- You can define functions of three or more variables in a similar manner. For example, $f(x, y, z) = x^2 - y^2 + \sin z$ is a function of three variables.

- You can add, subtract, and multiply functions of two or more variables. For example, if $f(x, y) = 2xy^2$ and $g(x, y) = \sin(xy)$, then the sum of the two functions is $(f + g)(x, y) = f(x, y) + g(x, y) = 2xy^2 + \sin(xy)$.

- Level curves extend naturally to level surfaces. For example, consider the function of three variables, $f(x, y, z) = 4x^2 + y^2 + z^2$. Each level surface is of the form $4x^2 + y^2 + z^2 = c$, which are ellipsoids.

- You will often see different letters used for the independent and dependent variables, as well as the names of the functions.

Pitfalls

- You cannot form the composition of two functions, each of two variables. However, if g is a function of a single variable and f is a function of two variables, then the following composition makes sense: $(g \circ f)(x, y) = g(f(x, y))$.

9

- Make sure you understand if you are working in the plane or in space. For example, the graph of the equation $y = x$ is a line in the plane, but a plane in space.

- The graph of a function of two variables is a surface in space, whereas its level curves are graphs in the xy-plane.

- Keep in mind that for a surface in space, its level curves lie in the xy-plane. On the other hand, a trace is the intersection of the surface with a plane.

Problems

1. Calculate $f(0, 5, 4)$ if $f(x, y, z) = \sqrt{x + y + z}$.

2. Describe the domain of the function $f(x, y) = \dfrac{x + y}{xy}$.

3. Describe the domain of the function $f(x, y) = \ln(4 - x - y)$.

4. Describe the graph of the function $f(x, y) = 4$.

5. Describe the graph of the function $f(x, y) = \sqrt{1 - x^2 - y^2}$.

6. Describe the level curves of the function $f(x, y) = 6 - 2x - 3y$ for $c = 0, 2, 4$.

7. Describe the level curves of the function $f(x, y) = xy$ for $c = \pm 1, \pm 3$.

8. Describe the level surface of the function $f(x, y, z) = x^2 + y^2 + z^2$ at $c = 9$.

9. Complete the square for the function $z = f(x, y) = 2x + 4y - x^2 - y^2$ to confirm that the largest value of the function is $z = 5$.

10. A propane tank is constructed by welding hemispheres to the ends of a right circular cylinder. Write the volume of the tank as a function of r and x, where r is the radius of the cylinder and hemispheres and x is the length of the cylinder.

Limits, Continuity, and Partial Derivatives
Lesson 3

Topics

- Limits of functions of two variables.

- Disks in the plane.

- The formal definition of limit.

- Continuity of functions of two variables.

- Partial derivatives.

Definitions and Theorems

- Let (x_0, y_0) be a point in the plane.

  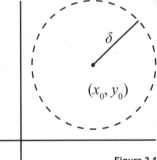

  Figure 3.1

  The open disk centered at (x_0, y_0) with radius δ is the set of points $\left\{ (x, y) : \sqrt{(x - x_0)^2 + (y - y_0)^2} < \delta \right\}$. (See **Figure 3.1**.)

- Let f be a function of two variables defined, except possibly at (x_0, y_0), on an open disk centered at (x_0, y_0), and let L be a real number.

  Then,

  $$\lim_{(x,y)\to(x_0,y_0)} f(x, y) = L$$

  if, for every $\varepsilon > 0$, there exists $\delta > 0$ such that

  $$\left| f(x, y) - L \right| < \varepsilon \text{ whenever } 0 < \sqrt{(x - x_0)^2 + (y - y_0)^2} < \delta.$$

- A function of two variables is **continuous** at a point (x_0, y_0) if $f(x_0, y_0)$ is defined and $\lim_{(x,y)\to(x_0,y_0)} f(x, y) = f(x_0, y_0)$.

- Definition of partial derivatives:

$$\frac{\partial f}{\partial x} = f_x(x,y) = \lim_{\Delta x \to 0} \frac{f(x+\Delta x, y) - f(x,y)}{\Delta x}.$$

$$\frac{\partial f}{\partial y} = f_y(x,y) = \lim_{\Delta y \to 0} \frac{f(x, y+\Delta y) - f(x,y)}{\Delta y}.$$

Summary

In this lesson, we continue to study the fundamental concepts of limits and continuity for functions of two variables. We will see that limits in multivariable calculus are more complicated, but we won't dwell on the theoretical aspects. We then present partial derivatives, the generalization of derivatives from elementary calculus. We will learn how to calculate partial derivatives and discover their geometric significance.

Example 1

Calculate the limit $\displaystyle\lim_{(x,y) \to (1,2)} \frac{5x^2 y}{x^2 + y^2}$.

Solution

The limit is easy to evaluate: $\displaystyle\lim_{(x,y) \to (1,2)} \frac{5x^2 y}{x^2 + y^2} = \frac{5(1)^2 2}{1^2 + 2^2} = \frac{10}{5} = 2.$

We were able to just plug in the point $(1, 2)$ in this example. The next example is more interesting.

Example 2

Show that the limit $\displaystyle\lim_{(x,y) \to (0,0)} \left(\frac{x^2 - y^2}{x^2 + y^2} \right)^2$ does not exist.

Solution

We approach the point $(0, 0)$ along two different paths.

Along the path $y = 0$, $\displaystyle\lim_{(x,0) \to (0,0)} \left(\frac{x^2 - 0^2}{x^2 + 0^2} \right)^2 = 1$. And along the path $y = x$, $\displaystyle\lim_{(x,x) \to (0,0)} \left(\frac{x^2 - x^2}{x^2 + x^2} \right)^2 = 0.$

Because these values do not agree, the limit does not exist.

Example 3

Calculate the partial derivatives of the function $f(x,y) = x^3 + \sin y$.

Solution

We calculate the partial derivative with respect to x by holding the variable y constant and differentiating with respect to x: $\frac{\partial f}{\partial x} = 3x^2$.

Similarly, the partial derivative with respect to y is calculated by holding the variable x constant: $\frac{\partial f}{\partial y} = \cos y$.

Study Tips

- Open disks are circles without boundaries. Closed disks contain the boundary.

- In elementary calculus, you can approach the point c in only two directions—from the left and from the right. The key difference in multivariable calculus is that you can approach the point (x_0, y_0) from any direction and along any path.

- You can define limits and continuity of functions of three or more variables in a similar manner.

- The definition of continuity is similar to that in elementary calculus: The function is continuous at a point if it is defined at the point, its limit exists at the point, and the limit equals the value of the function.

- Partial derivatives are rates of change with respect to one of the independent variables.

Pitfalls

- In Example 2, you cannot just plug in the value $(0, 0)$. Always be on the lookout for division by zero. In fact, there is a nonremovable discontinuity at this point.

- There are lots of notations for partial derivatives. For instance, if $z = f(x, y)$, then the partial derivative with respect to x might be written as

$$f_x(x, y) = \frac{\partial f}{\partial x} = \frac{\partial}{\partial x} f(x, y) = \frac{\partial z}{\partial x} = z_x.$$

Problems

1. Find the limit $\lim\limits_{(x, y) \to (2, 1)} \left(2x^2 + y\right)$.

2. Find the limit $\lim\limits_{(x, y) \to (1, 2)} e^{xy}$.

3. Find the limit $\lim\limits_{(x, y) \to (1, 1)} \frac{xy - 1}{1 + xy}$.

4. Discuss the continuity of the function $f(x, y) = \dfrac{y}{x^2 + y^2}$.

5. Discuss the continuity of the function $f(x, y) = \dfrac{1}{x^2 + y^2 - 4}$.

6. Show that the limit $\displaystyle\lim_{(x,y)\to(0,0)} \dfrac{xy}{x^2 + y^2}$ does not exist.

7. Show that the limit $\displaystyle\lim_{(x,y)\to(0,0)} \dfrac{-xy^2}{x^2 + y^4}$ does not exist.

8. Calculate the partial derivatives $\dfrac{\partial f}{\partial x}$ and $\dfrac{\partial f}{\partial y}$ for $f(x, y) = 2x - 5y + 3$.

9. Calculate the partial derivatives $\dfrac{\partial f}{\partial x}$ and $\dfrac{\partial f}{\partial y}$ for $f(x, y) = x\sqrt{y}$.

10. Calculate the partial derivatives $\dfrac{\partial f}{\partial x}$ and $\dfrac{\partial f}{\partial y}$ for $f(x, y) = \cos xy$.

Partial Derivatives—One Variable at a Time
Lesson 4

Topics

- Partial derivatives of functions of two variables.

- The geometric interpretation of partial derivatives.

- Partial derivatives of functions of three or more variables.

- Higher-order partial derivatives.

- Equality of mixed partial derivatives.

- Partial differential equations and Laplace's equation.

Definitions and Theorems

- Definition of partial derivatives:

$$\frac{\partial f}{\partial x} = f_x(x,y) = \lim_{\Delta x \to 0} \frac{f(x+\Delta x, y) - f(x,y)}{\Delta x}.$$

$$\frac{\partial f}{\partial y} = f_y(x,y) = \lim_{\Delta y \to 0} \frac{f(x, y+\Delta y) - f(x,y)}{\Delta y}.$$

- Higher-order partial derivatives:

$$\frac{\partial}{\partial x}\left(\frac{\partial f}{\partial x}\right) = \frac{\partial^2 f}{\partial x^2} = f_{xx}; \quad \frac{\partial}{\partial y}\left(\frac{\partial f}{\partial y}\right) = \frac{\partial^2 f}{\partial y^2} = f_{yy}.$$

$$\frac{\partial}{\partial y}\left(\frac{\partial f}{\partial x}\right) = \frac{\partial^2 f}{\partial y \partial x} = f_{xy}; \quad \frac{\partial}{\partial x}\left(\frac{\partial f}{\partial y}\right) = \frac{\partial^2 f}{\partial x \partial y} = f_{yx}.$$

- Laplace's partial differential equation: $\frac{\partial^2 z}{\partial x^2} + \frac{\partial^2 z}{\partial y^2} = 0$. A function that satisfies this equation is said to be **harmonic**.

Summary

In this lesson, we continue our study of partial derivatives. After reviewing how to calculate partial derivatives, we recall their geometric significance as rates of change. We then turn to higher-order partial derivatives and observe a surprising property of so-called mixed partial derivatives. Finally, we generalize differential equations to partial differential equations and look at Laplace's equation as an example.

Example 1

Find the first partial derivatives of the function $z = f(x, y) = x^3 + y^4 + \sin xy$.

Solution

The partial derivative with respect to x is $\dfrac{\partial z}{\partial x} = \dfrac{\partial f}{\partial x} = 3x^2 + \cos(xy)y$, and the partial derivative with respect to y is $\dfrac{\partial z}{\partial y} = \dfrac{\partial f}{\partial y} = 4y^3 + \cos(xy)x$.

Example 2

Find the slopes in the x-direction and in the y-direction of the surface given by the function $f(x, y) = 1 - (x - 1)^2 - (y - 2)^2$ at the point $(1, 2, 1)$.

Solution

The partial derivative with respect to x is
$f_x(x, y) = -2(x - 1)$ and $f_x(1, 2) = 0$.

The partial derivative with respect to y is
$f_y(x, y) = -2(y - 2)$ and $f_y(1, 2) = 0$.

Notice that the slopes are zero at the maximum point on the surface. Later, we will expand on the idea of using partial derivatives to find maximum and minimum values of functions. (See **Figure 4.1**.)

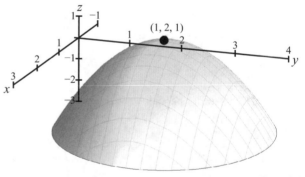

Figure 4.1

Example 3

Find $\dfrac{\partial f}{\partial x}$ for the function $f(x, y, z) = xy + yz^2 + xz$.

Solution

Calculating partial derivatives for functions of three or more variables is no different. We consider the variables y and z as constants and differentiate with respect to x: $\dfrac{\partial f}{\partial x} = y + z$.

Example 4

Calculate the four second-order partial derivatives for the function $f(x, y) = \sin x + e^y + xy$.

Solution

We begin by calculating the two first-order partial derivatives of the function: $\dfrac{\partial f}{\partial x} = \cos x + y$ and $\dfrac{\partial f}{\partial y} = e^y + x$.

The four second-order partial derivatives are obtained by differentiating the first partial derivatives.

$$f_{xx} = \frac{\partial}{\partial x}\left(\frac{\partial f}{\partial x}\right) = \frac{\partial}{\partial x}(\cos x + y) = -\sin x.$$

$$f_{yy} = \frac{\partial}{\partial y}\left(\frac{\partial f}{\partial y}\right) = \frac{\partial}{\partial y}(e^y + x) = e^y.$$

$$f_{yx} = \frac{\partial}{\partial x}\left(\frac{\partial f}{\partial y}\right) = \frac{\partial}{\partial x}(e^y + x) = 1.$$

$$f_{xy} = \frac{\partial}{\partial y}\left(\frac{\partial f}{\partial x}\right) = \frac{\partial}{\partial y}(\cos x + y) = 1.$$

Notice that the two mixed partial derivatives are equal. Under suitable hypotheses, this is always true for mixed partial derivatives.

Example 5

Show that $z = f(x, y) = e^x \sin y$ is a solution to Laplace's equation.

Solution

We have $\dfrac{\partial z}{\partial x} = e^x \sin y$, $\dfrac{\partial^2 z}{\partial x^2} = e^x \sin y$, $\dfrac{\partial z}{\partial y} = e^x \cos y$, and $\dfrac{\partial^2 z}{\partial y^2} = -e^x \sin y$.

Therefore, $\dfrac{\partial^2 z}{\partial x^2} + \dfrac{\partial^2 z}{\partial y^2} = e^x \sin y + \left(-e^x \sin y\right) = 0$.

Study Tips

- To calculate a partial derivative, hold one variable constant and differentiate with respect to the other variable.

- The partial derivative with respect to x is the slope of the graph in the x-direction. Similarly, the partial derivative with respect to y is the slope in the y-direction.

- Under suitable hypotheses, the mixed partial derivatives are equal: $f_{xy} = f_{yx}$.

Pitfalls

- The notation for partial derivatives can be confusing. Notice that for mixed second-order partials, you do the derivative "closest to f" first:

$$\frac{\partial}{\partial x}\left(\frac{\partial f}{\partial y}\right) = \frac{\partial^2 f}{\partial x \partial y} = \left(f_y\right)_x = f_{yx}.$$

- Although the mixed partial derivatives are equal for most common functions, there exist examples for which this is not true. For instance, they are not equal for the function

$$f(x,y) = \begin{cases} \dfrac{xy\left(x^2 - y^2\right)}{x^2 + y^2}, & (x,y) \neq (0,0) \\ 0, & (x,y) = (0,0) \end{cases}.$$

Problems

1. Find both first partial derivatives f_x and f_y for $f(x,y) = \sin 5x \cos 5y$.

2. Find both first partial derivatives f_x and f_y for $f(x,y) = ye^{y/x}$.

3. Find the slope of the surface $g(x,y) = 4 - x^2 - y^2$ in the x- and y-directions at the point $(1, 1, 2)$.

4. Find the first partial derivatives $f_x, f_y,$ and f_z for $f(x,y,z) = x^3yz^2$ at the point $(x, y, z) = (1, 1, 1)$.

5. Find the four second partial derivatives for the function $f(x,y) = x^2 - 2xy + 3y^2$.

6. Find the four second partial derivatives for the function $f(x,y) = e^x \tan y$.

7. For the function $f(x,y) = x^2 - xy + y^2 - 5x + y$, find all values of x and y such that $f_x(x,y) = 0$ and $f_y(x,y) = 0$.

8. For the function $f_x(x,y) = \dfrac{1}{x} + \dfrac{1}{y} + xy$, find all values of x and y such that $f_x(x,y) = 0$ and $f_y(x,y) = 0$.

9. Show that the function $z = \arctan \dfrac{y}{x}$ satisfies Laplace's equation, $\dfrac{\partial^2 z}{\partial x^2} + \dfrac{\partial^2 z}{\partial y^2} = 0$.

10. Show that the function $z = \sin(x - ct)$ satisfies the wave equation, $\dfrac{\partial^2 z}{\partial t^2} = c^2 \dfrac{\partial^2 z}{\partial x^2}$.

Total Differentials and Chain Rules
Lesson 5

Topics

- The total differential of a function of two variables.

- Differentiability for functions of two variables.

- The total differential and error analysis.

- Chain rules.

Definitions and Theorems

- Let $z = f(x, y)$, $dx = \Delta x$, and $dy = \Delta y$. The **total differential** of z is the expression
$$dz = \frac{\partial z}{\partial x} dx + \frac{\partial z}{\partial y} dy = f_x(x, y) dx + f_y(x, y) dy.$$

- A function $z = f(x, y)$ is **differentiable** at the point (x_0, y_0) if Δz can be written in the form
$\Delta z = f_x(x_0, y_0)\Delta x + f_y(x_0, y_0)\Delta y + \varepsilon_1 \Delta x + \varepsilon_2 \Delta y$, where ε_1 and ε_2 tend to zero as $(\Delta x, \Delta y) \to (0, 0)$.

- Let w be a function of x and y, and assume that x and y are both functions of t. Then, w is a function of t, and the **chain rule** says that

$$\frac{dw}{dt} = \frac{\partial w}{\partial x}\frac{dx}{dt} + \frac{\partial w}{\partial y}\frac{dy}{dt}.$$

Summary

In this lesson, we continue our study of functions of two or more independent variables. We first generalize differentials from elementary calculus to define the total differential of a function of two variables. We then define differentiability of a function of two variables and note that the definition looks quite different from the corresponding definition in elementary calculus. We apply the total differential to error analysis. Finally, we present one of the many chain rules in multivariable calculus.

Example 1

Find the total differential of the function $z = 2x \sin y - 3x^2 y^2$.

Solution

We have $dz = \frac{\partial z}{\partial x} dx + \frac{\partial z}{\partial y} dy = (2 \sin y - 6xy^2) dx + (2x \cos y - 6x^2 y) dy.$

Example 2

Use the total differential to approximate the change in the function
$z = f(x, y) = \sqrt{4 - x^2 - y^2}$ as (x, y) changes from $(1, 1)$ to $(1.01, 0.97)$.
(See **Figure 5.1**.)

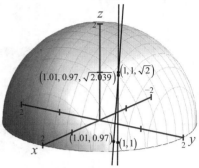

Figure 5.1

Solution

We have $(x, y) = (1, 1)$, $dx = \Delta x = 0.01$, and $dy = \Delta y = -0.03$.

The partial derivatives are $\dfrac{\partial z}{\partial x} = \dfrac{1}{2}\left(4 - x^2 - y^2\right)^{-\frac{1}{2}}(-2x) = \dfrac{-x}{\sqrt{4 - x^2 - y^2}}$ and $\dfrac{\partial z}{\partial y} = \dfrac{-y}{\sqrt{4 - x^2 - y^2}}$.

So, $\Delta z \approx dz = \dfrac{\partial z}{\partial x}\Delta x + \dfrac{\partial z}{\partial y}\Delta y = \dfrac{-x}{\sqrt{4 - x^2 - y^2}}\Delta x + \dfrac{-y}{\sqrt{4 - x^2 - y^2}}\Delta y$.

When $x = y = 1$, $\Delta z \approx \dfrac{-1}{\sqrt{2}}(0.01) + \dfrac{-1}{\sqrt{2}}(-0.03) \approx 0.0141$.

This compares favorably with the exact change:

$$\Delta z = f(1.01, 0.97) - f(1, 1) = \sqrt{4 - (1.01)^2 - (0.97)^2} - \sqrt{4 - 1^2 - 1^2} \approx 1.4279 - 1.4142 \approx 0.0137.$$

Example 3

Use the chain rule to find $\dfrac{dw}{dt}$ if $w = x^2 y - y^2$, $x = \sin t$, and $y = e^t$.

Solution

We have the following:

$$\frac{dw}{dt} = \frac{\partial w}{\partial x}\frac{dx}{dt} + \frac{\partial w}{\partial y}\frac{dy}{dt} = 2xy(\cos t) + (x^2 - 2y)e^t = 2(\sin t)(e^t)\cos t + (\sin^2 t - 2e^t)e^t.$$

Study Tips

- The total differential extends naturally to functions of three or more variables. For example, if $w = x^2 + y^3 + z^4$, then $dw = 2x\,dx + 3y^2\,dy + 4z^3\,dz$.

- We will see later that differentiability at a point implies that the surface can be approximated by a tangent plane at that point. This is similar to elementary calculus, where differentiability at a point implies that the graph can be approximated by a tangent line. (See **Figure 5.2**.)

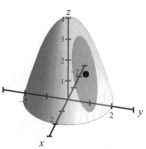

Figure 5.2

- There are many other chain rules in multivariable calculus, but we will not need them in this course.

- It is possible to solve Example 3 without the chain rule. First, express w as a function of t, and then differentiate:

$$w = x^2 y - y^2 = \left(\sin^2 t\right)e^t - \left(e^t\right)^2.$$

Next, find $\dfrac{dw}{dt}$ to verify that you obtain the same answer.

Pitfalls

- The definition of differentiability looks quite different from the definition in elementary calculus.

- Notice in the chain rule that some of the derivatives are ordinary derivatives, and others are partial derivatives.

Problems

1. Find the total differential if $z = 2x^2 y^3$.

2. Find the total differential if $z = e^x \sin y$.

3. Find the total differential if $w = \dfrac{x+y}{z-3y}$.

4. Use the total differential to approximate the quantity $(2.01)^2(9.02) - 2^2(9)$.

5. Use the total differential to approximate the quantity $\sin\left[(1.05)^2 + (0.95)^2\right] - \sin\left(1^2 + 1^2\right)$.

6. The radius r and height h of a right circular cylinder are measured with possible errors of 4% and 2%, respectively. Approximate the maximum possible percent error in measuring the volume.

7. Use the chain rule from elementary calculus to calculate the derivative of the function $h(x) = \sin\left(e^{3x^2}\right)$.

8. Use the chain rule to find $\dfrac{dw}{dt}$ if $w = xy$, $x = e^t$, and $y = e^{-2t}$.

9. Use the chain rule to find $\dfrac{dw}{dt}$ if $w = \cos(x - y)$, $x = t^2$, and $y = 1$.

10. Use the chain rule to find $\dfrac{dw}{dt}$ at $t = 1$ if $w = e^{xy}$, $x = t^2$, and $y = t$.

Extrema of Functions of Two Variables
Lesson 6

Topics

- Maximum and minimum values of functions of two variables.

- The extreme value theorem.

- Relative extrema and critical points.

- The second partials test for relative extrema.

- Applications.

Definitions and Theorems

- Let $z = f(x, y)$ be continuous on the closed and bounded region R in the plane. The values $f(a, b)$ and $f(c, d)$ satisfying $f(a, b) \leq f(x, y) \leq f(c, d)$ are the **maximum and minimum values** of f on R.

- The **extreme value theorem** says that if $z = f(x, y)$ is continuous on the closed and bounded region R in the plane, then there is at least one point in R at which f takes on a minimum value and at least one point in R at which f takes on a maximum value.

- Let f be a function defined on the region R containing the point (x_0, y_0). The function f has a **relative minimum** at (x_0, y_0) if $f(x, y) \geq f(x_0, y_0)$ for all (x, y) in some open disk containing (x_0, y_0). The definition of **relative maximum** is similar.

- Let f be defined on an open region R containing (x_0, y_0). The point (x_0, y_0) is a **critical point** if either $(1) f_x(x_0, y_0) = 0$ and $f_y(x_0, y_0) = 0$ or $(2) f_x(x_0, y_0)$ or $f_y(x_0, y_0)$ do not exist.

- Relative extrema occur at critical points. In other words, the critical points are the candidates for relative maxima and relative minima.

- **Second partials test**: Let (a, b) be a critical point of f.

  Define the quantity $d = f_{xx}(a,b) f_{yy}(a,b) - \left[f_{xy}(a,b) \right]^2$. Then, we have the following.

  1. $d > 0, f_{xx}(a, b) > 0 \Rightarrow$ relative minimum.
  2. $d > 0, f_{xx}(a, b) < 0 \Rightarrow$ relative maximum.

3. $d < 0, \Rightarrow$ saddle point.

4. $d = 0$: Test is inconclusive.

Summary

In this lesson, we develop techniques for finding maximum and minimum values of functions of two variables. We will see that the critical points of a function are the candidates for relative extrema, just as in elementary calculus. The second partials test can be used to determine the exact nature of these critical points. Finally, we close with an application from a previous lesson.

Example 1

If possible, find the highest and lowest points on the graph of the function $f(x, y) = 2x + 4y - x^2 - y^2$.

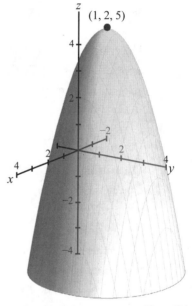

Figure 6.1

Solution

We set the partial derivatives $\dfrac{\partial f}{\partial x} = 2 - 2x$ and $\dfrac{\partial f}{\partial y} = 4 - 2y$ equal to zero and obtain the critical point $(x, y) = (1, 2)$.

By completing the square, we see that this point is a maximum and that there is no minimum value. (See **Figure 6.1**.)

$$\begin{aligned} f(x, y) &= 2x + 4y - x^2 - y^2 \\ &= -(x^2 - 2x + 1) - (y^2 - 4y + 4) + 5 \\ &= 5 - (x - 1)^2 - (y - 2)^2. \end{aligned}$$

Example 2

Determine the relative extrema of $f(x, y) = 2x^2 + y^2 + 8x - 6y + 20$.

Solution

We set the partial derivatives equal to zero to determine the critical point(s): $f_x = 4x + 8 = 0 \Rightarrow x = -2$ and $f_y = 2y - 6 = 0 \Rightarrow y = 3$. So, the only critical point is $(-2, 3)$.

By completing the square, $f(x, y) = 2(x + 2)^2 + (y - 3)^2 + 3$. Hence, $(-2, 3)$ is a relative minimum (and absolute minimum), and there is no relative maximum.

Example 3

Use the second partials test on Example 2 given the critical point $(-2, 3)$.

Solution

We first calculate the partial derivatives $f_x = 4x + 8, f_{xx} = 4, f_y = 2y - 6, f_{yy} = 2$, and $f_{xy} = 0$. So, we have

$$d = f_{xx}(a,b) f_{yy}(a,b) - \left[f_{xy}(a,b) \right]^2 = 4(2) - 0 = 8 > 0,$$

and $f_{xx} > 0$. Thus, by the second partials test, the point is a relative minimum.

Study Tips

- The definition of critical point is similar to the definition in elementary calculus, except that now we use partial derivatives.

- The critical points are the candidates for relative extrema. It is possible that none of the critical points are relative extrema. For instance, the critical point of the function $f(x, y) = y^2 - x^2$ is $(0, 0)$, which is neither a relative minimum nor relative maximum. Such points are called **saddle points**.

Pitfalls

- When using the extreme value theorem, make sure that the region R is closed and bounded. Otherwise, there might not be a maximum or minimum value. For instance, there was no minimum value in Example 1.

- Remember that both partial derivatives must be equal to zero (or one of them undefined) for there to be a critical point.

- Keep in mind that the relative extrema are not necessarily absolute extrema.

- The second partials test can fail in two ways: (1) The partial derivatives might not exist or (2) the discriminant $d = 0$.

Problems

1. Find the critical point(s) of the function $f(x, y) = \sqrt{x^2 + y^2 + 1}$.

2. Find the critical point(s) of the function $f(x, y) = -x^2 - y^2 + 10x + 12y - 64$.

3. Find the critical point(s) of the function $f(x, y) = \left(x^2 + y^2 \right)^{\frac{2}{3}}$.

4. Complete the square to determine the relative minimum of the function $f(x, y) = 2x^2 + y^2 + 8x - 6y + 20$.

5. Determine the relative extrema of $f(x, y) = xy$.

6. Use the second partials test to determine the relative extrema of the function
$f(x, y) = 3x^2 + 2y^2 - 6x - 4y + 16$.

7. Use the second partials test to determine the relative extrema of the function
$f(x, y) = -5x^2 + 4xy - y^2 + 16x + 10$.

8. Examine the function $f(x, y) = 2xy - \frac{1}{2}(x^4 + y^4) + 1$ for relative extrema.

9. Find the critical point(s) of the function $f(x, y) = x^{\frac{2}{3}} + y^{\frac{2}{3}}$ and determine the relative extrema.

10. An open box is to be constructed with 2 square meters of material. Determine the dimensions of the box so that the volume is a maximum.

11. Verify that that the partial derivative with respect to x for $V = xy\left[\dfrac{C - 3xy}{4(x+y)}\right]$ is
$$V_x = \frac{y^2}{4(x+y)^2}(C - 3x^2 - 6xy).$$

12. Verify that $V_x = \dfrac{y^2}{4(x+y)^2}(C - 3x^2 - 6xy) = 0$ and $V_y = \dfrac{x^2}{4(x+y)^2}(C - 3y^2 - 6xy) = 0$ gives the solution $x = y = 12$.

Applications to Optimization Problems
Lesson 7

Topics

- Applications of functions of two variables.

- Maximum and minimum values on closed and bounded regions.

Definitions and Theorems

- Let $z = f(x, y)$ be continuous on the closed and bounded region R in the plane. The values $f(a, b)$ and $f(c, d)$ satisfying $f(a, b) \leq f(x, y) \leq f(c, d)$ are the **maximum and minimum values** of f on R.

- The **extreme value theorem** says that if $z = f(x, y)$ is continuous on the closed and bounded region R in the plane, then there is at least one point in R at which f takes on a minimum value and at least one point in R at which f takes on a maximum value.

Summary

In this lesson, we continue our study of optimization applications of functions of two variables. We first look at maximum and minimum values for functions defined on closed and bounded regions. We then look at two real-life applications. The first one involves maximizing the volume of a package, and the second involves the construction of a water line through three different regions.

Example 1

Find the absolute extrema of the function $f(x, y) = 3x^2 + 2y^2 - 4y$ on the closed region bounded below by the parabola $y = x^2$ and above by the line $y = 4$. (See **Figure 7.1**.)

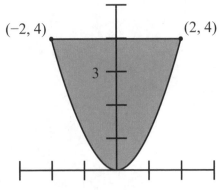

Figure 7.1

Solution

We first find the critical points in the region by setting the partial derivatives equal to zero: $f_x = 6x = 0, f_y = 4y - 4 = 0$.

Hence, the only critical point in the region is at $(0, 1)$, and $f(0, 1) = -2$.

Next, we analyze the boundary of the region.

Along the line segment $y = 4$, $-2 \le x \le 2$, we have $f(x, 4) = 3x^2 + 32 - 16 = 3x^2 + 16 = g(x)$. Because $g'(x) = 6x$, we evaluate $g(0) = 16$, $g(2) = 28$, and $g(-2) = 28$.

Along the parabola $y = x^2$, $-2 \le x \le 2$, $f(x, x^2) = h(x) = 3x^2 + 2(x^2)^2 - 4x^2 = 2x^4 - x^2$, $-2 \le x \le 2$. We have $h'(x) = 8x^3 - 2x = 2x(4x^2 - 1)$ and, hence, $h'(x) = 0 \Rightarrow x = 0, \pm\frac{1}{2}$.

We evaluate these points to obtain $h(0) = 0$, $h\left(\pm\frac{1}{2}\right) = -\frac{1}{8}$, and $h(\pm 2) = 28$.

Finally, we see that the absolute maximum is 28 at $(\pm 2, 4)$, and the absolute minimum is -2 at $(0, 1)$.

Example 2

A water line is to be built from point P to point S and must pass through regions where construction costs differ. The cost is 3 million dollars per kilometer from P to Q, 2 million dollars per kilometer from Q to R, and 1 million dollars from R to S. Find x and y so that the total cost is a minimum. (See **Figure 7.2**.)

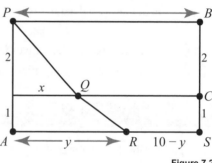

Figure 7.2

Solution

From the figure, we see that the total cost in millions of dollars is $C(x, y) = 3\sqrt{x^2 + 4} + 2\sqrt{(y-x)^2 + 1} + (10 - y)$.

The partial derivatives are

$$C_x = \frac{3x}{\sqrt{x^2 + 4}} - \frac{2(y-x)}{\sqrt{(y-x)^2 + 1}}$$

$$C_y = \frac{2(y-x)}{\sqrt{(y-x)^2 + 1}} - 1.$$

Setting these partial derivatives equal to zero yields (see Problem 7 for a derivation)

$$x = \frac{\sqrt{2}}{2} \approx 1.414, \quad y = \frac{\sqrt{3}}{3} + \frac{\sqrt{2}}{2} \approx 1.284.$$

These values yield the minimum cost $C\left(\frac{\sqrt{2}}{2}, \frac{\sqrt{3}}{3} + \frac{\sqrt{2}}{2}\right) \approx 17.39$.

You can verify that this is a minimum by the second partials test or by analyzing the values on the boundary. It is instructive to compare this minimum with other values for x and y: $C(0, 0) = 6 + 2 + 10 = 18$, $C(10, 10) = 3\sqrt{104} + 2 \approx 32.59$, and $C(1, 1) = 3\sqrt{5} + 2 + 9 \approx 17.71$.

Study Tips

- As illustrated in Example 1, the technique for finding absolute extrema for functions defined on closed and bounded regions requires two steps: You must find the critical points inside the region and also analyze the function values on the boundary of the region.

- When solving an applied optimization problem, make sure that your answer is indeed a maximum (or minimum). The second partials test can often be used.

Pitfalls

- When finding the critical points for a function defined on a closed and bounded region, make sure that the points are indeed in the region.

- Calculating partial derivatives is a calculus skill. But setting those derivatives equal to zero and solving the resulting equations is algebra. The algebra portion is often the most difficult.

Problems

1. Find the absolute extrema of the function $f(x, y) = x^2 - 4xy + 5$ on the region $R = \{(x, y): 1 \leq x \leq 4, 0 \leq y \leq 2\}$.

2. Find the absolute extrema of the function $f(x, y) = 12 - 3x - 2y$ on the triangular region in the xy-plane with vertices $(2, 0)$, $(0, 1)$, and $(1, 2)$.

3. Find the minimum distance from the point $(0, 0, 0)$ to the plane $x - y + z = 3$. Hint: To simplify the computations, minimize the square of the distance.

4. Find three positive integers such that their product is 27 and their sum is a minimum.

5. Show that a rectangular box of given volume and minimum surface area is a cube.

6. If $V_x = 108y - 4xy - 2y^2$ and $V_y = 108x - 2x^2 - 4xy$, $(x, y \neq 0)$, show that $V_x = V_y = 0$ implies that $x = y = 18$.

7. If $C_x = \dfrac{3x}{\sqrt{x^2 + 4}} - \dfrac{2(y-x)}{\sqrt{(y-x)^2 + 1}}$ and $C_y = \dfrac{2(y-x)}{\sqrt{(y-x)^2 + 1}} - 1$, $(0 \leq x \leq 10, x \leq y \leq 10)$, show that

   $C_x = C_y = 0$ implies that $x = \dfrac{\sqrt{2}}{2}$ and $y = \dfrac{\sqrt{3}}{3} + \dfrac{\sqrt{2}}{2}$.

Linear Models and Least Squares Regression
Lesson 8

Topics

- The least squares regression line.

- Application to systolic blood pressure.

- Nearly vertical data.

Definitions and Theorems

- Given a set of data $(x_1, y_1), (x_2, y_2), \ldots, (x_n, y_n)$, the **least squares regression line** $f(x) = ax + b$ is given by

$$a = \frac{n\sum_{i=1}^{n} x_i y_i - \sum_{i=1}^{n} x_i \sum_{i=1}^{n} y_i}{n\sum_{i=1}^{n} x_i^2 - \left(\sum_{i=1}^{n} x_i\right)^2}, \ b = \frac{1}{n}\left(\sum_{i=1}^{n} y_i - a\sum_{i=1}^{n} x_i\right).$$

Summary

In this lesson, we apply our optimization technique to curve fitting. Given a set of data points in the plane, we show how to find the line that best fits the data. This least squares regression line is used extensively in real-life models of data sets that are nearly linear. After we show an application to systolic blood pressure, we look briefly at the surprising situation in which the data is nearly vertical.

Example 1

Find the least squares regression line for the four points in the plane $(-3, 0), (-1, 1), (0, 2), (2, 3)$.

Solution

For this example, $n = 4$, and we have the following sums.

$$\sum_{i=1}^{4} x_i = -3 - 1 + 0 + 2 = -2, \sum_{i=1}^{4} y_i = 0 + 1 + 2 + 3 = 6.$$

$$\sum_{i=1}^{4} x_i y_i = 0 - 1 + 0 + 6 = 5, \sum_{i=1}^{4} (x_i)^2 = 9 + 1 + 0 + 4 = 14.$$

So, the slope is

$$a = \frac{n\sum_{i=1}^{n} x_i y_i - \sum_{i=1}^{n} x_i \sum_{i=1}^{n} y_i}{n\sum_{i=1}^{n} x_i^2 - \left(\sum_{i=1}^{n} x_i\right)^2} = \frac{4(5)-(-2)(6)}{4(14)-(-2)^2} = \frac{20+12}{56-4} = \frac{32}{52} = \frac{8}{13},$$

and the y-intercept is

$$b = \frac{1}{n}\left(\sum_{i=1}^{n} y_i - a\sum_{i=1}^{n} x_i\right) = \frac{1}{4}\left(6 - \frac{8}{13}(-2)\right) = \frac{1}{4}\left(\frac{6(13)+16}{13}\right) = \frac{1}{4}\left(\frac{94}{13}\right) = \frac{47}{26}.$$

The least squares regression line is $f(x) = ax + b = \frac{8}{13}x + \frac{47}{26}$.
(See **Figure 8.1**.)

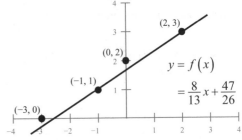

Figure 8.1

Example 2

The ages x (in years) and systolic blood pressures y of a man are shown in the graph. Find the least squares regression line for this data. Then, use the line to approximate the change in systolic blood pressure for each 1-year increase in age.
(See **Figure 8.2**.)

Solution

Using a graphing utility, you obtain the line $y = 1.6x + 84$. From the slope, you see that the systolic blood pressure changes by approximately 1.6 for each 1-year increase in age.

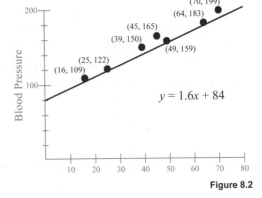

Figure 8.2

Study Tips

- The formula for the least squares regression line is derived by minimizing the sum of the squares of the differences between the data and the line:

$$S = \sum_{i=1}^{n}\left[f(x_i) - y_i\right]^2 = \sum_{i=1}^{n}\left[ax_i + b - y_i\right]^2.$$

- Most graphing utilities have built-in capabilities for calculating the least squares regression line. For Example 1, your calculator will give the very accurate approximation $y = 0.61538x + 1.80769$.

- You can also fit many other curves to sets of data, including polynomial, exponential, logarithmic, and trigonometric functions.

Pitfalls

- The least squares regression line is not a good approximation for nearly vertical data. For example, for the three points $(2, 2)$, $(2, 1)$, and $(2.1, 1.5)$, the least squares regression line is horizontal, $y = 1.5$.

- If your data is not nearly linear, you might want to use a different least squares model. For instance, if the data seems quadratic, you might use a second-degree polynomial to approximate the data.

Problems

1. Find the least squares regression line for the points $(1, 0)$, $(3, 3)$, and $(5, 6)$.

2. Find the least squares regression line for the points $(0, 0)$, $(1, 1)$, $(3, 4)$, $(4, 2)$, and $(5, 5)$.

3. Use a graphing utility or computer to find the least squares regression line for the points $(0, 6)$, $(4, 3)$, $(5, 0)$, $(8, -4)$, and $(10, -5)$.

4. Use a graphing utility or computer to find the least squares regression line for the points $(6, 4)$, $(1, 2)$, $(3, 3)$, $(8, 6)$, $(11, 8)$, and $(13, 8)$.

5. An agronomist used four test plots to determine the relationship between the wheat yield y (in bushels per acre) and the amount of fertilizer x (in hundreds of pounds per acre). The results are as follows.

   (x, y): $(1.0, 32)$, $(1.5, 41)$, $(2.0, 48)$, $(2.5, 53)$

   Use a graphing utility or computer to find the least squares regression line for the data, and use the model to estimate the yield for a fertilizer application of 160 pounds per acre.

6. A store manager wants to know the demand y for an energy bar as a function of price x. The daily sales for three different prices of the energy bar are as follows.

   (x, y): $(1.29, 450)$, $(1.49, 375)$, $(1.69, 330)$

   Use a graphing utility or computer to find the least squares regression line for the data, and use the model to estimate the demand when the price is $1.59.

Vectors and the Dot Product in Space
Lesson 9

Topics

- Vectors in space.

- The dot product of two vectors.

- The angle between two nonzero vectors.

- Lines in space.

Definitions and Theorems

- Vectors in space are denoted by $\mathbf{v} = \langle v_1, v_2, v_3 \rangle$, where v_1, v_2, and v_3 are the **components** of the vector. The **zero vector** is $\mathbf{0} = \langle 0, 0, 0 \rangle$, and the **standard unit vectors** are $\mathbf{i} = \langle 1, 0, 0 \rangle$, $\mathbf{j} = \langle 0, 1, 0 \rangle$, $\mathbf{k} = \langle 0, 0, 1 \rangle$.

- The **length** or **magnitude** of the vector $\mathbf{v}$ is $\|\mathbf{v}\| = \sqrt{v_1^2 + v_2^2 + v_3^2}$.

- Two vectors are **equal** if they have the same components—that is, if they have the same length and direction.

- Two nonzero vectors $\mathbf{u}$ and $\mathbf{v}$ are **parallel** if $\mathbf{u} = c\mathbf{v}$ for some nonzero scalar c.

- The **dot product** of $\mathbf{u} = \langle u_1, u_2, u_3 \rangle$ and $\mathbf{v} = \langle v_1, v_2, v_3 \rangle$ is $\mathbf{u} \cdot \mathbf{v} = u_1 v_1 + u_2 v_2 + u_3 v_3$.

- Two vectors are **orthogonal** (perpendicular) if their dot product is zero.

- If θ is the angle between the two nonzero vectors $\mathbf{u}$ and $\mathbf{v}$, then $\cos \theta = \dfrac{\mathbf{u} \cdot \mathbf{v}}{\|\mathbf{u}\| \|\mathbf{v}\|}$.

- **Lines in space**: Consider the line L through the point $P(x_1, y_1, z_1)$ and parallel to the **direction vector** $\mathbf{v} = \langle a, b, c \rangle$. The line L consists of all points $Q(x, y, z)$ for which $\overrightarrow{PQ}$ is parallel to $\mathbf{v}$, $\overrightarrow{PQ} = \langle x - x_1, y - y_1, z - z_1 \rangle = t \langle a, b, c \rangle = t\mathbf{v}$. The parametric equations for the line are

$$x = x_1 + at$$
$$y = y_1 + bt$$
$$z = z_1 + ct.$$

Summary

We extend our knowledge of vectors in the plane to vectors in space. The formulas for length, dot product, and angle are easy generalizations of the corresponding definitions from elementary calculus. We then show how to define lines in space using vectors. We develop the parametric equations for lines in space and illustrate this new idea with examples.

Example 1

Determine if the points $P(1, -2, 3)$, $Q(2, 1, 0)$, and $R(4, 7, -6)$ are collinear.

Solution

There are at least two ways to solve this problem. You could form the vectors $\overline{PQ}$ and $\overline{PR}$ and see if they are parallel. Or, you could see if the sum of the distances between two points equals the distance between the third pair. To this end, notice that

$$d(P,Q) = \sqrt{(2-1)^2 + (1+2)^2 + (0-3)^2} = \sqrt{19}$$

$$d(P,R) = \sqrt{(4-1)^2 + (7+2)^2 + (-6-3)^2} = \sqrt{171}$$

$$d(Q,R) = \sqrt{(4-2)^2 + (7-1)^2 + (-6-0)^2} = \sqrt{76}.$$

So, we have $PQ + QR = \sqrt{19} + \sqrt{76} = \sqrt{19} + 2\sqrt{19} = 3\sqrt{19} = \sqrt{171} = PR$, which implies that the points are collinear.

Example 2

Consider the three vectors $\mathbf{u} = \langle 3, -1, 2 \rangle$, $\mathbf{v} = \langle -4, 0, 2 \rangle$, and $\mathbf{w} = \langle 1, -1, -2 \rangle$. We have $\mathbf{u} \cdot \mathbf{v} = 3(-4) + (-1)0 + 2(2) = -8$ and $\mathbf{u} \cdot \mathbf{w} = 3(1) + (-1)(-1) + 2(-2) = 0$. This implies that the vectors $\mathbf{u}$ and $\mathbf{w}$ are orthogonal.

Example 3

Find the angle between the vectors $\mathbf{u} = \langle 3, -1, 2 \rangle$ and $\mathbf{v} = \langle -4, 0, 2 \rangle$.

Solution

The cosine of the angle is $\cos\theta = \dfrac{\mathbf{u} \cdot \mathbf{v}}{\|\mathbf{u}\|\|\mathbf{v}\|} = \dfrac{-8}{\sqrt{14}\sqrt{20}} = \dfrac{-4}{\sqrt{70}}$.

Using a graphing utility and the inverse cosine button, you obtain $\theta = \arccos\left(\dfrac{-4}{\sqrt{70}}\right) \approx 2.069 \approx 118.56°$.

Example 4

Find the parametric equation of the line that passes through the point $(1, -2, 4)$ and is parallel to the vector $\mathbf{v} = \langle 2, 4, -4 \rangle$.

Solution

Using the formula for parametric equations, we have $x = x_1 + at = 1 + 2t$, $y = y_1 + bt = -2 + 4t$, and $z = z_1 + ct = 4 - 4t$.

Study Tips

- Lines in space are described using a point and a direction vector. This is quite different from lines in the plane, for which we use slope and y-intercept.

- The parametric equations in Example 4 are $x = 1 + 2t$, $y = -2 + 4t$, and $z = 4 - 4t$. Notice that for $t = 0$, the equations yield the original point $(1, -2, 4)$. As t varies on the interval $(-\infty, \infty)$, the point (x, y, z) moves up and down the line.

Pitfall

- The dot product of two vectors is a scalar (real number). In the next lesson, we will define the cross product of two vectors, which is a vector.

Problems

1. Find the component form and magnitude of the vector having initial point $(3, 2, 0)$ and terminal point $(4, 1, 6)$.

2. Find the length of the vector $\mathbf{v} = \langle 1, 3, 4 \rangle$.

3. Determine if the points $(1, 2, 4)$, $(2, 5, 0)$, and $(0, 1, 5)$ are collinear.

4. Find the dot product of the vectors $\mathbf{u} = \langle 2, -1, 1 \rangle$ and $\mathbf{v} = \langle 1, 0, -1 \rangle$.

5. Find a unit vector in the direction of the vector $\mathbf{v} = \langle 2, 1, -2 \rangle$.

6. Find the angle between the vectors $\mathbf{u} = 3\mathbf{i} + 2\mathbf{j} + \mathbf{k}$ and $\mathbf{v} = 2\mathbf{i} - 3\mathbf{j}$.

7. Find the angle between the vectors $\mathbf{u} = 3\mathbf{i} + 4\mathbf{j}$ and $\mathbf{v} = 2\mathbf{j} + 3\mathbf{k}$.

8. Find a set of parametric equations for the line through the point $(0, 0, 0)$ and parallel to the vector $\mathbf{v} = \langle 3, 1, 5 \rangle$.

9. Find a set of parametric equations for the line through the point $(-3, 0, 2)$ and parallel to the vector $\mathbf{v} = \langle 0, 6, 3 \rangle$.

10. Find a set of parametric equations for the line through the points $(7, -2, 6)$ and $(-3, 0, 6)$.

The Cross Product of Two Vectors in Space
Lesson 10

Topics

- The cross product of two vectors in space.

- Properties of the cross product.

- The triple scalar product.

Definitions and Theorems

- The **cross product** of the vectors $\mathbf{u} = u_1\mathbf{i} + u_2\mathbf{j} + u_3\mathbf{k} = \langle u_1, u_2, u_3 \rangle$ and $\mathbf{v} = v_1\mathbf{i} + v_2\mathbf{j} + v_3\mathbf{k} = \langle v_1, v_2, v_3 \rangle$ is

$$\mathbf{u} \times \mathbf{v} = \begin{vmatrix} \mathbf{i} & \mathbf{j} & \mathbf{k} \\ u_1 & u_2 & u_3 \\ v_1 & v_2 & v_3 \end{vmatrix} = \left(u_2 v_3 - u_3 v_2 \right)\mathbf{i} - \left(u_1 v_3 - u_3 v_1 \right)\mathbf{j} + \left(u_1 v_2 - u_2 v_1 \right)\mathbf{k}.$$

- The cross product $\mathbf{u} \times \mathbf{v}$ is orthogonal to $\mathbf{u}$ and to $\mathbf{v}$. That is,

$$\left(\mathbf{u} \times \mathbf{v} \right) \cdot \mathbf{u} = 0 \quad \text{and} \quad \left(\mathbf{u} \times \mathbf{v} \right) \cdot \mathbf{v} = 0.$$

- Additional properties of the cross product:

$$\mathbf{u} \times \mathbf{u} = 0, \ \mathbf{u} \times \mathbf{v} = -(\mathbf{v} \times \mathbf{u}), \ \text{and} \ \mathbf{u} \times (\mathbf{v} + \mathbf{w}) = (\mathbf{u} \times \mathbf{v}) + (\mathbf{u} \times \mathbf{w}).$$

- The area of the parallelogram having the vectors $\mathbf{u}$ and $\mathbf{v}$ as adjacent sides is $\|\mathbf{u} \times \mathbf{v}\| = \|\mathbf{u}\|\|\mathbf{v}\|\sin\theta$.

- The **triple scalar product** is the scalar $\mathbf{u} \cdot \left(\mathbf{v} \times \mathbf{w} \right) = \begin{vmatrix} u_1 & u_2 & u_3 \\ v_1 & v_2 & v_3 \\ w_1 & w_2 & w_3 \end{vmatrix}.$

- The volume of the parallelepiped with $\mathbf{u}$, $\mathbf{v}$, and $\mathbf{w}$ as adjacent sides is $V = \left| \mathbf{u} \cdot \left(\mathbf{v} \times \mathbf{w} \right) \right|$.

Summary

The cross product of two vectors in space is a vector, not a scalar. We calculate cross products using a determinant formula. One of the most important properties states that the cross product of two nonzero vectors is a vector orthogonal (perpendicular) to both of the original vectors. In other words, the cross product is orthogonal to the plane determined by the original vectors. We present some of the basic properties of the cross product and close with the triple scalar product, which combines the dot product and cross product.

Example 1

Calculate the cross product of the vectors $\mathbf{u} = \mathbf{i} - 2\mathbf{j} + \mathbf{k}$ and $\mathbf{v} = 3\mathbf{i} + \mathbf{j} - 2\mathbf{k}$.

Solution

We evaluate the cross product by expanding the determinant along the first row.

$$\mathbf{u} \times \mathbf{v} = \begin{vmatrix} \mathbf{i} & \mathbf{j} & \mathbf{k} \\ 1 & -2 & 1 \\ 3 & 1 & -2 \end{vmatrix} = \begin{vmatrix} -2 & 1 \\ 1 & -2 \end{vmatrix}\mathbf{i} - \begin{vmatrix} 1 & 1 \\ 3 & -2 \end{vmatrix}\mathbf{j} + \begin{vmatrix} 1 & -2 \\ 3 & 1 \end{vmatrix}\mathbf{k}$$

$$= (4 - 1)\mathbf{i} - (-2 - 3)\mathbf{j} + (1 + 6)\mathbf{k} = 3\mathbf{i} + 5\mathbf{j} + 7\mathbf{k}.$$

Notice that the cross product is orthogonal to each of the original vectors.

Example 2

Find the area of the parallelogram having adjacent sides $\mathbf{u} = \mathbf{i} + \mathbf{j} + \mathbf{k}$ and $\mathbf{v} = \mathbf{j} + \mathbf{k}$. (See **Figure 10.1**.)

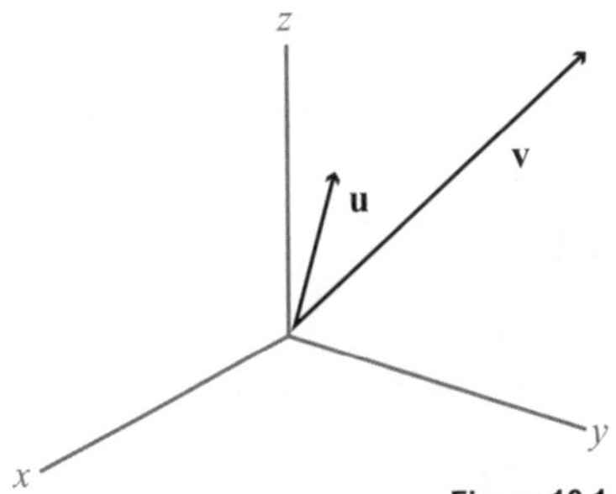

Figure 10.1

Solution

The cross product of the two vectors is $\mathbf{u} \times \mathbf{v} = -\mathbf{j} + \mathbf{k}$, and the area is therefore the length of this vector, $\|\mathbf{u} \times \mathbf{v}\| = \sqrt{2}$.

Example 3

Find the volume of the parallelepiped with adjacent sides $\mathbf{u} = \mathbf{i} + \mathbf{j}$, $\mathbf{v} = \mathbf{j} + \mathbf{k}$, and $\mathbf{w} = \mathbf{i} + \mathbf{k}$. (See **Figure 10.2**.)

Solution

The triple scalar product is $\mathbf{u} \cdot (\mathbf{v} \times \mathbf{w}) = \begin{vmatrix} 1 & 1 & 0 \\ 0 & 1 & 1 \\ 1 & 0 & 1 \end{vmatrix} = 2,$ which implies that the volume is 2.

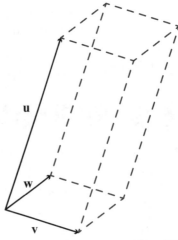

Figure 10.2

- Keep in mind that the cross product of two vectors is orthogonal to the original vectors. You can use this fact to check your calculations.

- The words "orthogonal" and "perpendicular" mean the same thing. Another term that we will use is "normal" in the sense that a vector is normal to a plane.

- The definition of the cross product is based on a determinant calculation. You might be familiar with 2×2 determinants,

$$\begin{vmatrix} a & b \\ c & d \end{vmatrix} = ad - bc.$$

For example, $\begin{vmatrix} 1 & 2 \\ 3 & 4 \end{vmatrix} = 1(4) - 2(3) = -2.$

- In the formula for the volume of a parallelepiped, notice that we are using the usual absolute value.

- In Example 1, we observed that the cross product was $\mathbf{u} \times \mathbf{v} = 3\mathbf{i} + 5\mathbf{j} + 7\mathbf{k}$. Reversing the order, you obtain the negative of the original cross product: $\mathbf{v} \times \mathbf{u} = -(3\mathbf{i} + 5\mathbf{j} + 7\mathbf{k}) = -3\mathbf{i} - 5\mathbf{j} - 7\mathbf{k} = -(\mathbf{u} \times \mathbf{v})$.

Pitfalls

- The cross product of two vectors in space is not commutative. In fact, $\mathbf{u} \times \mathbf{v} = -(\mathbf{v} \times \mathbf{u})$.

- Don't forget the minus sign in front of the $\mathbf{j}$ term when finding the cross product.

- The cross product is only defined for vectors in space (3-tuples). That said, you can find the cross product of $(1, 2, 0)$ and $(-3, 1, 0)$. The answer is $7\mathbf{k}$.

- The dot product of two vectors is a scalar (real number), whereas the cross product is a vector.

Problems

1. Find the cross products $\mathbf{k} \times \mathbf{i}$ and $\mathbf{i} \times \mathbf{k}$. What do you observe?

2. Find the cross product of the vectors $\mathbf{u} = \langle 7, 3, 2 \rangle$ and $\mathbf{v} = \langle 1, -1, 5 \rangle$.

3. Find the cross product of the vectors $\mathbf{u} = \langle 3, 1, -2 \rangle$ and $\mathbf{v} = \langle 1, -2, 1 \rangle$.

4. Show that the cross product of $\mathbf{i} + \mathbf{j} + \mathbf{k}$ and $\mathbf{j} + \mathbf{k}$ is orthogonal to each of these vectors.

5. Find a vector orthogonal to the vectors $\mathbf{i}$ and $2\mathbf{j} + \mathbf{k}$.

6. Let $\mathbf{v} = \langle 1, 0, -2 \rangle$ and calculate $\mathbf{v} \times \mathbf{v}$. What do you observe?

7. Find a unit vector orthogonal to the vectors $\langle 1, 2, 0 \rangle$ and $\langle 3, -4, 0 \rangle$.

8. Find the area of the parallelogram having adjacent sides $\langle 3, 2, -1 \rangle$ and $\langle 1, 2, 3 \rangle$.

9. Find the volume of the parallelepiped with adjacent edges $\langle 1, 3, 1 \rangle$, $\langle 0, 6, 6 \rangle$, and $\langle -4, 0, -4 \rangle$.

10. Find the volume of the parallelepiped with vertices $(0, 0, 0), (3, 0, 0), (0, 5, 1), (2, 0, 5), (3, 5, 1), (5, 0, 5),$ $(2, 5, 6), (5, 5, 6)$.

11. Find a vector orthogonal to the triangle formed by the points $A(1, 1, 2), B(2, 0, -1),$ and $C(4, -7, 0)$.

Lines and Planes in Space
Lesson 11

Topics

- The definition of a plane in space.

- The angle between two planes.

- Projections of vectors onto vectors.

- The distance between a point and a plane.

Definitions and Theorems

- Planes in space: Let $P(x_1, y_1, z_1)$ be a point on the plane, and let $\mathbf{n} = \langle a, b, c \rangle$ be a nonzero vector orthogonal to the plane. The **plane** consists of all points $Q(x, y, z)$ for which the vector $\overrightarrow{PQ}$ is orthogonal to $\mathbf{n}$. That is, the dot product is zero: $\mathbf{n} \cdot \overrightarrow{PQ} = \langle a, b, c \rangle \cdot \langle x - x_1, y - y_1, z - z_1 \rangle = 0$. Simplifying, we obtain the **standard form** of the equation of the plane, $a(x - x_1) + b(y - y_1) + c(z - z_1) = 0$.

- The **general form** of the equation of the plane is $ax + by + cz + d = 0$.

- The **projection** of the vector $\mathbf{u}$ onto the vector $\mathbf{v}$ is $\text{proj}_{\mathbf{v}}\,\mathbf{u} = \left(\dfrac{\mathbf{u} \cdot \mathbf{v}}{\|\mathbf{v}\|^2} \right) \mathbf{v}$.

- The **angle** between two planes is the same as the angle between their normal vectors.

- The **distance** between a plane and a point Q not in the plane is

$$D = \left\| \text{proj}_{\mathbf{n}}\,\overrightarrow{PQ} \right\| = \left\| \left(\dfrac{\overrightarrow{PQ} \cdot \mathbf{n}}{\|\mathbf{n}\|^2} \right) \mathbf{n} \right\| = \dfrac{\left| \overrightarrow{PQ} \cdot \mathbf{n} \right|}{\|\mathbf{n}\|},$$

where P is any point in the plane.

Summary

We define planes in space using a point in the plane and a normal (perpendicular) vector to the plane. This analysis gives rise to the standard equation and general equation of a plane in space. The cross product plays a major role in the discussion. The projection of one vector onto another was studied in elementary calculus, and we extend this idea to vectors in space. This leads to a beautiful formula for the distance between a point and a plane.

Example 1

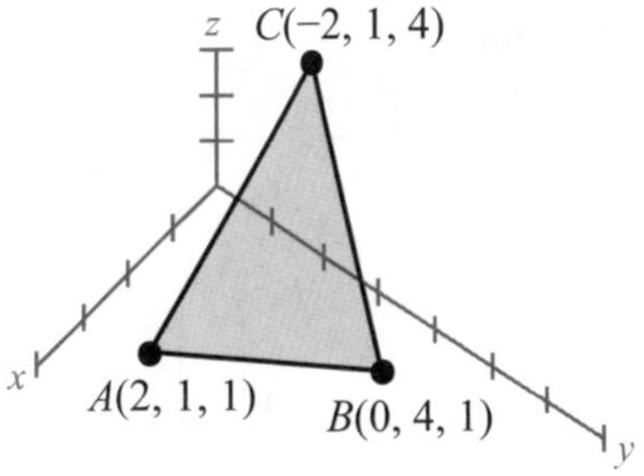

Find the general form of the equation of the plane containing the three points $A(2, 1, 1)$, $B(0, 4, 1)$, $C(-2, 1, 4)$. (See **Figure 11.1**.)

Solution

To find the equation, we need a point in the plane (there are three to choose from) and a normal vector to the plane. To find the normal vector, we compute the cross product of the vectors formed by joining the points:

$$\overrightarrow{AB} = \langle 0-2, 4-1, 1-1 \rangle = \langle -2, 3, 0 \rangle$$

$$\overrightarrow{AC} = \langle -2-2, 1-1, 4-1 \rangle = \langle -4, 0, 3 \rangle.$$

Their cross product is

$$\mathbf{n} = \overrightarrow{AB} \times \overrightarrow{AC} = \begin{vmatrix} \mathbf{i} & \mathbf{j} & \mathbf{k} \\ -2 & 3 & 0 \\ -4 & 0 & 3 \end{vmatrix} = 9\mathbf{i} + 6\mathbf{j} + 12\mathbf{k} = \langle 9, 6, 12 \rangle.$$

Using this normal vector and the point $A(2, 1, 1)$, we have the standard form of the plane, $a(x - x_1) + b(y - y_1) + c(z - z_1) = 9(x - 2) + 6(y - 1) + 12(z - 1) = 0$. This simplifies to the general form $3x + 2y + 4z - 12 = 0$. You can check that each of the original three points satisfies this equation.

Example 2

Find the angle between the two planes $x + 2y + 3z = 6$ and $2x + 3y - z = 0$.

Solution

The angle between the planes is the same as the angle between their normal vectors, $\mathbf{n}_1 = \langle 1, 2, 3 \rangle$ and $\mathbf{n}_2 = \langle 2, 3, -1 \rangle$.

The cosine of the angle between these vectors is $\cos\theta = \dfrac{\mathbf{n}_1 \cdot \mathbf{n}_2}{\|\mathbf{n}_1\| \|\mathbf{n}_2\|} = \dfrac{\langle 1, 2, 3 \rangle \cdot \langle 2, 3, -1 \rangle}{\sqrt{14}\sqrt{14}} = \dfrac{2 + 6 - 3}{14} = \dfrac{5}{14}$, which implies that $\theta \approx 69.1°$.

Example 3

Find the projection of the vector $\mathbf{u} = \langle 5, 10 \rangle$ onto the vector $\mathbf{v} = \langle 4, 3 \rangle$.

z $C(-2, 1, 4)$

x $A(2, 1, 1)$ $B(0, 4, 1)$ *y*

Figure 11.1

Solution

The formula for projection gives

$$\text{proj}_v \, \mathbf{u} = \left(\frac{\mathbf{u} \cdot \mathbf{v}}{\|\mathbf{v}\|^2}\right)\mathbf{v} = \left(\frac{\langle 5, 10 \rangle \cdot \langle 4, 3 \rangle}{\|\langle 4, 3 \rangle\|^2}\right)\langle 4, 3 \rangle = \frac{50}{25}\langle 4, 3 \rangle = 2\langle 4, 3 \rangle = \langle 8, 6 \rangle.$$

(See **Figure 11.2**.)

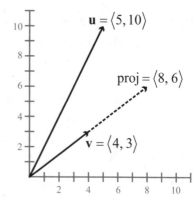

Figure 11.2

Example 4

Find the distance between the point $Q(0, 0, 0)$ and the plane $2x + 3y + z = 12$.

Solution

The normal vector to the plane is $\mathbf{n} = \langle 2, 3, 1 \rangle$.

Setting $y = z = 0$, we obtain the point $P(6, 0, 0)$ in the plane. Hence, $\overrightarrow{PQ} = \langle 0 - 6, 0 - 0, 0 - 0 \rangle = \langle -6, 0, 0 \rangle$.

The distance is $D = \dfrac{\left|\overrightarrow{PQ} \cdot \mathbf{n}\right|}{\|\mathbf{n}\|} = \dfrac{\left|\langle -6, 0, 0 \rangle \cdot \langle 2, 3, 1 \rangle\right|}{\sqrt{4 + 9 + 1}} = \dfrac{|-12|}{\sqrt{14}} = \dfrac{12}{\sqrt{14}}.$

Study Tips

- For the plane $ax + by + cz + d = 0$, the coefficients are the components of the normal vector to the plane, $\mathbf{n} = \langle a, b, c \rangle$.

- The words "orthogonal," "perpendicular," and "normal" pretty much mean the same thing.

- In Example 1, we could have used the normal vector $\langle 3, 2, 4 \rangle$, which is a scalar multiple of $\langle 9, 6, 12 \rangle$.

- Two distinct planes are parallel if their normal vectors are scalar multiples of each other. For instance, the planes $3x - 2y + z = 6$ and $6x - 4y + 2z = 7$ are parallel because their normal vectors $\mathbf{n}_1 = \langle 3, -2, 1 \rangle$ and $\mathbf{n}_2 = \langle 6, -4, 2 \rangle$ satisfy $\mathbf{n}_2 = 2\mathbf{n}_1$.

- Two planes are perpendicular (orthogonal) if their normal vectors are perpendicular—that is, if the dot product of the normal vectors is zero.

- In the formula for the distance between a point Q and a plane, the choice of the point P in the plane is arbitrary. For instance, you would have obtained the same answer in Example 4 if you had chosen the point $P(0, 2, 6)$.

Pitfall

- Three points in space do not necessarily determine a plane. If the points are collinear, then there is an infinite number of planes containing the three points.

Problems

1. Find an equation of the plane passing through the point $(1, 3, -7)$ and perpendicular to the vector $\mathbf{n} = \mathbf{j}$.

2. Find an equation of the plane passing through the point $(-1, 4, 0)$ and perpendicular to the line $x = -1 + 2t, y = 5 - t, z = 3 - 2t$.

3. Find an equation of the plane passing through the three points $(0, 0, 0)$, $(2, 0, 3)$, and $(-3, -1, 5)$.

4. Find the angle between the two planes $3x + 2y - z = 7$ and $x - 4y + 2z = 0$.

5. Determine whether the planes $5x - 3y + z = 4$ and $x + 4y + 7z = 1$ are parallel, orthogonal, or neither.

6. Determine whether the planes $3x + y - 4z = 3$ and $-9x - 3y + 12z = 4$ are parallel, orthogonal, or neither.

7. Find the parametric equations of the line that passes through the point $(2, 3, 4)$ and is perpendicular to the plane given by $3x + 2y - z = 6$.

8. Find the parametric equations of the line that passes through the point $(2, 3, 4)$ and is parallel to the xz-plane and the yz-plane.

9. Find the distance from the point $(0, 0, 0)$ to the plane $5x + y - z = 9$.

10. Find the distance from the point $(1, 3, -1)$ to the plane $3x - 4y + 5z = 6$.

Curved Surfaces in Space
Lesson 12

Topics

- Spheres and planes.

- Cylindrical surfaces.

- Quadric surfaces.

- Surfaces of revolution.

- The Möbius strip.

Definitions and Theorems

- **Sphere** of center (x_0, y_0, z_0) and radius r: $(x - x_0)^2 + (y - y_0)^2 + (z - z_0)^2 = r^2$.

- **Plane** in space: $ax + by + cz + d = 0$.

- Let C be a curve in a plane, and let L be a line not in a parallel plane. The set of all lines parallel to L and intersecting C is called a **cylinder**. C is the **generating curve**, and the parallel lines are the **rulings**.

- The general equation of a **quadric surface** is

$$Ax^2 + By^2 + Cz^2 + Dxy + Exz + Fyz + Gx + Hy + Iz + J = 0.$$

Summary

We have already seen many graphs of surfaces in space, including planes and spheres. In this lesson, we focus on various types of surfaces that play a role in our study of multivariable calculus. We first look at cylindrical surfaces, a generalization of the familiar cylinder. Then, we present the class of surfaces called quadric surfaces. We have already seen some of these, including paraboloids and ellipsoids. We briefly mention surfaces of revolution, which will seem familiar from elementary calculus. Finally, we show the famous Möbius strip, a surface with only one side.

Example 1

Sketch the surface $z = y^2$.

Solution

The graph is a cylinder whose generating curve $z = y^2$ is a parabola in the yz-plane. The rulings of the cylinder are parallel to the x-axis. (See **Figure 12.1**.)

Example 2

Sketch the surface given by $4x^2 - 3y^2 + 12z^2 + 12 = 0$.

Solution

We rewrite the equation as follows:

$$4x^2 - 3y^2 + 12z^2 = -12$$

$$\frac{x^2}{-3} + \frac{y^2}{4} - z^2 = 1$$

$$\frac{y^2}{4} - \frac{x^2}{3} - \frac{z^2}{1} = 1.$$

This is a hyperboloid of two sheets. The traces in the xy-plane $(z = 0)$ and in the yz-plane $(x = 0)$ are hyperbolas. There are no traces in the xz-plane $(y = 0)$. (See **Figure 12.2**.)

Example 3

Sketch the surface given by $x^2 + 2y^2 + z^2 - 4x + 4y - 2z + 3 = 0$.

Solution

By completing the square, you obtain the equation of an ellipsoid centered at the point $(2, -1, 1)$:

$$\frac{(x-2)^2}{4} + \frac{(y+1)^2}{2} + \frac{(z-1)^2}{4} = 1.$$

(See **Figure 12.3**.)

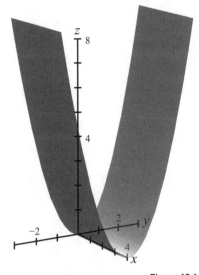

Figure 12.1

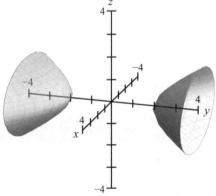

Figure 12.2

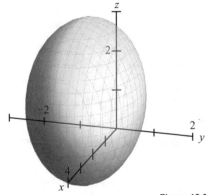

Figure 12.3

Example 4

If you rotate $y = \dfrac{1}{z}$, $z > 0$, about the z-axis, you obtain the surface of

revolution $x^2 + y^2 = \left(\dfrac{1}{z}\right)^2$. (See **Figure 12.4**.)

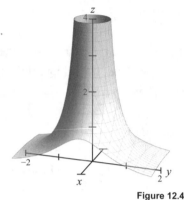

Figure 12.4

Study Tips

- Computers and graphing calculators are very useful in producing graphs of surfaces in space.

- Quadric surfaces are the three-dimensional analogs of conic sections.

- The Möbius strip is an example of a surface with only one side.

Pitfalls

- The word "cylinder" can be misleading. In calculus, a cylinder does not have to look like the usual "tin can," as illustrated in Example 1.

- The graph of an equation depends on whether you are working in a plane or space. For instance, the equation $z = x^2$ is a parabola in the xz-plane, but it is a cylinder in space.

Problems

1. Describe the surface $y = 5$.

2. Describe the surface $y^2 + z^2 = 9$.

3. Identify the quadric surface $\dfrac{x^2}{16} + \dfrac{y^2}{25} + \dfrac{z^2}{25} = 1$.

4. Identify the quadric surface $16x^2 - y^2 + 16z^2 = 4$.

5. Identify the quadric surface $4x^2 - y^2 - z^2 = 1$.

6. Identify the quadric surface $x^2 - y + z^2 = 0$.

7. Identify the quadric surface $16x^2 + 9y^2 + 16z^2 - 32x - 36y + 36 = 0$.

8. Identify the quadric surface $9x^2 + y^2 - 9z^2 - 54x - 4y - 54z + 4 = 0$.

9. Find an equation of the surface of revolution generated by revolving the curve $z^2 = 4y$ in the yz-plane about the y-axis.

10. Find an equation of the surface of revolution generated by revolving the curve $z = 2y$ in the yz-plane about the z-axis.

Vector-Valued Functions in Space
Lesson 13

Topics

- Vector-valued functions.

- The derivative of a vector-valued function.

- Integrals of vector-valued functions.

- Particle motion.

- The unit tangent vector.

- Arc length and the differential of arc length.

Definitions and Theorems

- Vector-valued functions: $\mathbf{r}(t) = f(t)\mathbf{i} + g(t)\mathbf{j} + h(t)\mathbf{k} = \langle f(t), g(t), h(t) \rangle$.

- The **derivative** of a vector-valued function: $\mathbf{r}'(t) = \lim\limits_{\Delta t \to 0} \dfrac{\mathbf{r}(t+\Delta t) - \mathbf{r}(t)}{\Delta t}$.

- The derivative of the cross product: $\dfrac{d}{dt}[\mathbf{r} \times \mathbf{u}] = \mathbf{r} \times \mathbf{u}' + \mathbf{r}' \times \mathbf{u}$.

- Particle motion

Position:	$\mathbf{r}(t) = x(t)\mathbf{i} + y(t)\mathbf{j} + z(t)\mathbf{k}$.
Velocity:	$\mathbf{v}(t) = \mathbf{r}'(t) = x'(t)\mathbf{i} + y'(t)\mathbf{j} + z'(t)\mathbf{k}$.
Acceleration:	$\mathbf{a}(t) = \mathbf{r}''(t) = x''(t)\mathbf{i} + y''(t)\mathbf{j} + z''(t)\mathbf{k}$.
Speed:	$\|\mathbf{v}(t)\| = \|\mathbf{r}'(t)\| = \sqrt{[x'(t)]^2 + [y'(t)]^2 + [z'(t)]^2}$.

- The **unit tangent vector**: $\mathbf{T}(t) = \dfrac{\mathbf{r}'(t)}{\|\mathbf{r}'(t)\|}$.

- **Arc length**: $s = \displaystyle\int_a^b \sqrt{[x'(t)]^2 + [y'(t)]^2 + [z'(t)]^2}\, dt = \int_a^b \|\mathbf{r}'(t)\|\, dt$.

- The **differential of arc length**: $ds = \sqrt{[x'(t)]^2 + [y'(t)]^2 + [z'(t)]^2}\, dt = \|\mathbf{r}'(t)\|\, dt$.

Summary

In this lesson, we extend our knowledge of vector-valued functions in the plane to functions in space. We recall the definition of the derivative of a vector-valued function and develop some of its properties. We then focus on one of the main themes of calculus—particle motion. We define the position, velocity, and acceleration functions. The unit tangent vector is introduced and will play an important role in upcoming lessons. Finally, we recall the definition of arc length of a curve.

Example 1

Calculate the first and second derivatives of the vector-valued function for the helix $\mathbf{r}(t) = \cos t\mathbf{i} + \sin t\mathbf{j} + 2t\mathbf{k}$.

Solution

We differentiate the components to obtain $\mathbf{r}'(t) = -\sin t\mathbf{i} + \cos t\mathbf{j} + 2t\mathbf{k}$ and $\mathbf{r}''(t) = -\cos t\mathbf{i} - \sin t\mathbf{j}$.

Example 2

Calculate the derivative of the dot product of the vector-valued functions $\mathbf{r}(t) = \frac{1}{t}\mathbf{i} - \mathbf{j} + \ln t\mathbf{k}$ and $\mathbf{u}(t) = t^2\mathbf{i} - 2t\mathbf{j} + \mathbf{k}$.

Solution

We can do this problem two ways. We could first take the dot product and differentiate the result:
$$\mathbf{r}(t) \cdot \mathbf{u}(t) = \frac{1}{t}(t^2) + (-1)(-2t) + \ln t(1) = t + 2t + \ln t = 3t + \ln t.$$

The derivative is therefore $\frac{d}{dt}\left[\mathbf{r}(t) \cdot \mathbf{u}(t)\right] = \frac{d}{dt}[3t + \ln t] = 3 + \frac{1}{t}$.

Or, we could use the product rule for the dot product, $\left[\mathbf{r}(t) \cdot \mathbf{u}(t)\right]' = \mathbf{r}(t) \cdot \mathbf{u}'(t) + \mathbf{r}'(t) \cdot \mathbf{u}(t)$. We will, of course, obtain the same answer.

Example 3

Find the antiderivative of the function $\mathbf{r}'(t) = \cos 2t\mathbf{i} - 2\sin t\mathbf{j} + \frac{1}{1+t^2}\mathbf{k}$.

Solution

We integrate term by term: $\mathbf{r}(t) = \frac{1}{2}\sin 2t\mathbf{i} + 2\cos t\mathbf{j} + \arctan t\mathbf{k} + \mathbf{C}$. Notice that the constant of integration is a vector, not a scalar.

Example 4

An object is moving with position function $\mathbf{r}(t) = 4\cos t\mathbf{i} + 4\sin t\mathbf{j} + 3t\mathbf{k}$. Find its velocity, acceleration, and speed.

Solution

We calculate the first and second derivatives to obtain the velocity and acceleration:

$$\mathbf{v}(t) = \mathbf{r}'(t) = -4\sin t\mathbf{i} + 4\cos t\mathbf{j} + 3\mathbf{k} \text{ and } \mathbf{a}(t) = \mathbf{r}''(t) = -4\cos t\mathbf{i} - 4\sin t\mathbf{j}.$$

The speed is given by

$$\|\mathbf{v}(t)\| = \|\mathbf{r}'(t)\| = \sqrt{\left[x'(t)\right]^2 + \left[y'(t)\right]^2 + \left[z'(t)\right]^2} = \sqrt{16\sin^2 t + 16\cos^2 t + 9} = \sqrt{16 + 9} = 5.$$

(See **Figure 13.1**.)

Example 5

Find the arc length of one turn of the helix

$$\mathbf{r}(t) = 4\cos t\mathbf{i} + 4\sin t\mathbf{j} + 3t\mathbf{k}, \ 0 \le t \le 2\pi.$$

Solution

The arc length is given by

$$s = \int_a^b \sqrt{\left[x'(t)\right]^2 + \left[y'(t)\right]^2 + \left[z'(t)\right]^2}\, dt$$

$$= \int_0^{2\pi} \sqrt{\left[-4\sin t\right]^2 + \left[4\cos t\right]^2 + \left[3\right]^2}\, dt$$

$$= \int_0^{2\pi} 5\, dt = 10\pi.$$

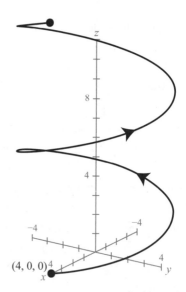

(4, 0, 0)

Figure 13.1

Study Tips

- You can evaluate the derivative of a vector-valued function by differentiating the individual components. That is, if $\mathbf{r}(t) = f(t)\mathbf{i} + g(t)\mathbf{j} + h(t)\mathbf{k}$, then the derivative is $\mathbf{r}'(t) = f'(t)\mathbf{i} + g'(t)\mathbf{j} + h'(t)\mathbf{k}$.

- The derivative vector is tangent to the curve and points in the direction of motion.

- The unit tangent vector in Example 4 is a unit vector pointing in the direction of motion,

$$\mathbf{T}(t) = \frac{\mathbf{r}'(t)}{\|\mathbf{r}'(t)\|} = \frac{1}{5}\left(-4\sin t\mathbf{i} + 4\cos t\mathbf{j} + 3\mathbf{k}\right).$$

- You can integrate a vector-valued function by integrating the individual components. Furthermore, you can combine the constants of integration into one constant $\mathbf{C}$, which is a vector.

Pitfall

- The constant of integration $\mathbf{C}$ for a vector-valued function is a vector, not a scalar.

Problems

1. Calculate the derivative of the function $\mathbf{r}(t) = \frac{1}{t}\mathbf{i} + 16t\mathbf{j} + \frac{t^2}{2}\mathbf{k}$.

2. Calculate the derivative of the function $\mathbf{r}(t) = \left\langle t^3, \cos 3t, \sin 3t \right\rangle$.

3. Calculate $\mathbf{r}'(t) \cdot \mathbf{r}''(t)$ if $\mathbf{r}(t) = \left\langle \frac{1}{2}t^2, -t, \frac{1}{6}t^3 \right\rangle$.

4. Find the indefinite integral $\int (2t\mathbf{i} + \mathbf{j} + \mathbf{k})\, dt$.

5. Evaluate the definite integral $\int_0^{\pi/4} \left[(\sec t \tan t)\mathbf{i} + (\tan t)\mathbf{j} + (2\sin t \cos t)\mathbf{k} \right] dt$.

6. Find the velocity, speed, and acceleration of a particle moving with position function $\mathbf{r}(t) = 4t\mathbf{i} + 4t\mathbf{j} + 2t\mathbf{k}$.

7. Find the unit tangent vector to the curve $\mathbf{r}(t) = \left\langle 2\cos t, 2\sin t, 4 \right\rangle$.

8. Find the unit tangent vector to the curve $\mathbf{r}(t) = t\mathbf{i} + t^2\mathbf{j} + t\mathbf{k}$ at the point $(0, 0, 0)$.

9. Find the arc length of the space curve $\mathbf{r}(t) = -t\mathbf{i} + 4t\mathbf{j} + 3t\mathbf{k}$ over the interval $0 \le t \le 1$.

10. Find the arc length of the space curve $\mathbf{r}(t) = \left\langle 2\sin t, 5t, 2\cos t \right\rangle$ over the interval $0 \le t \le \pi$.

Kepler's Laws—The Calculus of Orbits
Lesson 14

Topic

- Kepler's laws.

Definitions and Theorems

- Kepler's first law: The orbit of each planet is an ellipse, with the Sun at one of the two foci. (See **Figure 14.1**.)

- Kepler's second law: A line joining a planet and the Sun sweeps out equal areas during equal intervals of time. (See **Figure 14.2**.)

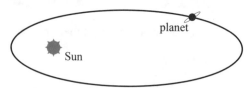

Figure 14.1

- Kepler's third law: The square of the orbital period of a planet is directly proportional to the cube of the semimajor axis of the orbit.

- Newton's second law of motion: $\mathbf{F} = m\mathbf{a}$.

- Newton's law of gravitation: $\mathbf{F} = -\dfrac{GMm}{r^3}\mathbf{r}$.

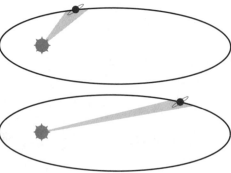

Here, $\mathbf{F}$ is the gravitational force on the planet, M is the mass of the Sun, m is the mass of the planet, G is a constant, and $r = \|\mathbf{r}\|$ is the length of the position vector.

Figure 14.2

Summary

Kepler's famous laws of planetary motion were announced by the German astronomer and mathematician Johannes Kepler (1571–1630). His three laws were based on a 20-year study of astronomical data compiled by the Danish astronomer Tycho Brahe. Isaac Newton later used calculus to derive these laws from basic laws of physics. In this lesson, we will study these three laws and use our calculus skills to prove the second law.

Example 1

Show that a given planet always moves in a plane.

Solution

Recall that the cross product of a vector with itself is zero. In fact, the cross product of parallel vectors is zero: If $\mathbf{u} = u_1\mathbf{i} + u_2\mathbf{j} + u_3\mathbf{k}$ and $\mathbf{v} = c\mathbf{u} = cu_1\mathbf{i} + cu_2\mathbf{j} + cu_3\mathbf{k}$ are parallel vectors, then

$$\mathbf{u} \times c\mathbf{u} = \begin{vmatrix} \mathbf{i} & \mathbf{j} & \mathbf{k} \\ u_1 & u_2 & u_3 \\ cu_1 & cu_2 & cu_3 \end{vmatrix} = \left(u_2 cu_3 - u_3 cu_2 \right)\mathbf{i} - \left(u_1 cu_3 - u_3 cu_1 \right)\mathbf{j} + \left(u_1 cu_2 - u_2 cu_1 \right)\mathbf{k} = 0.$$

From Newton's second law of motion and the law of gravitation,

$$\mathbf{F} = m\mathbf{a} = -\frac{GMm}{r^3}\mathbf{r} \Rightarrow \mathbf{a} = -\frac{GM}{r^3}\mathbf{r}.$$

This means that $\mathbf{a}$ and $\mathbf{r}$ are parallel, so their cross product is zero, $\mathbf{r} \times \mathbf{r}'' = \mathbf{r} \times \mathbf{a} = 0$.

Next, consider the following derivative: $\dfrac{d}{dt}\left[\mathbf{r} \times \mathbf{r}' \right] = \mathbf{r}' \times \mathbf{r}' + \mathbf{r} \times \mathbf{r}'' = 0$.

Because the derivative is zero, $\mathbf{r} \times \mathbf{r}'$ is a constant—for example, $\mathbf{r} \times \mathbf{r}' = \mathbf{L}$. So, the planet moves in a plane orthogonal to this constant vector $\mathbf{L}$. That is, the vector $\mathbf{r}$ lies in a plane orthogonal to $\mathbf{L}$.

Example 2

Prove Kepler's second law.

Solution

Begin by writing the position function in polar coordinates, $\mathbf{r} = r\left(\cos\theta\mathbf{i} + \sin\theta\mathbf{j} \right)$.

Then, we have $\|\mathbf{r}\| = r$ and $\mathbf{r}' = \dfrac{d\mathbf{r}}{dt} = r\left(-\sin\theta\mathbf{i} + \cos\theta\mathbf{j} \right)\dfrac{d\theta}{dt}$. We calculate the cross product of $\mathbf{r}$ and its derivative:

$$\mathbf{r} \times \mathbf{r}' = \begin{vmatrix} \mathbf{i} & \mathbf{j} & \mathbf{k} \\ r\cos\theta & r\sin\theta & 0 \\ -r\sin\theta & r\cos\theta & 0 \end{vmatrix}\frac{d\theta}{dt}$$

$$= r^2\left(\cos^2\theta + \sin^2\theta \right)\frac{d\theta}{dt}\mathbf{k} = r^2\frac{d\theta}{dt}\mathbf{k}.$$

So, now we have $\mathbf{r} \times \mathbf{r'} = r^2 \dfrac{d\theta}{dt} \mathbf{k}$ and $\mathbf{r} \times \mathbf{r'} = \mathbf{L}$, which implies that $\|\mathbf{r} \times \mathbf{r'}\| = \|\mathbf{L}\| = r^2 \dfrac{d\theta}{dt}$.

Consider the area swept out between $\theta = \alpha$ and $\theta = \beta$. In polar coordinates, the area is

$$A = \frac{1}{2} \int_\alpha^\beta r^2 \, d\theta = \frac{1}{2} \int_{t_0}^{t_1} r^2 \frac{d\theta}{dt} \, dt = \frac{1}{2} \int_{t_0}^{t_1} \|\mathbf{L}\| \, dt = \frac{1}{2} \|\mathbf{L}\| (t_1 - t_0).$$

So, for the time interval $[t_0, t_1]$, the area swept out is constant. In other words, for time intervals of equal length, the areas swept out are the same, which proves Kepler's second law.

Example 3

For the planet Mercury, $a = 0.3871$ and $P = 0.2408$. Kepler's third law is verified because $a^3 = 0.05800$ and $P^2 = 0.05798$, which are very close.

Study Tips

- The orbital period for Earth is $P = 1$ year.

- The semimajor axis of the ellipse $\dfrac{x^2}{a^2} + \dfrac{y^2}{b^2} = 1, a > b$, is a. In astronomical units (AU), $a = 1$.

- Recall the formula for area in polar coordinates: $A = \dfrac{1}{2} \int_\alpha^\beta r^2 \, d\theta$.

Problems

1. Halley's Comet has an elliptical orbit with the Sun at one focus and has an eccentricity of $e \approx 0.967$. The length $(2a)$ of the major axis of the orbit is approximately 35.88 astronomical units (AU). (An astronomical unit is defined as the mean distance between Earth and the Sun, 93 million miles.) A polar equation for the orbit is

$$r = \frac{ed}{1 + e \sin \theta}.$$

Find the value of d. Then, use the fact that $c = ea$ is the distance between the focus and the center to determine how close the comet comes to the Sun.

2. The asteroid Apollo has a period of 661 Earth days, and its orbit is approximated by the ellipse

$$r = \frac{1}{1 + \left(\frac{5}{9}\right) \cos \theta} = \frac{9}{9 + 5 \cos \theta},$$

where r is measured in astronomical units. The area of this ellipse is approximately 5.46507. Use a graphing utility to approximate the time it takes Apollo to move from the position given by $\theta = -\pi/2$ to $\theta = \pi/2$.

Directional Derivatives and Gradients
Lesson 15

Topics

- Directional derivatives.

- The gradient of a function of two or more variables.

- Properties of the gradient.

- Gradients and level curves.

- Gradients and level surfaces.

Definitions and Theorems

- Let $\mathbf{u} = \cos\theta\mathbf{i} + \sin\theta\mathbf{j}$ be a unit vector in the plane, and let f be a differentiable function of x and y. The **directional derivative** of f in the direction of $\mathbf{u}$ is

$$D_{\mathbf{u}}f(x, y) = f_x(x, y)\cos\theta + f_y(x, y)\sin\theta.$$

- Let $z = f(x, y)$ be a function whose partial derivatives exist. The **gradient** of f is the vector
  $$\mathbf{grad}\, f(x, y) = \nabla f(x, y) = f_x(x, y)\mathbf{i} + f_y(x, y)\mathbf{j}.$$

- Theorem: $D_{\mathbf{u}}f(x, y) = \nabla f(x, y) \cdot \mathbf{u}$.

- Theorem: $D_{\mathbf{u}}f(x, y) = \|\nabla f(x, y)\|\cos\phi$, where φ is the angle between the gradient and the unit vector $\mathbf{u}$. The directional derivative is a maximum when $\cos\phi = 1$ and a minimum when $\cos\phi = -1$.

- Theorem: If f is differentiable at the point (x_0, y_0) and $\nabla f(x_0, y_0) \neq \mathbf{0}$, then $\nabla f(x_0, y_0)$ is orthogonal to the level curve through the point (x_0, y_0). In a similar manner, gradients of functions of three variables are orthogonal to level surfaces.

Summary

In this lesson, we continue our study of functions of two or more independent variables. We first generalize the concept of partial derivative to the so-called directional derivative. This leads to the definition of the gradient of a function of two (or more) variables. We will see that the gradient is a vector that points in the direction of maximum increase (steepest ascent). Finally, we discover that the gradient vector in the plane is orthogonal to level curves. And in space, the gradient is orthogonal to level surfaces. This will be a key result when we develop tangent planes to surfaces in the next lesson.

Example 1

Find the directional derivative of $f(x, y) = 4 - x^2 - \frac{1}{4}y^2$ at the point $(1, 2)$ in the direction of $\mathbf{u} = \left(\cos\frac{\pi}{3}\right)\mathbf{i} + \left(\sin\frac{\pi}{3}\right)\mathbf{j}$.

Solution

$$D_{\mathbf{u}}f(x, y) = f_x(x, y)\cos\theta + f_y(x, y)\sin\theta = (-2x)\cos\theta + \left(-\frac{y}{2}\right)\sin\theta.$$

We have $\theta = \frac{\pi}{3}$, $x = 1, y = 2$, so $D_{\mathbf{u}}f(1, 2) = (-2)\left(\frac{1}{2}\right) + (-1)\left(\frac{\sqrt{3}}{2}\right) = -1 - \frac{\sqrt{3}}{2} \approx -1.866$.

Example 2

Find the gradient of the function $f(x, y) = y\ln x + xy^2$ at the point $(1, 2)$.

Solution

The partial derivatives are $f_x(x, y) = \frac{y}{x} + y^2$ and $f_y(x, y) = \ln x + 2xy$.

So, we have $\nabla f(x, y) = f_x(x, y)\mathbf{i} + f_y(x, y)\mathbf{j} = \left(\frac{y}{x} + y^2\right)\mathbf{i} + (\ln x + 2xy)\mathbf{j}$.

At the point $(1, 2)$, $\nabla f(1, 2) = \left(\frac{2}{1} + 2^2\right)\mathbf{i} + (\ln 1 + 2(1)(2))\mathbf{j} = 6\mathbf{i} + 4\mathbf{j}$.

Example 3

The gradient of the function of three variables $f(x, y, z) = x^2 + y^2 - 4z$ is

$$\nabla f(x, y, z) = f_x(x, y, z)\mathbf{i} + f_y(x, y, z)\mathbf{j} + f_z(x, y, z)\mathbf{k} = 2x\mathbf{i} + 2y\mathbf{j} - 4\mathbf{k}.$$

At the point $(2, -1, 1)$, $\nabla f(2, -1, 1) = 4\mathbf{i} - 2\mathbf{j} - 4\mathbf{k}$.

Consider a level surface through this point
$f(2, -1, 1) = 2^2 + (-1)^2 - 4(1) = 1$. The gradient vector
is orthogonal to the level surface through the point
$x^2 + y^2 - 4z = 1 \Rightarrow z = \frac{1}{4}(x^2 + y^2 - 1)$.

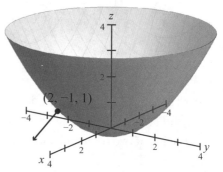

Figure 15.1

In this case, the gradient is pointing downward at the point
$(2, -1, 1)$ on the paraboloid. (See **Figure 15.1**.)

Study Tips

- The directional derivative is a number. If $\theta = 0$, then the directional derivative is just the partial derivative $f_x(x, y)$. Similarly, if $\theta = 90° = \pi/2$, then the directional derivative is $f_y(x, y)$.

- The gradient of a function of two (or more) variables is a vector-valued function.

- Gradients of functions of two variables are orthogonal to level curves, and gradients of functions of three variables are orthogonal to level surfaces.

Pitfalls

- In the definition of directional derivative, the direction vector $\mathbf{u}$ must be a unit vector.

- Furthermore, the function f must be differentiable. You can consult a calculus textbook for a more general definition of directional derivative involving limits.

Problems

1. Find the directional derivative of the function $f(x, y) = 3x - 4xy + 9y$ at the point $P(1, 2)$ in the direction of $\mathbf{v} = \dfrac{3}{5}\mathbf{i} + \dfrac{4}{5}\mathbf{j}$.

2. Find the directional derivative of the function $f(x, y) = e^x \sin y$ at the point $P(1, \pi/2)$ in the direction of $\mathbf{v} = -\mathbf{i}$.

3. Find the directional derivative of the function $f(x, y, z) = x^2 + y^2 + z^2$ at the point $P(1, 1, 1)$ in the direction of $\mathbf{v} = \mathbf{i} - \mathbf{j} + \mathbf{k}$.

4. Find the gradient of the function $f(x, y) = 3x + 5y^2 + 1$ at the point $(2, 1)$.

5. Find the gradient of the function $z = \ln(x^2 - y)$ at the point $(2, 3)$.

6. Find the gradient of the function $f(x, y, z) = 3x^2 - 5y^2 + 2z^2$ at the point $(1, 1, -2)$.

7. Find the maximum value of the directional derivative of the function $f(x, y) = x^2 + 2xy$ at the point $(1, 0)$.

8. Find the maximum value of the directional derivative of the function $f(x, y, z) = xy^2z^2$ at the point $(2, 1, 1)$.

9. Find a normal vector to the level curve $f(x, y) = 6 - 2x - 3y = 6$ at the point $P(0, 0)$.

10. The temperature at the point (x, y) on a metal plate is $T = \dfrac{x}{x^2 + y^2}$. Find the direction of greatest increase in heat from the point $(3, 4)$.

Tangent Planes and Normal Vectors to a Surface
Lesson 16

Topics

- Normal vectors to surfaces.

- Tangent planes to surfaces.

Definitions and Theorems

- Consider a surface given by $F(x, y, z) = 0$. This is a level surface, so the gradient vector $\mathbf{n} = \langle a, b, c \rangle$ is normal to the surface at any point (x_0, y_0, z_0) on the surface. This vector, together with the point, determines the **tangent plane** to the surface. The equation of the tangent plane is
  $a(x - x_0) + b(y - y_0) + c(z - z_0) = 0.$

- The equation of the tangent plane can be written as

$$F_x\left(x_0, y_0, z_0\right)\left(x - x_0\right) + F_y\left(x_0, y_0, z_0\right)\left(y - y_0\right) + F_z\left(x_0, y_0, z_0\right)\left(z - z_0\right) = 0.$$

Summary

In this lesson, we show how to find the equation of a tangent plane to a surface. The secret is to use the fact from the previous lesson that gradients are orthogonal to level surfaces. We also show that approximations by the total differential are equivalent to using the tangent plane to approximate the surface.

Example 1

The level surface $F(x, y, z) = 0$ for the function of three variables $F(x, y, z) = x^2 + y^2 + z^2 - 9$ is a sphere of radius 3, $F(x, y, z) = x^2 + y^2 + z^2 - 9 = 0$, or $x^2 + y^2 + z^2 = 9$.

The gradient of the function is $\nabla F(x, y, z) = 2x\mathbf{i} + 2y\mathbf{j} + 2z\mathbf{k}$, which is normal to the surface at the point $(1, 2, 2)$, $\nabla F(1, 2, 2) = 2\mathbf{i} + 4\mathbf{j} + 4\mathbf{k}$. (See **Figure 16.1**.)

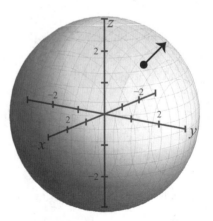

Figure 16.1

Example 2

Find the equation of the tangent plane to the surface $z = x^2 + y^2$ at the point $(1, 1, 2)$.

Solution

Define the function of three variables $F(x, y, z) = f(x, y) - z = x^2 + y^2 - z$ and consider the level surface $F(x, y, z) = x^2 + y^2 - z = 0$.

The gradient is $\nabla F(x, y, z) = \langle 2x, 2y, -1 \rangle$, and $\nabla F(1, 1, 2) = \langle 2, 2, -1 \rangle$. This vector is normal to the surface at the point $(1, 1, 2)$.

Using this normal vector and the given point, we have $2(x - 1) + 2(y - 1) - 1(z - 2) = 0$. So, the equation of the tangent plane is $2x + 2y - z = 2$. (See **Figure 16.2**.)

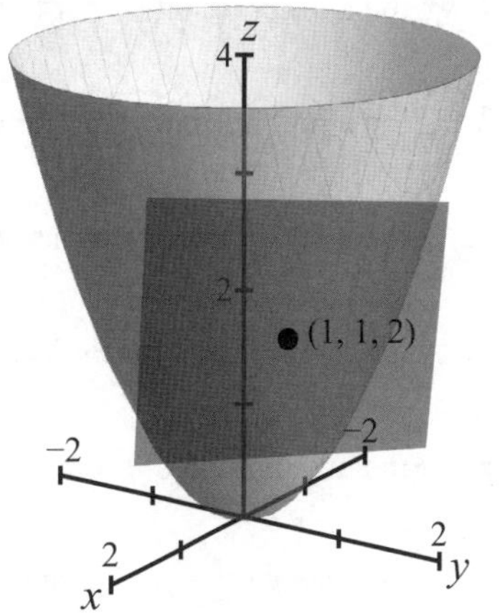

Example 3

Show that approximations by the total differential are equivalent to approximating a surface by its tangent plane.

Solution

Figure 16.2

Consider the surface $z = f(x, y)$ and form the function $F(x, y, z) = f(x, y) - z$.

The tangent plane at the point (x_0, y_0, z_0) is given by

$$F_x(x - x_0) + F_y(y - y_0) + F_z(z - z_0) = 0$$
$$f_x(x_0 - y_0)(x - x_0) + f_y(x_0 - y_0)(y - y_0) - (z - z_0) = 0$$
$$z - z_0 = f_x(x_0 - y_0)(x - x_0) + f_y(x_0 - y_0)(y - y_0).$$

Compare this to the error formula given by the total differential

$$\Delta z \approx f_x(x_0, y_0)\Delta x + f_y(x_0, y_0)\Delta y.$$

Study Tips

- For functions of three variables, the gradient vector $\nabla F(x_0, y_0, z_0)$ is normal (orthogonal) to the level surface through the point (x_0, y_0, z_0).

- The key to finding the tangent plane to a surface $z = f(x, y)$ is to express the equation as the level surface of a function of three variables, $F(x, y, z) = f(x, y) - z = 0$, as we did in Example 2.

- As mentioned in a previous lesson, the total differential is a tangent plane approximation to a surface. This is similar to the tangent line approximation to a curve in elementary calculus.

Pitfall

- A function $F(x, y, z)$ has to be "nice" in order to have a tangent plane at a point. For example, there is no tangent plane defined at the vertex of a cone.

Problems

1. Find a unit normal vector to the surface $3x + 4y + 12z = 0$ at the point $(0, 0, 0)$.

2. Find a unit normal vector to the surface $x^2 + y^2 + z^2 = 6$ at the point $(1, 1, 2)$.

3. Find a normal vector to the surface $z - x \sin y = 4$ at the point $(6, \pi/6, 7)$.

4. Find a normal vector to the surface $z = x^3$ at the point $(2, -1, 8)$.

5. Find an equation of the tangent plane to the surface $z = x^2 + y^2 + 3$ at the point $(2, 1, 8)$.

6. Find an equation of the tangent plane to the surface $f(x, y) = \dfrac{y}{x}$ at the point $(1, 2, 2)$.

7. Find an equation of the tangent plane to the surface $x^2 + 2z^2 = y^2$ at the point $(1, 3, -2)$.

8. Find an equation of the tangent plane to the surface $x^2 + 4y^2 + z^2 = 36$ at the point $(2, -2, 4)$.

9. Find the point(s) on the surface $z = 3 - x^2 - y^2 + 6y$ at which the tangent plane is horizontal.

10. Find the point(s) on the surface $z = xy + \dfrac{1}{x} + \dfrac{1}{y}$ at which the tangent plane is horizontal.

Lagrange Multipliers—Constrained Optimization
Lesson 17

Topics

- Lagrange multipliers.

- Applications to optimization problems with constraints.

Definitions and Theorems

- Lagrange's theorem: Let f and g have continuous first partial derivatives such that f has an extremum at (x_0, y_0) on the smooth constraint curve $g(x, y) = k$. If $\nabla g(x_0, y_0) \neq 0$, then there is a real number λ such that $\nabla f(x_0, y_0) = \lambda \nabla g(x_0, y_0)$. The number λ is called a **Lagrange multiplier**.

Summary

The method of Lagrange multipliers is a powerful technique for solving optimization problems that have constraints. For instance, you might want to find the maximum volume of a box with the constraint that the cost of the material for the box is fixed. We begin this lesson with a simple example of maximizing the value of a function of two variables given a certain constraint on those variables. Then, we solve the same box problem we saw in our previous lesson on maximum/minimum applications.

Example 1

Find the maximum value of the function $f(x, y) = 4xy$, where $x, y > 0$, subject to the constraint

$$g(x, y) = \frac{x^2}{3^2} + \frac{y^2}{4^2} = 1.$$

Solution

The gradients are $\nabla f(x, y) = 4y\mathbf{i} + 4x\mathbf{j}$ and $\nabla g(x, y) = \frac{2x}{9}\mathbf{i} + \frac{y}{8}\mathbf{j}$.

We solve the equation $\nabla f(x, y) = \lambda g(x, y)$, which implies that $4y\mathbf{i} + 4x\mathbf{j} = \lambda \frac{2x}{9}\mathbf{i} + \lambda \frac{y}{8}\mathbf{j}$.

Hence, we have the three equations $4y = \lambda \frac{2x}{9}$, $4x = \lambda \frac{y}{8}$, and $\frac{x^2}{3^2} + \frac{y^2}{4^2} = 1$.

We now use our algebra skills to solve these equations. From the first equation, $\lambda = \dfrac{18y}{x}$.

Substitute this into the second equation: $4x = \lambda \dfrac{y}{8} = \left(\dfrac{18y}{x}\right)\dfrac{y}{8} \Rightarrow 4x = \dfrac{9y^2}{4x} \Rightarrow \dfrac{x^2}{9} = \dfrac{y^2}{16}$.

Next, use the constraint equation $\dfrac{x^2}{3^2} + \dfrac{y^2}{4^2} = 1 \Rightarrow \dfrac{y^2}{16} + \dfrac{y^2}{16} = 1 \Rightarrow 2y^2 = 16 \Rightarrow y^2 = 8$.

Thus, we have $y = 2\sqrt{2}$ and $x^2 = \dfrac{9}{16}y^2 = \dfrac{9}{16}(8) = \dfrac{9}{2} \Rightarrow x = \dfrac{3\sqrt{2}}{2}$.

With these values of x and y, the maximum value is $f\left(\dfrac{3\sqrt{2}}{2}, 2\sqrt{2}\right) = 4\left(\dfrac{3\sqrt{2}}{2}\right)(2\sqrt{2}) = 24$.

Example 2

The material for constructing the base of an open box costs \$3 per square foot, and the material for constructing the sides costs \$2 per square foot. For a fixed amount of money $C = \$1296$, find the dimensions of the box of largest volume that can be made. (See **Figure 17.1**.)

Solution

We want to maximize the volume of the box, $f(x, y, z) = xyz$, subject to the constraint $g(x, y, z) = 3xy + 4xz + 4yz = 1296$. Using Lagrange multipliers, we have

$$\nabla f(x, y, z) = \lambda \nabla g(x, y, z)$$
$$yz\mathbf{i} + xz\mathbf{j} + xy\mathbf{k} = \lambda\left[(3y + 4z)\mathbf{i} + (3x + 4z)\mathbf{j} + (4x + 4y)\mathbf{k}\right].$$

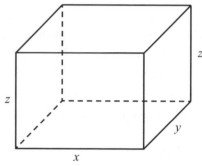

Figure 17.1

So, we must solve the following four equations in four unknowns:

$$yz = \lambda(3y + 4z)$$
$$xz = \lambda(3x + 4z)$$
$$xy = \lambda(4x + 4y)$$
$$3xy + 4xz + 4yz = 1296.$$

This requires a lot of algebra, and the final solution is $x = y = 12$, $z = 9$, and $\lambda = \dfrac{3}{2}$. The maximum volume is $xyz = 12 \times 12 \times 9 = 1296$ cubic feet.

Study Tips

- Lagrange multipliers are particularly useful for optimization applications having side conditions or constraints.

- You can extend Lagrange multipliers to problems with more than one constraint.

- When using Lagrange multipliers, the algebra can be quite difficult.

- You can write the constraint in different ways, but the gradient will be the same. For instance, in Example 1, we used $g(x, y) = \dfrac{x^2}{3^2} + \dfrac{y^2}{4^2} = 1$, but we could have used $g(x, y) = \dfrac{x^2}{3^2} + \dfrac{y^2}{4^2} - 1 = 0$.

- Notice that the answer to Example 2 is the same as the one we obtained in Lesson 6. Which method do you prefer?

Pitfalls

- The technique of Lagrange multipliers can fail $\nabla g(x_0, y_0) = 0$.

- The greatest difficulty with Lagrange multipliers is in solving the system of equations. Make sure that you check your answer with the original equations.

Problems

1. Use Lagrange multipliers to find the minimum value of $f(x, y) = x^2 + y^2$ subject to the constraint $x + 2y - 5 = 0$. Assume that x and y are positive.

2. Use Lagrange multipliers to find the maximum value of $f(x, y) = x^2 - y^2$ subject to the constraint $2y - x^2 = 0$. Assume that x and y are positive.

3. Use Lagrange multipliers to find the maximum value of $f(x, y) = 2x + 2xy + y$ subject to the constraint $2x + y = 100$. Assume that x and y are positive.

4. Use Lagrange multipliers to find the minimum value of $f(x, y, z) = x^2 + y^2 + z^2$ subject to the constraint $x + y + z - 9 = 0$. Assume that x, y, and z are positive.

5. Use Lagrange multipliers to find the maximum value of $f(x, y, z) = xyz$ subject to the constraint $x + y + z - 3 = 0$. Assume that x, y, and z are positive.

6. Use Lagrange multipliers to find the minimum distance from the line $x + y = 1$ to the point $(0, 0)$.

7. Use Lagrange multipliers to find the minimum distance from the parabola $y = x^2$ to the point $(0, 3)$.

8. A cargo container in the shape of a rectangular solid must have a volume of 480 cubic feet. The bottom will cost \$5 per square foot to construct, and the sides and the top will cost \$3 per square foot to construct. Use Lagrange multipliers to find the dimensions of the container of this size that has minimum cost.

Applications of Lagrange Multipliers
Lesson 18

Topics

- Applications of Lagrange multipliers.

- Maximizing the volume of a package.

- Snell's law of refraction.

Definitions and Theorems

- Lagrange's theorem: Let f and g have continuous first partial derivatives such that f has an extremum at (x_0, y_0) on the smooth constraint curve $g(x, y) = k$. If $\nabla g(x_0, y_0) \neq 0$, then there is a real number λ such that $\nabla f(x_0, y_0) = \lambda \nabla g(x_0, y_0)$. The number λ is called a **Lagrange multiplier**.

- When light waves traveling in a transparent medium strike the surface of a second transparent medium, they tend to "bend" in order to follow the path of minimum time. This tendency is called **refraction**, and it is described by **Snell's law of refraction**.

    Let v_1 and v_2 be the velocities of light in the two media, and let the angles be as indicated in the figure. Then,

    $$\frac{\sin \theta_1}{v_1} = \frac{\sin \theta_2}{v_2}.$$

    (See **Figure 18.1**.)

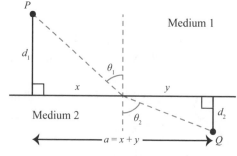

Figure 18.1

Summary

We continue our study of constrained optimization applications using Lagrange multipliers. We first use them to maximize the volume of a package, given a certain constraint on the dimensions. We saw this problem in Lesson 7, but it will be easier with Lagrange multipliers. Then, we derive Snell's law of refraction.

Example 1

The sum of the length and girth (perimeter of a cross section) of a package carried by a delivery service cannot exceed 108 inches. Find the dimensions of the rectangular package of largest volume that can be sent. (See **Figure 18.2**.)

Solution

We want to maximize the volume of the box, $V(x, y, z) = xyz$, subject to the constraint $g(x, y, z) = x + 2y + 2z = 108$. Using Lagrange multipliers, we have

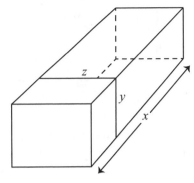

$$\nabla V = yz\,\mathbf{i} + xz\,\mathbf{j} + xy\,\mathbf{k}$$
$$\nabla g = \mathbf{i} + 2\mathbf{j} + 2\mathbf{k}$$
$$\nabla V(x, y, z) = \lambda \nabla g(x, y, z).$$

Figure 18.2

Hence, we must solve the following four equations in four unknowns:

$$yz = \lambda$$
$$xz = 2\lambda$$
$$xy = 2\lambda$$
$$x + 2y + 2z = 108.$$

The calculus portion of the problem is over, and next we need to use a lot of algebra. From the second and third equations, $xz = 2\lambda$ and $xy = 2\lambda$, we have $xz = xy \Rightarrow z = y$. From the first and third equations, $yz = \lambda$ and $xy = 2\lambda$, we have $2yz = 2\lambda = xy \Rightarrow x = 2z$. So, we have $y = z$, $x = 2y = 2z$. Next, use the constraint equation:

$$x + 2y + 2z = 108$$
$$2y + 2y + 2y = 6y = 108.$$

So, we have $y = 18$, $x = 36$, $z = 18$. The dimensions are $18 \times 18 \times 36$ inches.

Example 2

Use Lagrange multipliers to derive Snell's law of refraction.

Solution

Consider the **Figure 18.3**.

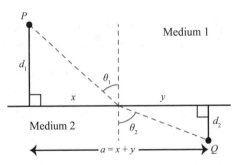

Figure 18.3

The distance from P to Q is $\sqrt{d_1^2 + x^2} + \sqrt{d_2^2 + y^2}$.

Because speed = distance/time, we have time = distance/speed, which is what we want to minimize.

Hence, we want to minimize $T(x, y) = \dfrac{\sqrt{d_1^2 + x^2}}{v_1} + \dfrac{\sqrt{d_2^2 + y^2}}{v_2}$ subject to the constraint $g(x, y) = x + y = a$.

Using Lagrange multipliers,

$$\nabla T(x, y) = \lambda \nabla g(x, y)$$

$$\frac{x}{v_1 \sqrt{d_1^2 + x^2}} \mathbf{i} + \frac{y}{v_2 \sqrt{d_2^2 + x^2}} \mathbf{j} = \lambda \mathbf{i} + \lambda \mathbf{j}.$$

So, we need to solve the three equations

$$\frac{x}{v_1 \sqrt{d_1^2 + x^2}} = \lambda$$

$$\frac{y}{v_2 \sqrt{d_2^2 + y^2}} = \lambda$$

$$x + y = a.$$

Hence, $\dfrac{x}{v_1 \sqrt{d_1^2 + x^2}} = \dfrac{y}{v_2 \sqrt{d_2^2 + y^2}}$.

From the figure, $\sin \theta_1 = \dfrac{x}{\sqrt{d_1^2 + x^2}}$ and $\sin \theta_2 = \dfrac{y}{\sqrt{d_2^2 + y^2}}$, which gives Snell's law, $\dfrac{\sin \theta_1}{v_1} = \dfrac{\sin \theta_2}{v_2}$.

Study Tip

- It's worth repeating that often the most difficult step in solving a Lagrange multiplier problem is the algebra.

Pitfall

- The technique of Lagrange multipliers can fail if $\nabla g(x_0, y_0) = 0$.

Problems

1. The Cobb-Douglas production function for a software manufacturer is given by $f(x, y) = 100 x^{3/4} y^{1/4}$, where x represents the units of labor (at \$150 per unit) and y represents the units of capital (at \$250 per unit). The total cost of labor and capital is limited to \$50,000. Find the maximum production level for this manufacturer.

2. Find the extreme values of $f(x, y) = x^2 + 2y^2 - 2x + 3$ subject to the constraint $x^2 + y^2 \leq 10$.

3. The volume of an ellipsoid $\dfrac{x^2}{a^2} + \dfrac{y^2}{b^2} + \dfrac{z^2}{c^2} = 1$ is $\dfrac{4\pi}{3} abc$. For a fixed sum $a + b + c$, show that the ellipsoid of maximum volume is a sphere.

4. Find the dimensions of a right circular cylinder with volume V_0 cubic units and minimum surface area.

5. Find the minimum distance from the point $(2, 1, 1)$ to the plane $x + y + z = 1$.

Iterated Integrals and Area in the Plane
Lesson 19

Topics

- Iterated integrals.

- Iterated integrals and area.

- Reversing the order of integration.

Definitions and Theorems

- Iterated integrals are of the form $\int_c^d \left[\int_{h_1(y)}^{h_2(y)} f(x,y) \, dx \right] dy$ and $\int_a^b \left[\int_{g_1(x)}^{g_2(x)} f(x,y) \, dy \right] dx$.

Summary

We now turn to the theory of integration for multivariable calculus. We begin with iterated integrals, which are nothing more than repeated simple integrals. We show how an iterated integral can be used to calculate the area of a planar region. We end the lesson by studying how you can reverse the order of integration. In fact, for some iterated integrals, you must reverse the order of integration.

Example 1

Calculate the iterated integral $\int_2^4 \left[\int_1^x 2xy \, dy \right] dx$.

Solution

First, we evaluate the integral in the brackets with respect to y, and then we integrate the result with respect to x.

$$\int_2^4 \left[\int_1^x 2xy \, dy \right] dx = \int_2^4 \left[xy^2 \right]_1^x dx = \int_2^4 \left(x^3 - x \right) dx = \left[\frac{x^4}{4} - \frac{x^2}{2} \right]_2^4 = (64 - 8) - (4 - 2) = 54.$$

Example 2

Use an iterated integral to find the area of the region bounded by the graphs of $f(x) = \sin x$ and $g(x) \cos x$ between $x = \frac{\pi}{4}$ and $x = \frac{5\pi}{4}$. (See **Figure 19.1**.)

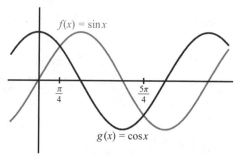

Figure 19.1

Solution

We have the following:

$$A = \int_{\pi/4}^{5\pi/4} \int_{\cos x}^{\sin x} dy\, dx$$

$$= \int_{\pi/4}^{5\pi/4} \left[y\right]_{\cos x}^{\sin x} dx$$

$$= \int_{\pi/4}^{5\pi/4} \left[\sin x - \cos x\right] dx$$

$$= \left[-\cos x - \sin x\right]_{\pi/4}^{5\pi/4} = 2\sqrt{2}.$$

Example 3

Sketch the region whose area is represented by the iterated integral $\int_0^2 \int_{y^2}^4 dx\, dy$.

Solution

We know that $y^2 \le x \le 4$. So, the region is bounded on the left by $x = y^2 \Leftrightarrow y = \sqrt{x}$ and on the right by $x = 4$.

Furthermore, $0 \le y \le 2$, so the region is as shown in **Figure 19.2**.

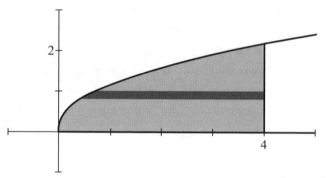

Figure 19.2

Example 4

Sketch the region of integration represented by the iterated integral $\int_0^2 \int_x^2 e^{-y^2} dy\, dx$. Then, evaluate the integral by reversing the order of integration.

Solution

The region of integration is shown in **Figure 19.3**.

Reversing the order, we have $\int_0^2 \int_x^2 e^{-y^2} dy\, dx = \int_0^2 \int_0^y e^{-y^2} dx\, dy$.

Although the original integral could not be evaluated using the fundamental theorem of calculus, the new integral can easily be evaluated using substitution.

The answer is $\frac{1}{2}\left(1 - \frac{1}{e^4}\right)$.

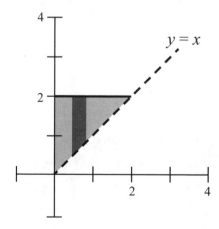

Figure 19.3

Study Tips

- Iterated integrals are similar to partial derivatives in that you integrate with respect to one variable while holding the other variable fixed. For example, if

$$f_x(x,y) = 2xy \text{, then } f(x,y) = \int f_x(x,y)\,dx = \int 2xy\,dx = x^2 y + C(y).$$

  Notice that the "constant of integration" is a function of y.

- Iterated integrals are usually written without brackets or parentheses. For instance, the iterated integral in Example 1 is usually written as follows:

$$\int_2^4 \left[\int_1^x 2xy\,dy \right] dx = \int_2^4 \int_1^x 2xy\,dy\,dx.$$

- Representative rectangles can be very useful in describing the region of integration.

Pitfalls

- For area computations, the outer limits of integration must be constants. For instance, the following iterated integral is incorrect: $\int_0^x \int_{y^2}^4 dx\,dy.$

- Keep in mind that the variable of integration can never appear as a limit of integration. For example, the following integral is incorrect: $\int_0^x y\,dx.$

Problems

1. Evaluate the integral $\int_0^x (x+2y)\,dy.$

2. Evaluate the integral $\int_1^{2y} \dfrac{y}{x}\,dx.$

3. Evaluate the iterated integral $\int_0^1 \int_0^2 (x+y)\,dy\,dx.$

4. Evaluate the iterated integral $\int_0^{\pi/2} \int_0^1 y\cos x\,dy\,dx.$

5. Evaluate the iterated integral $\int_1^3 \int_0^y \dfrac{4}{x^2+y^2}\,dx\,dy.$

6. Use an iterated integral to find the area of the region bounded by $\sqrt{x} + \sqrt{y} = 2$, $x = 0$, and $y = 0$.

7. Evaluate the iterated integral $\int_0^1 \int_{-\sqrt{1-y^2}}^{\sqrt{1-y^2}} dx\,dy$.

Then, reverse the order of integration and evaluate the resulting iterated integral.

8. Evaluate the iterated integral $\int_0^2 \int_{1/2}^1 dy\,dx$.

Then, reverse the order of integration and evaluate the resulting iterated integral.

9. Evaluate the iterated integral $\int_0^1 \int_{2x}^2 4e^{y^2}\,dy\,dx$.

10. Evaluate the iterated integral $\int_0^2 \int_{y^2}^4 \sqrt{x}\sin x\,dx\,dy$.

Double Integrals and Volume
Lesson 20

Topics

- Double integrals and volume.

- Properties of double integrals.

- Average value.

Definitions and Theorems

- Properties of double integrals:

$$\iint_R cf(x,y)\,dA = c\iint_R f(x,y)\,dA$$
$$\iint_R \left[f(x,y)+g(x,y)\right]\,dA = \iint_R f(x,y)\,dA + \iint_R g(x,y)\,dA.$$

- Let f be integrable over the plane region R of area A. The **average value** of f over R is

$$\frac{1}{A}\iint_R f(x,y)\,dA.$$

Summary

We continue our study of integration of functions of two variables. We show that the volume of a solid can be represented by a double integral. These double integrals have many of the same properties as single integrals. Although the motivation for double integrals was area and volume, we will see in upcoming lessons that there are many more applications of such integrals. We end the lesson with the familiar topic of average value.

Example 1

Calculate the volume below the surface $z = 6 - 2y$ and above the rectangle given by $0 \le x \le 4$, $0 \le y \le 2$.

Solution

The volume is given by the double integral $\iint\limits_R f(x,y)\,dA = \int_0^4 \int_0^2 (6-2y)\,dy\,dx$.

We evaluate the integral as follows:

$$\int_0^4 \int_0^2 (6-2y)\,dy\,dx = \int_0^4 \left[6y - y^2\right]_0^2 dx = \int_0^4 8\,dx = \left[8x\right]_0^4 = 32.$$

(See Figure **20.1**.)

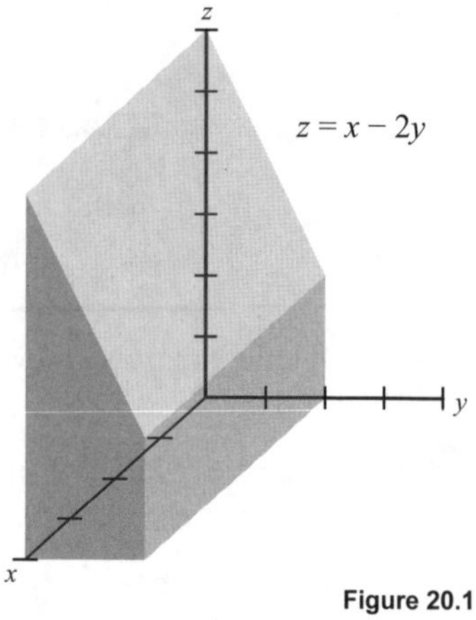

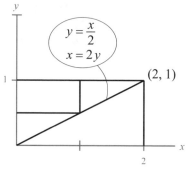

$z = x - 2y$

Figure 20.1

Example 2

The double integral for the volume under the surface $z = \sin y^2 = \sin(y^2)$ and above the region bounded by $y = \dfrac{x}{2}$, $x = 0$, and $y = 1$ is $V = \int_0^2 \int_{x/2}^1 \sin y^2 \, dy\,dx$. Reverse the order of integration.

Solution

The region of integration is a triangle, and the given integral uses vertical representative rectangles. (See **Figure 20.2**.)

If instead we use horizontal representative rectangles, we obtain the integral

$$V = \int_0^2 \int_{x/2}^1 \sin y^2 \, dy\,dx = \int_0^1 \int_0^{2y} \sin y^2 \, dx\,dy.$$

Notice that the first integral cannot be done easily, whereas the second integral is straightforward. The answer is $-\cos 1 + 1 \approx 0.4597$.

$y = \dfrac{x}{2}$

$x = 2y$

$(2, 1)$

Figure 20.2

Example 3

Find the average value of $f(x,y) = \dfrac{1}{2}xy$ over the rectangular region R with vertices $(0, 0)$, $(4, 0)$, $(4, 3)$, and $(0, 3)$.

Solution

The area of the region is $4 \times 3 = 12$. The average value is

$$\frac{1}{A}\iint\limits_R f(x,y)\,dA = \frac{1}{12}\int_0^4 \int_0^3 \frac{1}{2}xy\,dy\,dx.$$

This integral is easy to evaluate, and the final answer is $\dfrac{3}{2}$.

Study Tips

- Double integrals do not only represent areas and volumes. We will see many other applications in upcoming lessons.

- It is very helpful to draw the region of integration together with a representative rectangle.

- Computers and graphing calculators can evaluate double integrals. Sometimes the answer might be an approximation. The following are two results from a calculator:

$$\int_0^1 \int_0^{2y} \sin y^2 \, dx \, dy = \cos(1) - 1$$

$$\int_0^2 \int_{x/2}^1 \sin y^2 \, dy \, dx = 0.4596976941.$$

Pitfalls

- Remember that the outer limits of integration must be constants, and the variable of integration can never appear as a limit of integration. For example, the following double integral is incorrect for two reasons: $\int_y^2 \int_{x/2}^1 \sin y^2 \, dx \, dy$.

- In Example 2, the given integral cannot be evaluated by the fundamental theorem of calculus because the integrand, $\sin y^2$, does not have an elementary antiderivative.

Problems

1. Find the volume of the solid bounded by the surface $z = \dfrac{y}{2}$ and above the rectangle $0 \le x \le 4$, $0 \le y \le 2$.

2. Find the volume of the solid bounded by the surface $z = 1 - xy$ and above the triangle bounded by $y = x$, $y = 1$, and $x = 0$.

3. Set up the double integral for the volume of the solid in the first octant bounded by $z = xy$, $z = 0$, $y = x$, and $x = 1$.

4. Set up the double integral for the volume of the solid bounded by $x^2 + y^2 + z^2 = r^2$.

5. Set up the double integral for the volume of the solid in the first octant bounded by $y = 4 - x^2$ and $z = 4 - x^2$.

6. Evaluate the iterated integral $\int_0^1 \int_{y/2}^{1/2} e^{-x^2} \, dx \, dy$ by switching the order of integration.

7. Evaluate the iterated integral $\int_0^2 \int_{x/2}^2 \sqrt{y} \cos y \, dy \, dx$ by switching the order of integration.

8. Find the average value of the function $f(x, y) = x$ over the rectangle with vertices $(0, 0)$, $(4, 0)$, $(4, 2)$, and $(0, 2)$.

9. Find the average value of the function $f(x, y) = \sin(x + y)$ over the rectangle with vertices $(0, 0)$, $(\pi, 0)$, (π, π), and $(0, \pi)$.

10. Why is the expression $\int_0^2 \int_0^y (x + y) \, dy \, dx$ invalid?

Double Integrals in Polar Coordinates
Lesson 21

Topics

- Polar coordinates.

- Double integrals in polar coordinates.

Definitions and Theorems

- Conversion formulas:

$$x = r\cos\theta, y = r\sin\theta$$

$$x^2 + y^2 = r^2, \tan\theta = \frac{y}{x}.$$

- Double integrals in polar coordinates: Let R be a planar region consisting of all points $(x, y) = (r\cos\theta, r\sin\theta)$ satisfying $0 \le g_1(\theta) \le r \le g_2(\theta)$, $\alpha \le \theta \le \beta$, and $0 \le (\beta - \alpha) \le 2\pi$.

    Then, $\displaystyle\iint_R f(x, y)\, dA = \int_\alpha^\beta \int_{g_1(\theta)}^{g_2(\theta)} f(r\cos\theta, r\sin\theta)\, r\, dr\, d\theta.$

Summary

In this lesson, we develop double integrals in polar coordinates. This conversion is especially useful if the region of integration or the integrand is easily expressed in polar coordinates. We begin with a review of polar coordinates and then develop the formula for a double integral in polar coordinates. In this case, the differential of area, dA, becomes $r\, dr\, d\theta$. Don't forget the extra r factor. We illustrate these ideas with area and volume examples.

Example 1

Use polar coordinates to describe the region in **Figure 21.1**.

Solution

The region is a quarter circle of radius 2: $\left\{(r, \theta) : 0 \le r \le 2, 0 \le \theta \le \frac{\pi}{2}\right\}$.

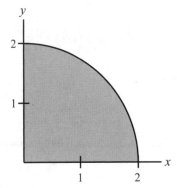

Figure 21.1

Example 2

Evaluate the double integral $\int_0^2 \int_0^{\sqrt{4-y^2}} y\,dx\,dy$ by converting to polar coordinates.

Solution

The region is a quarter circle of radius 2.

In polar coordinates, the integral becomes $\int_0^2 \int_0^{\sqrt{4-y^2}} y\,dx\,dy = \int_0^{\pi/2} \int_0^2 (r\sin\theta)r\,dr\,d\theta$.

This integral is easy to evaluate because the limits of integration are constants:

$$\int_0^{\pi/2} \int_0^2 (r\sin\theta)r\,dr\,d\theta = \int_0^{\pi/2}\left[\frac{r^3}{3}\sin\theta\right]_0^2 d\theta$$

$$= \frac{8}{3}\int_0^{\pi/2}\sin\theta\,d\theta = \frac{8}{3}\left[-\cos\theta\right]_0^{\pi/2}$$

$$= \frac{8}{3}\left[0-(-1)\right] = \frac{8}{3}.$$

Example 3

Set up the double integral in polar coordinates to find the area of the region bounded by the polar graph $r = 3\cos 3\theta$. (See **Figure 21.2**.)

Solution

The graph is a rose curve with 3 petals.

One petal is defined by $-\dfrac{\pi}{6} \leq \theta \leq \dfrac{\pi}{6}$, where $0 \leq r \leq 3\cos 3\theta$.

So, the total area is $A = 3\int_{-\pi/6}^{\pi/6} \int_0^{3\cos 3\theta} r\,dr\,d\theta = \dfrac{9\pi}{4}$.

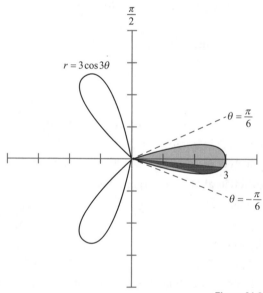

Figure 21.2

Example 4

Set up the double integral for the volume of the ice-cream cone bounded above by the hemisphere $z = \sqrt{2-x^2-y^2}$ and bounded below by the cone $z = \sqrt{x^2+y^2}$.

Solution

We first determine where the surfaces intersect by equating the equations:

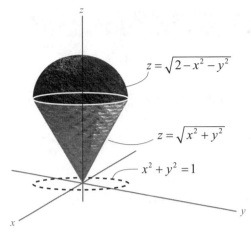

$$\sqrt{2-x^2-y^2} = \sqrt{x^2+y^2}$$
$$2-x^2-y^2 = x^2+y^2$$
$$2 = 2x^2+2y^2$$
$$x^2+y^2 = 1.$$

(See **Figure 21.3**.)

Figure 21.3

In polar coordinates, the equations are

$$z = \sqrt{2-x^2-y^2} = \sqrt{2-r^2} \quad \text{and} \quad z = \sqrt{x^2+y^2} = r.$$

The volume is therefore

$$V = \int_0^{2\pi} \int_0^1 \left[\sqrt{2-r^2} - r \right] r\, dr\, d\theta.$$

The evaluation requires substitution, and you obtain

$$V = \frac{4\left(\sqrt{2}-1\right)}{3} \pi.$$

Study Tips

- The area of a polar sector is $A = r\Delta r\Delta\theta$. Hence, the differential of area in rectangular coordinates, $dA = dy\,dx = dx\,dy$ becomes $r\,dr\,d\theta$ in polar coordinates.

- In polar coordinates, area is given by $\iint\limits_R dA = \iint\limits_R r\,dr\,d\theta$.

- The r value can be negative in polar coordinates.

Pitfall

- Remember that the differential of area in polar coordinates is $dA = r\,dr\,d\theta$. Don't forget the r.

Problems

1. Evaluate the iterated integral $\int_0^3 \int_0^{\sqrt{9-x^2}} x\,dy\,dx$ by converting to polar coordinates.

2. Evaluate the iterated integral $\int_{-2}^2 \int_0^{\sqrt{4-x^2}} \left(x^2 + y^2\right) dy\,dx$ by converting to polar coordinates.

3. Evaluate the iterated integral $\int_0^2 \int_0^{\sqrt{2x-x^2}} xy\,dy\,dx$ by converting to polar coordinates.

4. Use a double integral in polar coordinates to find the area of the region enclosed by the graph of the equation $r = 6\cos\theta$.

5. Use a double integral in polar coordinates to find the area of the region enclosed by the graphs of the equations $r = 2$ and $r = 4$.

6. Use a double integral in polar coordinates to find the area bounded by the three-leaved rose curve $r = 2\sin 3\theta$.

7. Use a double integral in polar coordinates to find the volume of the solid in the first octant bounded by $z = xy$ and $x^2 + y^2 = 1$.

8. Use a double integral in polar coordinates to find the volume of the solid bounded by $z = \sqrt{x^2 + y^2}$, $z = 0$, and $x^2 + y^2 = 25$.

9. Use a double integral in polar coordinates to find the volume of the solid inside the hemisphere $z = \sqrt{16 - x^2 - y^2}$ and outside the cylinder $x^2 + y^2 = 1$.

10. Set up the double integral in polar coordinates for the area inside the circle $r = 2\cos\theta$ and outside the circle $r = 1$.

Centers of Mass for Variable Density
Lesson 22

Topics

- Mass.

- Moments.

- Centers of mass for variable density.

Definitions and Theorems

- If the planar lamina given by the region R has variable density $\rho(x, y)$, then the **mass** is

$$m = \iint\limits_{R} \rho(x, y)\, dA \,.$$

- The **moments of mass** with respect to the x- and y-axes are

$$M_x = \iint\limits_{R} y\rho(x, y)\, dA, \; M_y = \iint\limits_{R} x\rho(x, y)\, dA \,.$$

- If m is the mass of the lamina, the **center of mass** is $(\overline{x}, \overline{y}) = \left(\dfrac{M_y}{m}, \dfrac{M_x}{m} \right)$.

Summary

In this lesson, we apply our knowledge of double integrals to the calculation of mass and centers of mass. The formula for mass is the double integral of the density function. The formulas for the moments with respect to the axes are much simpler than the corresponding formulas in elementary calculus. In some examples, polar coordinates yield easier integrals than Cartesian coordinates.

Example 1

Find the mass of the triangular lamina with vertices $(0, 0)$, $(0, 3)$, and $(2, 3)$ if the density at the point (x, y) is $\rho(x, y) = 2x + y$. (See **Figure 22.1**.)

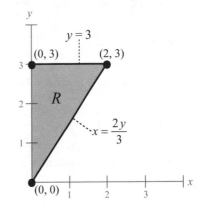

Figure 22.1

Solution

The boundaries of the triangular region are $x = 0$, $y = 3$, and $x = \dfrac{2y}{3}$.

Using a horizontal representative rectangle, the mass is

$$m = \iint_R (2x + y)\, dA = \int_0^3 \int_0^{2y/3} (2x + y)\, dx\, dy = 10.$$

Example 2

Find the center of mass of the lamina corresponding to the parabolic region $0 \le y \le 4 - x^2$ if the density at the point (x, y) is constant, $\rho(x, y) = 1$.

Solution

The mass is

$$m = \int_{-2}^{2} \int_0^{4-x^2} 1\, dy\, dx = \int_{-2}^{2} [y]_0^{4-x^2}\, dx = \int_{-2}^{2} (4 - x^2)\, dx$$

$$= \left[4x - \frac{x^3}{3} \right]_{-2}^{2} = \left[\left(8 - \frac{8}{3} \right) - \left(-8 + \frac{8}{3} \right) \right] = \frac{32}{3}.$$

By symmetry, the center of mass lies on the y-axis, so $M_y = 0$.

The moment about the x-axis is $M_x = \int_{-2}^{2} \int_0^{4-x^2} y\, dy\, dx = \dfrac{256}{15}$.

So, we have $\overline{y} = \dfrac{M_x}{m} = \dfrac{256/15}{32/3} = \dfrac{8}{5}$, and the center of mass is $(\overline{x}, \overline{y}) = \left(0, \dfrac{8}{5} \right)$.

Example 3

Solve the previous example assuming that the density is not constant but, rather, given by $\rho(x, y) = 2y$.

Solution

The computations are very similar to the previous example.

The mass is $m = \int_{-2}^{2} \int_0^{4-x^2} 2y\, dy\, dx = \dfrac{512}{15}$. By symmetry, $M_y = 0$.

The moment about the x-axis is $M_x = \int_{-2}^{2} \int_0^{4-x^2} y(2y)\, dy\, dx = \dfrac{8192}{105}$.

So, $\bar{y} = \dfrac{M_x}{m} = \dfrac{8192/105}{512/15} = \dfrac{16}{7}$.

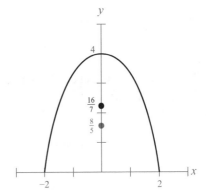

Figure 22.2

Finally, the center of mass is $(\bar{x}, \bar{y}) = \left(0, \dfrac{16}{7}\right)$.

Notice that the balancing point has moved up a bit from the previous example. (See **Figure 22.2**.)

Study Tips

- Usually, density is mass per unit of volume. But for planar laminas, density is mass per unit of surface area.

- The formulas for center of mass are equivalent to those studied in elementary calculus.

- The setup of the problem is the most important step. Calculating the resulting integrals can be done by hand or by using computers and graphing calculators.

- Notice how we took advantage of symmetry in Examples 2 and 3.

Pitfall

- The formula for M_x involves y, and the formula for M_y involves x. Similarly, the formula for $\bar{x}$ involves y, and the formula for $\bar{y}$ involves x.

Problems

1. Find the mass of the square lamina bounded by $0 \le x \le 2$ and $0 \le y \le 2$ if the density is $\rho(x, y) = xy$.

2. Find the mass of the lamina bounded by $0 \le x \le 1$ and $0 \le y \le \sqrt{1 - x^2}$ if the density is $\rho(x, y) = xy$.

3. Find the mass and center of mass of the triangular lamina with vertices $(0, 0)$, $(0, 3)$, and $(3, 3)$ if the density is $\rho(x, y) = 4y$.

4. Find the mass and center of mass of the triangular lamina with vertices $(0, 0)$, $(0, 3)$, and $(3, 3)$ if the density is $\rho(x, y) = 4x$.

5. Find the mass and center of mass of the lamina bounded by $y = \sqrt{x}$, $y = 0$, and $x = 1$ if the density is $\rho(x, y) = 5y$.

6. Find the mass and center of mass of the lamina bounded by $y = x^2$, $y = 0$, and $x = 2$ if the density is $\rho(x, y) = 3xy$.

7. Find the mass and center of mass of the lamina bounded by $x^2 + y^2 = 16$, $0 \leq x$, and $0 \leq y$ if the density is $\rho(x, y) = 3(x^2 + y^2)$.

Surface Area of a Solid
Lesson 23

Topics

- Surface area of solids in space.

- The differential of arc length and the differential of surface area.

- Surface area in polar coordinates.

Definitions and Theorems

- Let the function f represent a smooth curve on the interval $[a,b]$. The **arc length** between a and b is

$$s = \int_a^b \sqrt{1 + \left[f'(x) \right]^2}\, dx.$$

- If a piece of arc length is rotated about the x-axis, the **surface area** of the resulting surface of revolution is

$$A = 2\pi \int_a^b f(x) \sqrt{1 + \left[f'(x) \right]^2}\, dx.$$

- If a piece of arc length is rotated about the y-axis, the **surface area** of the resulting surface of revolution is

$$A = 2\pi \int_a^b x \sqrt{1 + \left[f'(x) \right]^2}\, dx.$$

- The **differential of arc length** is

$$ds = \sqrt{1 + \left[f'(x) \right]^2}\, dx.$$

- For a surface given by $z = f(x, y)$ defined over a region R in the xy-plane, the **surface area** is

$$S = \iint_R \sqrt{1 + \left[f_x(x, y) \right]^2 + \left[f_y(x, y) \right]^2}\, dA.$$

- The **differential of surface area** is

$$dS = \sqrt{1 + \left[f_x(x, y) \right]^2 + \left[f_y(x, y) \right]^2}\, dA.$$

Summary

The formula for surface area is similar to that of arc length. Both involve an important differential: the differential of arc length and the differential of surface area. After a brief review of arc length and surfaces of revolution, we present the general formula for surface area of graphs of functions of two variables. In some examples, we will see that polar coordinates are useful in simplifying the computations.

Example 1

Find the surface area of the plane $z = 2 - x - y$ in the first octant. (See **Figure 23.1**.)

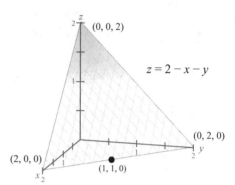

Figure 23.1

Solution

We have $f_x(x, y) = -1, f_y(x, y) = -1$, and

$$dS = \sqrt{1 + (f_x)^2 + (f_y)^2}\, dA = \sqrt{1 + 1 + 1}\, dA = \sqrt{3}\, dA.$$

So, the surface area is

$$S = \iint_R \sqrt{1 + \left[f_x(x, y) \right]^2 + \left[f_y(x, y) \right]^2}\, dA = \iint_R \sqrt{3}\, dA = \sqrt{3} \iint_R dA.$$

Using a vertical representative rectangle, $S = \sqrt{3} \int_0^2 \int_0^{2-x} dy\, dx = 2\sqrt{3}$.

Example 2

Set up the double integral for the surface area of the portion of the surface $f(x, y) = 1 - x^2 + y$ that lies above the triangular region with vertices $(1, 0, 0)$, $(0, -1, 0)$, and $(0, 1, 0)$.

Solution

The partial derivatives are $f_x(x, y) = -2x$ and $f_y(x, y) = 1$. Hence,

$$S = \iint_R \sqrt{1 + \left[f_x(x, y) \right]^2 + \left[f_y(x, y) \right]^2}\, dA$$

$$= \iint_R \sqrt{1 + 4x^2 + 1}\, dA$$

$$= \iint_R \sqrt{2 + 4x^2}\, dA.$$

We now need to find the bounds for the region determined by the three points. (See **Figure 23.2**.)

We see that $0 \le x \le 1$, $x - 1 \le y \le 1 - x$. Hence, the integral for surface area becomes

$$S = \iint_R \sqrt{2 + 4x^2}\, dA = \int_0^1 \int_{x-1}^{1-x} \sqrt{2 + 4x^2}\, dy\, dx.$$

This integral is difficult to evaluate. A calculator gives

$$S = \ln\left(\sqrt{3} + \sqrt{2}\right) + \frac{\sqrt{2}}{3} \approx 1.618.$$

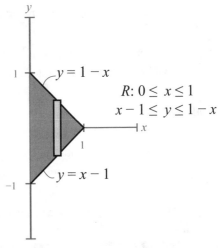

$R: 0 \le x \le 1$
$x - 1 \le y \le 1 - x$

Figure 23.2

Example 3

Find the surface area of the ice-cream cone $z = \sqrt{x^2 + y^2}$ that lies above the circular region $x^2 + y^2 \le 1$.

Solution

The partial derivatives are $f_x = \dfrac{x}{\sqrt{x^2 + y^2}}$ and $f_y = \dfrac{y}{\sqrt{x^2 + y^2}}$. The differential of surface area is

$$dS = \sqrt{1 + \left(\frac{x}{\sqrt{x^2 + y^2}}\right)^2 + \left(\frac{y}{\sqrt{x^2 + y^2}}\right)^2}\, dA$$

$$= \sqrt{1 + \frac{x^2}{x^2 + y^2} + \frac{y^2}{x^2 + y^2}}\, dA$$

$$= \sqrt{\frac{2x^2 + 2y^2}{x^2 + y^2}}\, dA = \sqrt{\frac{2(x^2 + y^2)}{x^2 + y^2}}\, dA = \sqrt{2}\, dA.$$

Hence, the surface area of the ice-cream cone is

$$S = \iint_R dS = \iint_R \sqrt{2}\, dA = \sqrt{2} \iint_R dA = \sqrt{2}\left(\text{Area of circle}\right) = \sqrt{2}\left(\pi\right) = \pi\sqrt{2}.$$

Study Tips

- Notice the similarity between the differential of arc length and the differential of surface area:

$$ds = \sqrt{1 + \left[f'(x)\right]^2}\, dx \quad \text{differential of arc length}$$

$$dS = \sqrt{1 + \left[f_x(x, y)\right]^2 + \left[f_y(x, y)\right]^2}\, dA \quad \text{differential of surface area.}$$

- Surface area is the double integral of the differential of surface area: $S = \iint\limits_{R} dS$.

- You could have used elementary geometry to solve Example 3. The surface area of a right circular cone of height h and radius r is $S = \pi r \sqrt{r^2 + h^2}$. In Example 3, $r = h = 1$, and hence, $S = \pi\sqrt{2}$.

Pitfalls

- In elementary calculus, many of the integrands for arc length and surface are difficult to integrate. This is also true in multivariable calculus, as we saw in Example 2.

- Don't forget the extra r when using polar coordinates: $dA = r\,dr\,d\theta$.

Problems

1. Find the area of the surface given by $f(x, y) = 2x + 2y$ over the triangular region R with vertices $(0, 0)$, $(4, 0)$, and $(0, 4)$.

2. Find the area of the surface given by $f(x, y) = 15 + 2x - 3y$ over the square region R with vertices $(0, 0)$, $(3, 0)$, $(0, 3)$, and $(3, 3)$.

3. Find the area of the surface given by $f(x, y) = 12 + 2x - 3y$ over the circular region R given by $R = \{(x, y): x^2 + y^2 \le 9\}$.

4. Find the area of the portion of the plane $z = 24 - 3x - 2y$ in the first octant.

5. Set up the double integral for the area of the portion of the paraboloid $z = 16 - x^2 - y^2$ in the first octant.

6. Set up the double integral for the area of the surface $f(x, y) = 2y + x^2$ over the triangular region R with vertices $(0, 0)$, $(1, 0)$, and $(1, 1)$.

7. Set up the double integral in polar coordinates for the area of the surface $f(x, y) = 9 - x^2 - y^2$ over the region R given by $R = \{(x, y): 0 \le f(x, y)\}$.

8. Set up the double integral for the area of the surface $f(x, y) = e^x$ over the region R given by $R = \{(x, y): 0 \le x \le 1, 0 \le y \le 1\}$.

9. Show that the surface area of the cone $z = k\sqrt{x^2 + y^2}$, $k > 0$, over the circular region $x^2 + y^2 \le r^2$ in the xy-plane is $\pi r^2 \sqrt{k^2 + 1}$.

Triple Integrals and Applications
Lesson 24

Topics

- Triple integrals.

- Changing the order of integration.

- Triple integrals and mass.

Definitions and Theorems

- Mass in triple integrals: $m = \iiint\limits_{Q} \rho(x, y, z)\, dV$.

Summary

In this lesson, we extend our knowledge of double integrals to triple integrals. We begin by using triple integrals to calculate volume, in which the integrand is 1. Later in the lesson, we use triple integrals to calculate the mass of a solid. An important skill with triple integrals is changing the order of integration. In general, there are six possible orders of integration.

Example 1

Evaluate the triple integral $\int_0^4 \int_0^3 \int_0^2 1\, dz\, dy\, dx$.

Solution

This triple integral represents the volume of a box. We evaluate the integral in the same manner as we evaluated double integrals,

$$\int_0^4 \int_0^3 \int_0^2 dz\, dy\, dx = \int_0^4 \int_0^3 [z]_0^2 \, dy\, dx$$
$$= \int_0^4 \int_0^3 2\, dy\, dx$$
$$= \int_0^4 [2y]_0^3 \, dx$$
$$= \int_0^4 6\, dx$$
$$= [6x]_0^4 = 24.$$

(See **Figure 24.1**.)

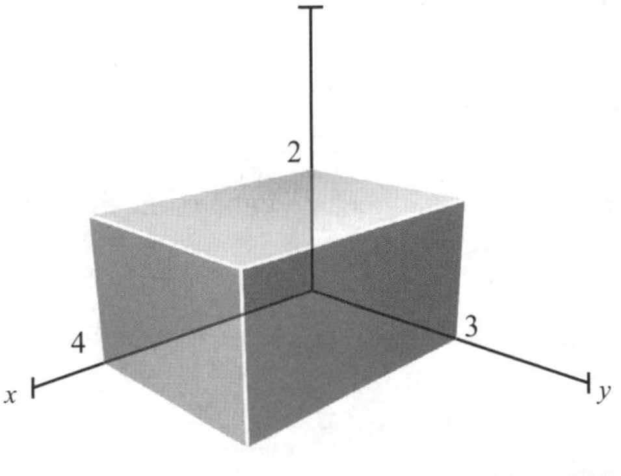

Figure 24.1

Example 2

Sketch the solid whose volume is represented by the triple integral
$\int_0^1 \int_0^2 \int_0^{1-y} dz\, dx\, dy$. Then, rewrite the integral in the order $dy\, dz\, dx$.

Solution

The limits of integration determine the shape of the solid.
(See **Figure 24.2**.)

Because $z = 1 - y \Leftrightarrow y = 1 - z$, $\int_0^1 \int_0^2 \int_0^{1-y} dz\, dx\, dy = \int_0^2 \int_0^1 \int_0^{1-z} dy\, dz\, dx$.
Both integrals give the same volume of 1.

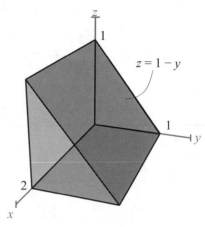

Figure 24.2

Example 3

Set up the triple integral for the volume of the solid region bounded
below by the surface $z = x^2 + y^2$ and above by $z = 2 - x^2 - y^2$.
(See **Figure 24.3**.)

Solution

We must first find the intersection of the two paraboloids by setting
the equations equal to each other:

$$z = 2 - x^2 - y^2 = x^2 + y^2 \Rightarrow 2 = 2x^2 + 2y^2 \Rightarrow x^2 + y^2 = 1.$$

The region of integration is the unit circle. The volume is

$$V = \int_{-1}^1 \int_{-\sqrt{1-x^2}}^{\sqrt{1-x^2}} \int_{x^2+y^2}^{2-x^2-y^2} dz\, dy\, dx.$$

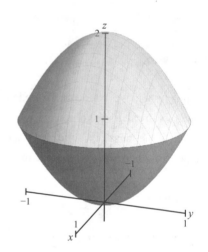

Figure 24.3

This integral is difficult, and the answer is π. In the next lesson, we will see how to solve the problem using
cylindrical coordinates.

Example 4

Find the mass of the unit cube in the first octant given that the density at the point (x, y, z) is the square of its
distance to the origin.

Solution

The density is $\rho(x, y, z) = k(x^2 + y^2 + z^2)$. Hence, the mass is given by

$$m = \iiint_Q \rho(x, y, z) \, dV = \int_0^1 \int_0^1 \int_0^1 k(x^2 + y^2 + z^2) \, dz \, dy \, dx.$$

This integral is not difficult to evaluate, and the final answer is k.

Study Tips

- Just as with double integrals, we often omit integrands of 1. For instance, in Example 1,
$$\int_0^4 \int_0^3 \int_0^2 1 \, dz \, dy \, dx = \int_0^4 \int_0^3 \int_0^2 \, dz \, dy \, dx.$$

- There are six orders of integration for triple integrals in Cartesian coordinates: $dz \, dy \, dx$, $dz \, dx \, dy$, $dy \, dz \, dx$, $dy \, dx \, dz$, $dx \, dy \, dz$, $dx \, dz \, dy$.

- It is worth repeating that the setup of a problem is more important than the actual integrations.

Pitfall

- Remember that the variable of integration cannot appear as a limit of integration. The following triple integral is incorrect: $\int_0^1 \int_0^2 \int_0^{1-z} \, dz \, dx \, dy$.

Problems

1. Evaluate the triple integral $\int_0^5 \int_0^2 \int_0^1 dy \, dx \, dz$. What does this represent?

2. Evaluate the triple integral $\int_0^3 \int_0^2 \int_0^1 (x + y + z) \, dx \, dz \, dy$.

3. Evaluate the triple integral $\int_{-1}^1 \int_{-1}^1 \int_{-1}^1 x^2 y^2 z^2 \, dx \, dy \, dz$.

4. Set up the triple integral for the volume of the solid in the first octant bounded by the coordinate planes and the plane $z = 5 - x - y$.

5. Set up the triple integral for the volume of the solid bounded by $z = 9 - x^2$, $z = 0$, $y = 0$, and $y = 2x$.

6. Set up the triple integral for the volume of the solid bounded by $z = 6 - x^2 - y^2$ and $z = 0$.

7. Set up the integral for the mass of the solid bounded by $2x + 3y + 6z = 12$, $x = 0$, $y = 0$, and $z = 0$ if the density is $\rho(x, y, z) = 3$.

8. Set up the integral for the mass of the solid bounded by $3x + 3y + 5z = 15$, $x = 0$, $y = 0$, and $z = 0$ if the density is $\rho(x, y, z) = 3y$.

9. Rewrite the iterated integral $\int_0^1 \int_{-1}^0 \int_0^{y^2} dz\, dy\, dx$ using the order $dy\, dz\, dx$.

10. Rewrite the iterated integral $\int_0^4 \int_0^{(4-x)/2} \int_0^{(12-3x-6y)/4} dz\, dy\, dx$ using the order $dy\, dx\, dz$.

Triple Integrals in Cylindrical Coordinates
Lesson 25

Topics

- Cylindrical coordinates.

- Conversion formulas.

- Triple integrals in cylindrical coordinates.

- The differential of volume in cylindrical coordinates.

- Applications of triple integrals in cylindrical coordinates.

Definitions and Theorems

- Let $P = (x, y, z)$ be a point in space. Its **cylindrical coordinates** are (r, θ, z), where (r, θ) are the polar coordinates of the projection of the point onto the xy-plane. The z coordinate is the same.

- Conversion formulas:

$$x = r\cos\theta, y = r\sin\theta, z = z$$

$$r^2 = x^2 + y^2, \tan\theta = \frac{y}{x}, \ z = z.$$

- The **differential of volume** in cylindrical coordinates is $dV = r\,dz\,dr\,d\theta$.

Summary

The cylindrical coordinate system is the three-dimensional generalization of polar coordinates. These coordinates are especially useful for representing cylindrical surfaces and surfaces of revolution. The conversion formulas are similar to the conversion formulas between polar coordinates and Cartesian coordinates. We'll study examples of triple integrals in cylindrical coordinates and note that the differential of volume has the extra r factor, $dV = r\,dz\,dr\,d\theta$.

Example 1

Convert the point $(r, \theta, z) = \left(4, \frac{5\pi}{6}, 3\right)$ to Cartesian coordinates.

Solution

We use the conversion formulas: $x = r\cos\theta = 4\cos\dfrac{5\pi}{6} = 4\left(-\dfrac{\sqrt{3}}{2}\right) = -2\sqrt{3}$, $\; y = r\sin\theta = 4\sin\dfrac{5\pi}{6} = 4\left(\dfrac{1}{2}\right) = 2$, and $z = 3$.

The Cartesian coordinates of the point are $(x, y, z) = \left(-2\sqrt{3}, 2, 3\right)$.

Example 2

Convert the point $(x, y, z) = \left(1, \sqrt{3}, 2\right)$ to cylindrical coordinates.

Solution

We have $r^2 = x^2 + y^2 = 1 + 3 = 4 \Rightarrow r = \pm 2$, and $\tan\theta = \dfrac{y}{x} = \dfrac{\sqrt{3}}{1} = \sqrt{3}$, which gives $\theta = \dfrac{\pi}{3} + n\pi$. Of course, $z = 2$.

There are many possible cylindrical coordinates. For example, $(r, \theta, z) = \left(2, \dfrac{\pi}{3}, 2\right)$ or $(r, \theta, z) = \left(-2, \dfrac{4\pi}{3}, 2\right)$.

Example 3

The surface $\theta = c$ is a vertical plane. (See **Figure 25.1**.)

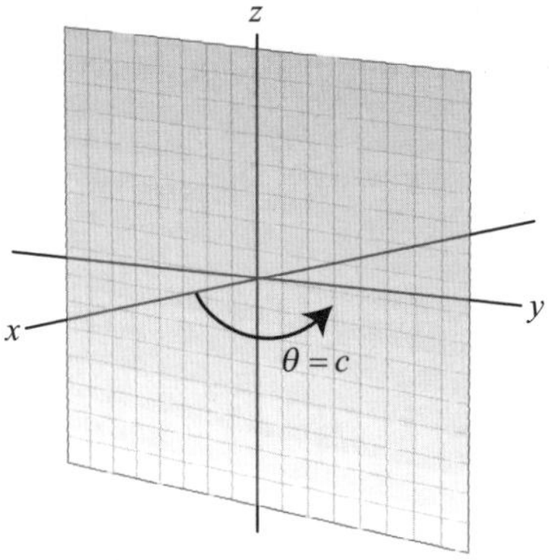

Example 4

Find the volume of the solid bounded below by $z = x^2 + y^2$ and above by $z = 2 - x^2 - y^2$. (See **Figure 25.2**.)

Solution

The intersection of the two paraboloids is obtained by setting the equations equal to each other:

$$z = 2 - x^2 - y^2 = x^2 + y^2 \;\Rightarrow\; 2 = 2x^2 + 2y^2 \;\Rightarrow\; x^2 + y^2 = 1.$$

Converting to cylindrical coordinates, $z = 2 - x^2 - y^2 = 2 - r^2$ and $z = x^2 + y^2 = r^2$.

The volume is $V = \iiint\limits_{Q} dV = \displaystyle\int_0^{2\pi}\!\int_0^1\!\int_{r^2}^{2-r^2} r\, dz\, dr\, d\theta$.

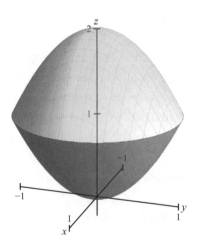

Figure 25.1

Figure 25.2

This integral is easy to evaluate:

$$V = \int_0^{2\pi} \int_0^1 \left[rz \right]_{r^2}^{2-r^2} dr\, d\theta$$

$$= \int_0^{2\pi} \int_0^1 \left[r\left(2 - r^2 - r^2 \right) \right] dr\, d\theta$$

$$= \int_0^{2\pi} \int_0^1 \left[2r - 2r^3 \right] dr\, d\theta$$

$$= \int_0^{2\pi} \left[r^2 - \frac{r^4}{2} \right]_0^1 d\theta$$

$$= \int_0^{2\pi} \frac{1}{2} d\theta = \left[\frac{1}{2}\theta \right]_0^{2\pi} = \pi.$$

Study Tips

- Notice that cylindrical coordinates are the natural extension of Cartesian coordinates to three dimensions.

- When converting from one coordinate system to another, you can always check your answer by converting back to the original coordinates.

- It is helpful to identify the coordinate system representing a given point. For instance, in Example 1, write $(r, \theta, z) = \left(4, \frac{5\pi}{6}, 3 \right)$ and $(x, y, z) = \left(-2\sqrt{3}, 2, 3 \right)$.

Pitfalls

- The cylindrical coordinates of a point are not unique. In particular, the r-value can be positive or negative. And there are infinitely many choices for the angle θ.

- Don't forget the extra r in the differential of volume, $dV = r\, dz\, dr\, d\theta$.

Problems

1. Convert the point $(r, \theta, z) = (1, -\pi, -4)$ to rectangular coordinates.

2. Convert the point $(r, \theta, z) = (3, \frac{\pi}{4}, 1)$ to rectangular coordinates.

3. Convert the point $(x, y, z) = \left(2\sqrt{2}, -2\sqrt{2}, 4 \right)$ to cylindrical coordinates.

4. Find an equation in cylindrical coordinates for the rectangular equation $x = 9$.

5. Find an equation in rectangular coordinates for the cylindrical equation $r^2 + z^2 = 5$.

6. Find an equation in rectangular coordinates for the cylindrical equation $r = 2\sin\theta$.

7. Verify that $V = 2\int_0^{2\pi}\int_{R_2}^{R_1}\int_0^{\sqrt{R_1^2-r^2}} r\,dz\,dr\,d\theta = \frac{4\pi}{3}\left(R_1^2 - R_2^2\right)^{3/2}$.

8. Convert the integral $\int_{-2}^{2}\int_{-\sqrt{4-x^2}}^{\sqrt{4-x^2}}\int_{x^2+y^2}^{4} x\,dz\,dy\,dx$ to cylindrical coordinates.

9. Set up the triple integral in cylindrical coordinates for the volume of the solid bounded above by $z = 2x$ and below by $z = 2x^2 + 2y^2$.

10. Set up the triple integral in cylindrical coordinates for the volume of the solid inside the sphere $x^2 + y^2 + z^2 = 4$ and above the upper nappe of the cone $z^2 = x^2 + y^2$.

Triple Integrals in Spherical Coordinates
Lesson 26

Topics

- Spherical coordinates.

- Conversion formulas.

- Triple integrals in spherical coordinates.

- The differential of volume in spherical coordinates.

- Applications of triple integrals in spherical coordinates.

Definitions and Theorems

- Let $P = (x, y, z)$ be a point in space. Its **spherical coordinates** are (ρ, θ, ϕ), where ρ is the distance from P to the origin, θ is the same angle as used in cylindrical coordinates, and ϕ is the angle between the positive z-axis and the line segment $\overline{OP}$, $0 \le \phi \le \pi$.

- Conversion formulas:

$$r = \rho \sin \phi, z = \rho \cos \phi$$

$$x = r \cos \theta = \rho \sin \phi \cos \theta$$

$$y = r \sin \theta = \rho \sin \phi \sin \theta$$

$$\rho^2 = x^2 + y^2 + z^2 \implies \rho = \sqrt{x^2 + y^2 + z^2}$$

$$\tan \theta = \frac{y}{x}$$

$$\cos \phi = \frac{z}{\rho} = \frac{z}{\sqrt{x^2 + y^2 + z^2}}.$$

- The **differential of volume** in spherical coordinates is $dV = \rho^2 \sin \phi \, d\rho \, d\phi \, d\theta$.

Summary

Spherical coordinates are similar to the longitude and latitude coordinates on Earth. The first coordinate is a distance, and the other two coordinates are angles. We begin by defining spherical coordinates in space and develop their conversion formulas. After looking at some examples of surfaces in spherical coordinates, we apply them to the calculation of volumes and mass. For spherical coordinates, the differential of volume is a bit complicated: $dV = \rho^2 \sin\phi \, d\rho \, d\phi \, d\theta$.

Example 1

Convert the point $(\rho, \theta, \phi) = \left(4, \dfrac{\pi}{6}, \dfrac{\pi}{4}\right)$ to Cartesian coordinates.

Solution

We use the conversion formulas:

$$x = \rho \sin\phi \cos\theta = 4\sin\frac{\pi}{4}\cos\frac{\pi}{6} = 4\left(\frac{\sqrt{2}}{2}\right)\left(\frac{\sqrt{3}}{2}\right) = \sqrt{6}$$

$$y = \rho \sin\phi \sin\theta = 4\sin\frac{\pi}{4}\sin\frac{\pi}{6} = 4\left(\frac{\sqrt{2}}{2}\right)\left(\frac{1}{2}\right) = \sqrt{2}$$

$$z = \rho \cos\phi = 4\cos\frac{\pi}{4} = 4\left(\frac{\sqrt{2}}{2}\right) = 2\sqrt{2}.$$

Hence, the Cartesian coordinates are $(x, y, z) = \left(\sqrt{6}, \sqrt{2}, 2\sqrt{2}\right)$.

Example 2

Convert the point $(x, y, z) = (4, 0, 0)$ to spherical coordinates.

Solution

We have $\rho = \sqrt{x^2 + y^2 + z^2} = \sqrt{4^2 + 0 + 0} = 4$, $\tan\theta = \dfrac{y}{x} = \dfrac{0}{4} = 0 \Rightarrow \theta = 0$, and $\cos\phi = \dfrac{z}{\rho} = 0 \Rightarrow \phi = \dfrac{\pi}{2}$.

Therefore, $(\rho, \theta, \phi) = \left(4, 0, \dfrac{\pi}{2}\right)$. (See **Figure 26.1**.)

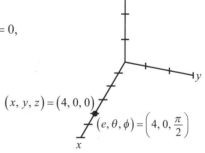

Figure 26.1

Example 3

The surface $\rho = c$ is a sphere centered at the origin. (See **Figure 26.2**.)

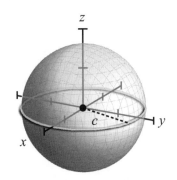

Figure 26.2

Example 4

Find the volume of the ice-cream cone bounded above by the upper half of the sphere $x^2 + y^2 + z^2 = 2$ and below by $z = \sqrt{x^2 + y^2}$. (See **Figure 26.3**.)

Solution

The intersection of the two surfaces is obtained by setting the equations equal to each other:

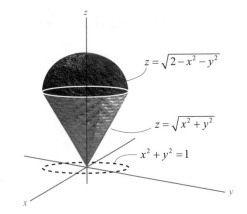

Figure 26.3

$$\sqrt{x^2 + y^2} = z \Rightarrow z^2 = x^2 + y^2$$
$$x^2 + y^2 + z^2 = x^2 + y^2 + \left(x^2 + y^2 \right) = 2$$
$$\Rightarrow x^2 + y^2 = 1 \Rightarrow z = 1.$$

Converting to spherical coordinates,

$$x^2 + y^2 + z^2 = 2 = \rho^2 \Rightarrow \rho = \sqrt{2} \text{ and } z = \rho \cos\phi \Rightarrow 1 = \sqrt{2} \cos\phi \Rightarrow \cos\phi = \frac{1}{\sqrt{2}} \Rightarrow \phi = \frac{\pi}{4}.$$

Also, $0 \le \theta \le 2\pi$. The ice-cream cone is given by $0 \le \rho \le \sqrt{2}, 0 \le \phi \le \frac{\pi}{4}, 0 \le \theta \le 2\pi$. The volume is

$$V = \iiint_Q dV = \int_0^{2\pi} \int_0^{\pi/4} \int_0^{\sqrt{2}} \rho^2 \sin\phi \, d\rho \, d\phi \, d\theta = \frac{4\pi}{3} \left[\sqrt{2} - 1 \right].$$

You are asked to verify this integration in Problem 7.

Study Tips

- Spherical coordinates are especially useful for spheres, which have a center of symmetry.

- It is helpful to identify the coordinate system representing a given point. For instance, in Example 1, write $(\rho, \theta, \phi) = \left(4, \frac{\pi}{6}, \frac{\pi}{4} \right)$ and $(x, y, z) = \left(\sqrt{6}, \sqrt{2}, 2\sqrt{2} \right)$.

- For spherical coordinates, $0 \le \phi \le \pi$ and $\rho \ge 0$. Furthermore, θ is the same angle as in polar coordinates for $r \ge 0$.

- There can be confusion if the coordinate system is not made explicit. For instance, $(0, \pi, 0)$ is the origin in spherical coordinates, but it is a point on the y-axis in rectangular coordinates.

- Don't forget the complicated differential of volume in spherical coordinates, $dV = \rho^2 \sin\phi \, d\rho \, d\phi \, d\theta$.

Problems

1. Convert the point $(\rho, \theta, \phi) = \left(12, -\dfrac{\pi}{4}, 0\right)$ to rectangular coordinates.

2. Convert the point $(\rho, \theta, \phi) = \left(5, \dfrac{\pi}{4}, \dfrac{3\pi}{4}\right)$ to rectangular coordinates.

3. Convert the point $(x, y, z) = \left(-2, 2\sqrt{3}, 4\right)$ to spherical coordinates.

4. Find an equation in spherical coordinates for the rectangular equation $z = 6$.

5. Find an equation in rectangular coordinates for the spherical equation $\phi = \dfrac{\pi}{6}$.

6. Convert the integral $\displaystyle\int_{-2}^{2} \int_{-\sqrt{4-x^2}}^{\sqrt{4-x^2}} \int_{2}^{2+\sqrt{4-x^2-y^2}} x \, dz \, dy \, dx$ to spherical coordinates.

7. Verify that $V = \displaystyle\iiint_Q dV = \int_0^{2\pi} \int_0^{\pi/4} \int_0^{\sqrt{2}} \rho^2 \sin\phi \, d\rho \, d\phi \, d\theta = \dfrac{4\pi}{3}\left[\sqrt{2} - 1\right]$.

8. Set up the triple integral in spherical coordinates for the volume of the solid inside the sphere $x^2 + y^2 + z^2 = 9$, outside $z = \sqrt{x^2 + y^2}$, and above the xy-plane.

9. Set up the triple integral in spherical coordinates for the volume of the torus given by $\rho = 4\sin\phi$.

10. Set up the triple integral in spherical coordinates for the mass of the sphere of radius 3 if the density is proportional to the distance of the point to the z-axis.

Vector Fields—Velocity, Gravity, Electricity
Lesson 27

Topics

- Vector fields.

- Rotation and radial vector fields.

- The gradient as a vector field.

- Gravitational fields.

- Electric force fields.

- Conservative vector fields.

- Calculating the potential for a conservative vector field in the plane.

Definitions and Theorems

- A **vector field** over a planar region R is a function $\mathbf{F}$ that assigns a vector $\mathbf{F}(x, y)$ to each point in R.

- A **vector field** over a solid region Q is a function $\mathbf{F}$ that assigns a vector $\mathbf{F}(x, y, z)$ to each point in Q.

- **Newtons's law of gravitation** states that the force of attraction exerted on a particle of mass m_1 located at (x, y, z) by a particle of mass m_2 located at $(0, 0, 0)$ is

$$\mathbf{F}(x, y, z) = \frac{-Gm_1m_2}{x^2 + y^2 + z^2}\mathbf{u}.$$

  Here, G is the gravitational constant, and $\mathbf{u}$ is the unit vector from the origin to (x, y, z).

- **Coulomb's law** states that the force exerted on a particle with electric charge q_1 located at (x, y, z) by a particle of charge q_2 located at $(0, 0, 0)$ is $\mathbf{F}(x, y, z) = \dfrac{cq_1q_2}{\|\mathbf{r}\|^2}\mathbf{u}$.

- A vector field $\mathbf{F}$ is **conservative** if there exists a differentiable function f (the **potential**) such that $\mathbf{F} = \nabla f$.

- Theorem: Let M and N have continuous first partial derivatives on an open disk R. The vector field given by $\mathbf{F}(x, y) = M\mathbf{i} + N\mathbf{j}$ is conservative if and only if $\dfrac{\partial N}{\partial x} = \dfrac{\partial M}{\partial y}$.

Summary

In this lesson, we develop the concept of a vector field. In the plane, a vector field is a function that assigns a vector to each point in the plane. Similarly, in space, a vector field assigns a vector to each point in space. We begin by describing typical vector fields, including rotational fields, gravitational fields, and electric fields. In fact, the gradient of a function is a vector field. We define what is meant by a conservative vector field, one that is the gradient of a potential function. Most of the important fields in applications are conservative. We develop a test for conservative vector fields in the plane and show how to find the potential function.

Example 1

Sketch some vectors in the vector field given by $\mathbf{F}(x, y) = -y\mathbf{i} + x\mathbf{j}$.

Solution

We first compute some points to get an idea of the field:

$$\mathbf{F}(x, y) = -y\mathbf{i} + x\mathbf{j}$$
$$\mathbf{F}(1, 0) = 0\mathbf{i} + 1\mathbf{j} = \mathbf{j}$$
$$\mathbf{F}(0, 1) = -1\mathbf{i} + 0\mathbf{j} = -\mathbf{i}$$
$$\mathbf{F}(2, 2) = -2\mathbf{i} + 2\mathbf{j}.$$

By plotting these vectors, we obtain the following example of a **rotation vector field**. (See **Figure 27.1**.)

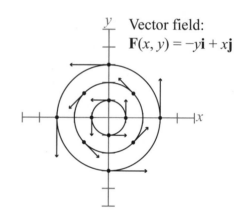

Vector field:
$\mathbf{F}(x, y) = -y\mathbf{i} + x\mathbf{j}$

Figure 27.1

Example 2

Sketch some vectors in the vector field $\mathbf{F}(x, y) = x\mathbf{i} + y\mathbf{j}$.

Solution

We first compute some points to get an idea of the field:

$$\mathbf{F}(x, y) = x\mathbf{i} + y\mathbf{j}$$
$$\mathbf{F}(1, 1) = \mathbf{i} + \mathbf{j}$$
$$\mathbf{F}(-1, -1) = -\mathbf{i} - \mathbf{j}$$
$$\mathbf{F}(-2, 2) = -2\mathbf{i} + 2\mathbf{j}.$$

By plotting these vectors, we obtain the following example of a **radial vector field**. (See **Figure 27.2**.)

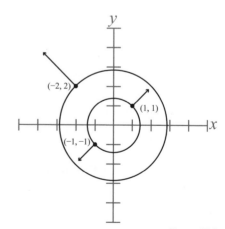

Figure 27.2

Example 3

The gradient of a function f is a vector field.

For example, if $f(x, y) = x^2 y - \dfrac{y^2}{2}$, then $\nabla f(x, y) = f_x(x, y)\mathbf{i} + f_y(x, y)\mathbf{j} = 2xy\mathbf{i} + (x^2 - y)\mathbf{j}$ is a vector field.

At each point (x, y) in the plane, the gradient assigns a vector.

Example 4

The vector field $\mathbf{F}(x, y) = (10x + 3y)\mathbf{i} + (3x + 2y)\mathbf{j}$ is conservative with potential $f(x, y) = 5x^2 + 3xy + y^2$ because $\mathbf{F} = \nabla f$.

Example 5

The vector field $\mathbf{F}(x, y) = x^2 y\mathbf{i} + xy\mathbf{j}$ is not conservative because $M = x^2 y$, $\dfrac{\partial M}{\partial y} = x^2$, $N = xy$, $\dfrac{\partial N}{\partial x} = y$, and $x^2 \neq y$.

Example 6

Find a potential for the conservative vector field $\mathbf{F}(x, y) = 2xy\mathbf{i} + (x^2 - y)\mathbf{j}$.

Solution

Note that the field is conservative because $\dfrac{\partial M}{\partial y} = 2x$ and $\dfrac{\partial N}{\partial x} = 2x$.

We need to find a function $f(x, y)$ such that $\nabla f(x, y) = 2xy\mathbf{i} + (x^2 - y)\mathbf{j}$. That is, $f_x(x, y) = 2xy$ and $f_y(x, y) = x^2 - y$.

Integrating the first equation,

$$f(x, y) = \int f_x(x, y)\,dx = \int 2xy\,dx = x^2 y + g(y).$$

Integrating the second equation,

$$f(x, y) = \int f_y(x, y)\,dy = \int (x^2 - y)\,dy = x^2 y - \frac{y^2}{2} + h(x).$$

From these two versions of the function f, we have

$$f(x, y) = x^2 y - \frac{y^2}{2} + K.$$

Study Tips

- A vector field assigns a *vector* to each point in the domain.

- Gravitational fields and electric fields have the same form and are examples of **inverse square fields**. Given $\mathbf{r} = x\mathbf{i} + y\mathbf{j} + z\mathbf{k}$, the vector field $\mathbf{F}$ is an inverse square field if $\mathbf{F}(x, y, z) = \dfrac{k}{\|\mathbf{r}\|^2}\mathbf{u}$.

- Every inverse square field is conservative. Hence, gravitational fields and electric force fields are conservative.

- After calculating the potential for a conservative vector field, you can check your answer by taking the gradient of the potential.

  For instance, in Example 6, $\nabla f(x, y) = \nabla\left(x^2 y - \dfrac{y^2}{2} + K\right) = 2xy\mathbf{i} + \left(x^2 - y\right)\mathbf{j}$, which is the original vector field.

Pitfalls

- For conservative vector fields, $\mathbf{F} = \nabla f$, keep in mind that f is a function of two or three variables, whereas $\mathbf{F}$ is a vector field.

- Notice in Example 6 that the "constants of integration" are functions of the "other" variable. The final answer has a true constant.

Problems

1. Describe the vector field $\mathbf{F}(x, y) = \mathbf{i} + \mathbf{j}$ and compute $\|\mathbf{F}\|$.

2. Describe the vector field $\mathbf{F}(x, y, z) = \mathbf{i} + \mathbf{j} + \mathbf{k}$ and compute $\|\mathbf{F}\|$.

3. Determine whether or not the vector field $\mathbf{F}(x, y) = 5y^2(y\mathbf{i} + 3x\mathbf{j})$ is conservative.

4. Determine whether or not the vector field $\mathbf{F}(x, y) = \dfrac{1}{\sqrt{x^2 + y^2}}(\mathbf{i} + \mathbf{j})$ is conservative.

5. Find the conservative vector field for the potential function $f(x, y) = x^2 - \dfrac{1}{4}y^2$.

6. Find the conservative vector field for the potential function $f(x, y, z) = 6xyz$.

7. Find the conservative vector field for the potential function $f(x, y, z) = z + ye^{x^2}$.

8. Find a potential function for the conservative vector field $\mathbf{F}(x, y) = y\mathbf{i} + x\mathbf{j}$.

9. Find a potential function for the conservative vector field $\mathbf{F}(x, y) = \dfrac{x}{x^2 + y^2}\mathbf{i} + \dfrac{y}{x^2 + y^2}\mathbf{j}$.

10. Find a potential function for the conservative vector field $\mathbf{F}(x, y) = 3x^2y^2\mathbf{i} + 2x^3y\mathbf{j}$.

Curl, Divergence, Line Integrals
Lesson 28

Topics

- The curl of a vector field.

- The divergence of a vector field.

- Line integrals of functions defined on curves.

- Applications to mass.

Definitions and Theorems

- The **curl** of the vector field $\mathbf{F}(x, y, z)$ is

$$\operatorname{curl} \mathbf{F}(x, y, z) = \left(\frac{\partial P}{\partial y} - \frac{\partial N}{\partial z} \right)\mathbf{i} - \left(\frac{\partial P}{\partial x} - \frac{\partial M}{\partial z} \right)\mathbf{j} + \left(\frac{\partial N}{\partial x} - \frac{\partial M}{\partial y} \right)\mathbf{k}$$

$$= \nabla \times \mathbf{F}(x, y, z) = \begin{vmatrix} \mathbf{i} & \mathbf{j} & \mathbf{k} \\ \dfrac{\partial}{\partial x} & \dfrac{\partial}{\partial y} & \dfrac{\partial}{\partial z} \\ M & N & P \end{vmatrix}.$$

- Under suitable hypotheses, a vector field is conservative if and only if $\operatorname{curl} \mathbf{F} = 0$.

- The **divergence** of the field $\mathbf{F}(x, y, z)$ is $\operatorname{div} \mathbf{F}(x, y, z) = \nabla \cdot \mathbf{F} = \dfrac{\partial M}{\partial x} + \dfrac{\partial N}{\partial y} + \dfrac{\partial P}{\partial z}$.

- Let C be a planar curve given by $\mathbf{r}(t) = x(t)\mathbf{i} + y(t)\mathbf{j}$, $a \leq t \leq b$.

  The line integral of f is $\displaystyle\int_C f(x, y)\,ds = \int_a^b f(x(t), y(t))\sqrt{[x'(t)]^2 + [y'(t)]^2}\,dt.$

  A similar definition holds for curves in space.

- Differential of arc length: $ds = \sqrt{[x'(t)]^2 + [y'(t)]^2 + [z'(t)]^2}\,dt.$

Summary

Recall that most of the important vector fields in applications are conservative. Hence, we begin this lesson with a test for conservative vector fields in space. This test involves the concept of the curl of a vector field, an operation related to the cross product. The curl of a velocity field is related to its tendency to rotate. Another important operation on a vector field is the divergence, which is related to sources and sinks for velocity fields. Finally, we introduce line integrals for functions of two and three variables. These integrals are motivated by the calculation of mass for a thin wire.

Example 1

Calculate the curl of the vector field $\mathbf{F}(x, y, z) = 2xy\mathbf{i} + (x^2 + z^2)\mathbf{j} + 2yz\mathbf{k}$.

Solution

We use the determinant definition of curl:

$$\operatorname{curl}\mathbf{F}(x, y, z) = \begin{vmatrix} \mathbf{i} & \mathbf{j} & \mathbf{k} \\ \dfrac{\partial}{\partial x} & \dfrac{\partial}{\partial y} & \dfrac{\partial}{\partial z} \\ M & N & P \end{vmatrix} = \begin{vmatrix} \mathbf{i} & \mathbf{j} & \mathbf{k} \\ \dfrac{\partial}{\partial x} & \dfrac{\partial}{\partial y} & \dfrac{\partial}{\partial z} \\ 2xy & x^2 + z^2 & 2yz \end{vmatrix}$$

$$= \begin{vmatrix} \dfrac{\partial}{\partial y} & \dfrac{\partial}{\partial z} \\ x^2 + z^2 & 2yz \end{vmatrix}\mathbf{i} - \begin{vmatrix} \dfrac{\partial}{\partial x} & \dfrac{\partial}{\partial z} \\ 2xy & 2yz \end{vmatrix}\mathbf{j} + \begin{vmatrix} \dfrac{\partial}{\partial x} & \dfrac{\partial}{\partial y} \\ 2xy & x^2 + z^2 \end{vmatrix}\mathbf{k}$$

$$= (2z - 2z)\mathbf{i} - (0 - 0)\mathbf{j} + (2x - 2x)\mathbf{k} = 0.$$

Notice that the curl is zero, so the vector field is conservative.

Example 2

Calculate the divergence of $\mathbf{F}(x, y, z) = x^3 y^2 z\mathbf{i} + x^2 z\mathbf{j} + x^2 y\mathbf{k}$.

Solution

We have $\operatorname{div}\mathbf{F}(x, y, z) = \dfrac{\partial M}{\partial x} + \dfrac{\partial N}{\partial y} + \dfrac{\partial P}{\partial z} = \dfrac{\partial}{\partial x}\left[x^3 y^2 z\right] + \dfrac{\partial}{\partial y}\left[x^2 z\right] + \dfrac{\partial}{\partial z}\left[x^2 y\right]$.

Hence, $\operatorname{div}\mathbf{F} = 3x^2 y^2 z + 0 + 0 = 3x^2 y^2 z$.

Example 3

Evaluate the line integral $\int_C (x^2 - y + 3z) ds$, where C is the line segment given by $\mathbf{r}(t) = t\mathbf{i} + 2t\mathbf{j} + t\mathbf{k}$, $0 \le t \le 1$.

Solution

We first compute ds. Because $x'(t) = 1$, $y'(t) = 2$, $z'(t) = 1$,

$$ds = \sqrt{[x'(t)]^2 + [y'(t)]^2 + [z'(t)]^2} \, dt = \sqrt{1^2 + 2^2 + 1^2} \, dt = \sqrt{6} \, dt.$$

The line integral becomes

$$\int_C (x^2 - y + 3z) ds = \int_0^1 (t^2 - 2t + 3t)\sqrt{6} \, dt = \frac{5\sqrt{6}}{6}.$$

Example 4

Calculate the mass of a spring in the shape of the circular helix
$\mathbf{r}(t) = \cos t\mathbf{i} + \sin t\mathbf{j} + t\mathbf{k}$, $0 \le t \le 6\pi$, if the density of the spring is
$\rho(x, y, z) = 1 + z$. (See **Figure 28.1**.)

Solution

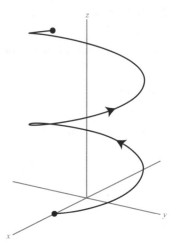

Figure 28.1

We have $\mathbf{r}'(t) = -\sin t\mathbf{i} + \cos t\mathbf{j} + \mathbf{k}$ and $ds = \sqrt{\sin^2 t + \cos^2 t + 1} \, dt = \sqrt{2} \, dt$.

So, the line integral is $\int_C (1 + z) ds = \int_0^{6\pi} (1 + t)\sqrt{2} \, dt = 6\pi\sqrt{2}(3\pi + 1)$.

You are asked to verify this integration in Problem 10.

Study Tips

- You will often see the cross product notation for curl: $\text{curl } \mathbf{F} = \nabla \times \mathbf{F}$.

- The vector field in Example 1 is conservative. The potential function is $f(x, y, z) = x^2 y + yz^2 + K$.

- Loosely speaking, curl is a measure of a field's tendency to rotate. If $\text{curl } \mathbf{F} = \mathbf{0}$, we say that the field is **irrotational**. For example, the radial field $\mathbf{F}(x, y) = x\mathbf{i} + y\mathbf{j}$ is irrotational, whereas the field $\mathbf{F}(x, y) = y\mathbf{i} - x\mathbf{j}$ is not.

- You will often see the dot product notation for divergence: $\text{div } \mathbf{F} = \nabla \cdot \mathbf{F}$.

- Loosely speaking, the divergence of a velocity field measures the tendency of the fluid to diverge from a point. If the divergence of the field is positive, we have a **source**. If it is negative, we have a **sink**. And if the divergence is zero, we say that the field is **divergence free** or **incompressible**.

- The line integral discussed in this lesson is motivated by mass of a thin wire. Hence, the value of the integral does not depend on the parameterization of the curve C. Furthermore, if the integrand is 1, we have the formula for arc length.

- Notice the differential of arc length $ds = \sqrt{\left[x'(t)\right]^2 + \left[y'(t)\right]^2 + \left[z'(t)\right]^2}\, dt$ in the definition of line integral.

Pitfalls

- The divergence of a vector field is a scalar function, whereas the curl is a vector field.

- Line integrals should really be called "curve integrals" because they are defined on curves in the plane or space.

Problems

1. Find the curl of the vector field $\mathbf{F}(x, y, z) = xyz\mathbf{i} + xyz\mathbf{j} + xyz\mathbf{k}$.

2. Find the curl of the vector field $\mathbf{F}(x, y, z) = e^x \sin y\mathbf{i} - e^x \cos y\mathbf{j}$.

3. Verify that the curl of the vector field $\mathbf{F}(x, y) = -y\mathbf{i} + x\mathbf{j}$ is $\mathrm{curl}\mathbf{F} = 2\mathbf{k}$.

4. Determine if the vector field $\mathbf{F}(x, y, z) = \sin z\mathbf{i} + \sin x\mathbf{j} + \sin y\mathbf{k}$ is conservative.

5. Find a potential function for the conservative vector field $\mathbf{F}(x, y, z) = xy^2 z^2\mathbf{i} + x^2 yz^2\mathbf{j} + x^2 y^2 z\mathbf{k}$.

6. Find the divergence of the vector field $\mathbf{F}(x, y) = x^2\mathbf{i} + 2y^2\mathbf{j}$.

7. Find the divergence of the vector field $\mathbf{F}(x, y, z) = \sin x\mathbf{i} + \cos y\mathbf{j} + z^2\mathbf{k}$.

8. Evaluate the line integral $\int_C xy\, ds$, where C is the path $\mathbf{r}(t) = 4t\mathbf{i} + 3t\mathbf{j}$, $0 \le t \le 1$.

9. Evaluate the line integral $\int_C \left(x^2 + y^2 + z^2\right) ds$, where C is the path $\mathbf{r}(t) = \sin t\mathbf{i} + \cos t\mathbf{j} + 2\mathbf{k}$, $0 \le t \le \frac{\pi}{2}$.

10. Verify that $\int_0^{6\pi} (1+t)\sqrt{2}\, dt = 6\pi\sqrt{2}(3\pi + 1)$.

More Line Integrals and Work by a Force Field
Lesson 29

Topics

- Line integrals of vector fields.

- Work.

- Line integrals in differential form.

Definitions and Theorems

- Let C be a planar curve given by $\mathbf{r}(t) = x(t)\mathbf{i} + y(t)\mathbf{j}$, $a \le t \le b$. If $\mathbf{F}$ is a vector field with unit tangent vector $\mathbf{T}$, then the **line integral** of $\mathbf{F}$ is

$$\int_C \mathbf{F} \cdot d\mathbf{r} = \int_C \mathbf{F} \cdot \mathbf{T}\, ds = \int_a^b \mathbf{F}\big(x(t), y(t)\big) \cdot \mathbf{r}'(t)\, dt.$$

A similar definition holds for curves in space.

- The **increment of work** is $dW \approx \mathbf{F} \cdot \mathbf{T}\, ds = \mathbf{F} \cdot d\mathbf{r}$.

- Line integrals in **differential form**: If $\mathbf{F}(x, y) = M\mathbf{i} + N\mathbf{j}$, then $\displaystyle \int_C \mathbf{F} \cdot d\mathbf{r} = \int_C M\, dx + N\, dy$.

A similar definition holds for curves in space.

Summary

The extension of line integrals to vector fields is motivated by the calculation of work. We illustrate the definition with examples of line integrals for vector fields. In all cases, the line integral is converted to a single integral. We will see that the orientation of the path matters, unlike the situation with line integrals of functions developed in the previous lesson. We close the lesson by introducing the differential form of the line integral.

Example 1

Let C be the quarter circle $\mathbf{r}(t) = \cos t\, \mathbf{i} + \sin t\, \mathbf{j}$, $0 \le t \le \dfrac{\pi}{2}$, and let $\mathbf{F}(x, y) = 3x\mathbf{i} + 4y\mathbf{j}$. Calculate the line integral $\displaystyle \int_C \mathbf{F} \cdot d\mathbf{r}$. (See **Figure 29.1.**)

Solution

We have $\int_C \mathbf{F} \cdot d\mathbf{r} = \int_a^b \mathbf{F}\big(x(t), y(t)\big) \cdot \mathbf{r}'(t)\, dt$ and $\mathbf{r}'(t) = -\sin t\mathbf{i} + \cos t\mathbf{j}$.

So, $\mathbf{F}(x, y) = 3x\mathbf{i} + 4y\mathbf{j} = 3\cos t\mathbf{i} + 4\sin t\mathbf{j}$.

Finally,

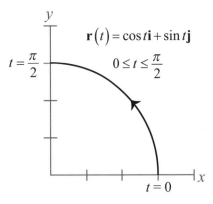

$$\int_C \mathbf{F} \cdot d\mathbf{r} = \int_a^b \mathbf{F}\big(x(t), y(t)\big) \cdot \mathbf{r}'(t)\, dt$$

$$= \int_0^{\pi/2} \big[3\cos t\mathbf{i} + 4\sin t\mathbf{j}\big] \cdot \big[-\sin t\mathbf{i} + \cos t\mathbf{j}\big]\, dt$$

$$= \int_0^{\pi/2} \big[-3\cos t \sin t + 4\sin t \cos t\big]\, dt$$

$$= \int_0^{\pi/2} \sin t \cos t\, dt = \left[\frac{\sin^2 t}{2}\right]_0^{\pi/2} = \frac{1}{2}.$$

Figure 29.1

Example 2

Find the work done by the force field $\mathbf{F}(x, y, z) = -\dfrac{1}{2}x\mathbf{i} - \dfrac{1}{2}y\mathbf{j} + \dfrac{1}{4}\mathbf{k}$ on a particle as it moves along the helix $\mathbf{r}(t) = \cos t\mathbf{i} + \sin t\mathbf{j} + t\mathbf{k}$ from $(1, 0, 0)$ to $(-1, 0, 3\pi)$.

Solution

$\mathbf{r}'(t) = -\sin t\mathbf{i} + \cos t\mathbf{j} + \mathbf{k}$. For the path between the two points, $0 \le t \le 3\pi$.

The force field is $\mathbf{F}(x, y, z) = -\dfrac{1}{2}x\mathbf{i} - \dfrac{1}{2}y\mathbf{j} + \dfrac{1}{4}\mathbf{k} = -\dfrac{1}{2}\cos t\mathbf{i} - \dfrac{1}{2}\sin t\mathbf{j} + \dfrac{1}{4}\mathbf{k}$.

The work is

$$W = \int_C \mathbf{F} \cdot d\mathbf{r} = \int_a^b \mathbf{F} \cdot \mathbf{r}'(t)\, dt$$

$$= \int_0^{3\pi} \left(-\frac{1}{2}\cos t\mathbf{i} - \frac{1}{2}\sin t\mathbf{j} + \frac{1}{4}\mathbf{k}\right) \cdot \left(-\sin t\mathbf{i} + \cos t\mathbf{j} + \mathbf{k}\right)\, dt$$

$$= \int_0^{3\pi} \left(\frac{1}{2}\sin t \cos t - \frac{1}{2}\sin t \cos t + \frac{1}{4}\right)\, dt$$

$$= \int_0^{3\pi} \frac{1}{4}\, dt = \left[\frac{1}{4}t\right]_0^{3\pi} = \frac{3\pi}{4}.$$

Example 3

Evaluate the line integral $\int_C y\,dx + x^2\,dy$, where C is the parabola $y = 4x - x^2$ from $(4, 0)$ to $(1, 3)$.

Solution

We have $y = 4x - x^2 \Rightarrow dy = (4 - 2x)\,dx$. Notice that x goes from 4 to 1. So,

$$\int_C y\,dx + x^2\,dy = \int_4^1 \left[\left(4x - x^2\right)dx + x^2\left(4 - 2x\right)dx \right]$$

$$= \int_4^1 \left[4x + 3x^2 - 2x^3 \right]dx.$$

This integral is easy to evaluate, and the final answer is $\dfrac{69}{2}$.

Study Tips

- From the definition of line integral, you see that work is greater if the force is applied in the direction of motion.

- Line integrals of force fields do not depend on the parameterization of the curve.

- The line integrals discussed in the previous lesson were motivated by mass of a thin wire. Hence, the value of the integral does not depend on the orientation of the curve C. However, for line integrals of vector fields, the orientation is important.

- If we reverse the orientation of the path—for instance, in Example 3—the value of the line integral would be the negative of the original answer.

Pitfalls

- Remember that line integrals of vector fields depend on the orientation of the path, whereas line integrals of functions $f(x, y, z)$ do not.

- The notation for line integrals of vector fields can be confusing. Remember that if $\mathbf{F}(x, y) = M\mathbf{i} + N\mathbf{j}$, then $\int_C \mathbf{F} \cdot d\mathbf{r} = \int_a^b \mathbf{F} \cdot \mathbf{r}'(t)\,dt = \int_C M\,dx + N\,dy$.

1. Evaluate the line integral $\int_C \mathbf{F} \cdot d\mathbf{r}$, where $\mathbf{F}(x, y) = x\mathbf{i} + y\mathbf{j}$ and C is the curve given by $\mathbf{r}(t) = t\mathbf{i} + t\mathbf{j}, 0 \leq t \leq 1$.

2. Evaluate the line integral $\int_C \mathbf{F} \cdot d\mathbf{r}$, where $\mathbf{F}(x, y) = 3x\mathbf{i} + 4y\mathbf{j}$ and C is the curve given by $\mathbf{r}(t) = t\mathbf{i} + \sqrt{4 - t^2}\,\mathbf{j}, -2 \leq t \leq 2$.

3. Evaluate the line integral $\int_C \mathbf{F} \cdot d\mathbf{r}$, where $\mathbf{F}(x, y, z) = xy\mathbf{i} + xz\mathbf{j} + yz\mathbf{k}$ and C is the curve given by $\mathbf{r}(t) = t\mathbf{i} + t^2\mathbf{j} + 2t\mathbf{k}, 0 \leq t \leq 1$.

4. Evaluate the line integral $\int_C \mathbf{F} \cdot d\mathbf{r}$, where $\mathbf{F}(x, y, z) = x\mathbf{i} + y\mathbf{j} - 5z\mathbf{k}$ and C is the curve given by $\mathbf{r}(t) = 2\cos t\mathbf{i} + 2\sin t\mathbf{j} + t\mathbf{k}, 0 \leq t \leq 2\pi$.

5. Find the work done by the force field $\mathbf{F}(x, y) = x\mathbf{i} + 2y\mathbf{j}$ on a particle moving along the path $C: x = t, y = t^3$ from $(0, 0)$ to $(2, 8)$.

6. Find the work done by the force field $\mathbf{F}(x, y, z) = yz\mathbf{i} + xz\mathbf{j} + xy\mathbf{k}$ on a particle moving along the line C from $(0, 0, 0)$ to $(5, 3, 2)$.

7. Evaluate the line integral $\int_C (3y - x)\,dx + y^2\,dy$, where C is the path given by $x = 2t, y = 10t, 0 \leq t \leq 1$.

8. Evaluate the line integral $\int_C (x + 3y^2)\,dy$, where C is the path given by $x = 2t, y = 10t, 0 \leq t \leq 1$.

9. Evaluate the line integral $\int_C \mathbf{F} \cdot d\mathbf{r}$, where $\mathbf{F}(x, y) = x^2\mathbf{i} + xy\mathbf{j}$ and C is the curve given by $\mathbf{r}(t) = 2t\mathbf{i} + (t - 1)\mathbf{j}, 1 \leq t \leq 3$.

10. Evaluate the same line integral in Problem 9 but with the orientation reversed: $\mathbf{r}(t) = 2(3 - t)\mathbf{i} + (2 - t)\mathbf{j}, 0 \leq t \leq 2$. What do you observe?

Fundamental Theorem of Line Integrals
Lesson 30

Topics

- The fundamental theorem of line integrals.

- Smooth curves, piecewise smooth curves, simple curves, and closed curves.

- Path independence.

Definitions and Theorems

- The **fundamental theorem of line integrals**: Let C be a piecewise smooth curve in the open region R given by $\mathbf{r}(t) = x(t)\mathbf{i} + y(t)\mathbf{j}$, $a \leq t \leq b$. Let $\mathbf{F} = M\mathbf{i} + N\mathbf{j}$ be conservative, M and N continuous, and f a potential for $\mathbf{F}$. Then,

$$\int_C \mathbf{F} \cdot d\mathbf{r} = \int_C \nabla f \cdot d\mathbf{r} = f\big(x(b), y(b)\big) - f\big(x(a), y(a)\big).$$

A similar property holds for line integrals in space.

- The curve $\mathbf{r}(t) = x(t)\mathbf{i} + y(t)\mathbf{j} + z(t)\mathbf{k}$, $a \leq t \leq b$ is **smooth** if the derivatives of the component functions are continuous and are not simultaneously zero. The curve is **piecewise smooth** if it can be partitioned into a finite number of subintervals, on each of which the curve is smooth. The curve is **simple** if it does not cross itself, except possibly at the endpoints. The curve is **closed** if $\mathbf{r}(a) = \mathbf{r}(b)$.

- A region is **simply connected** if it is connected (one piece) and every simple closed curve in the region encloses only points that lie in the region.

- Under suitable hypotheses, the following are equivalent: (1) $\mathbf{F}$ is conservative, (2) the line integral is independent of path, and (3) the line integral is zero for any closed curve.

- Law of conservation of energy: In a conservative force field, the sum of potential and kinetic energies of an object remain constant from point to point.

Summary

Many of the important vector fields for applications are conservative, such as gravitational and electric fields. For such fields, the line integral between any two points is simply the difference of the potential function evaluated at those points. In other words, the line integral is independent of path. In this lesson, we present this fundamental theorem of line integrals and illustrate it with examples. We study properties of curves in space, including smooth curves, piecewise smooth curves, simple curves, and closed curves. We obtain an important theorem for conservative vector fields defined on simply connected regions. Finally, we discuss the famous law of conservation of energy.

Example 1

Find the work done by the force field $\mathbf{F}(x, y) = 2xy\mathbf{i} + x^2\mathbf{j}$ on a particle that moves from $(0, 0)$ to $(1, 1)$ along the path $y = x$.

Solution

The path is $\mathbf{r}(t) = t\mathbf{i} + t\mathbf{j}$, $0 \le t \le 1$ and $\mathbf{r}'(t) = \dfrac{d\mathbf{r}}{dt} = \mathbf{i} + \mathbf{j}$.

The vector field is $\mathbf{F}(x, y) = 2xy\mathbf{i} + x^2\mathbf{j} = 2(t)(t)\mathbf{i} + t^2\mathbf{j} = 2t^2\mathbf{i} + t^2\mathbf{j}$. Hence, the work is

$$W = \int_C \mathbf{F} \cdot d\mathbf{r} = \int_0^1 \left(2t^2\mathbf{i} + t^2\mathbf{j}\right)\cdot(\mathbf{i} + \mathbf{j})\,dt = \int_0^1 3t^2\,dt = \left[t^3\right]_0^1 = 1.$$

Example 2

Calculate the line integral $\int_C \mathbf{F} \cdot d\mathbf{r}$, where C is a piecewise smooth curve from $(-1, 4)$ to $(1, 2)$ and $\mathbf{F}(x, y) = 2xy\mathbf{i} + (x^2 - y)\mathbf{j}$.

Solution

The vector field is conservative with potential function

$$f(x, y) = x^2 y - \frac{1}{2}y^2$$

because

$$\nabla f(x, y) = \nabla\left(x^2 y - \frac{1}{2}y^2\right) = 2xy\mathbf{i} + (x^2 - y)\mathbf{j} = \mathbf{F}(x, y).$$

By the fundamental theorem of line integrals, we have

$$\begin{aligned}
\int_C \mathbf{F} \cdot d\mathbf{r} &= \int_C \nabla f \cdot d\mathbf{r} \\
&= f\big(x(b), y(b)\big) - f\big(x(a), y(a)\big) \\
&= f(1, 2) - f(-1, 4) \\
&= \left[1^2(2) - \frac{1}{2}2^2\right] - \left[(-1)^2(4) - \frac{1}{2}4^2\right] = 4.
\end{aligned}$$

Example 3

Evaluate the line $\int_C \mathbf{F} \cdot d\mathbf{r}$, where C is a piecewise smooth curve from $(1, 1, 0)$ to $(0, 2, 3)$ and $\mathbf{F}(x, y, z) = 2xy\mathbf{i} + (x^2 + z^2)\mathbf{j} + 2yz\mathbf{k}$.

Solution

The curl of $\mathbf{F}$ is zero, so the vector field is conservative. The potential function is $f(x, y, z) = x^2y + yz^2$. By the fundamental theorem of line integrals,

$$\int_C \mathbf{F} \cdot d\mathbf{r} = \int_C \nabla f \cdot d\mathbf{r} = f(0, 2, 3) - f(1, 1, 0) = \left[(0^2)(2) + 2(3)^2\right] - \left[(1^2)(1) + 1(0)^2\right] = 17.$$

Example 4

Calculate $\int_C \mathbf{F} \cdot d\mathbf{r}$, where $\mathbf{F}(x, y) = (y^3 + 1)\mathbf{i} + (3xy^2 + 1)\mathbf{j}$ and C is the semicircular path from $(0, 0)$ to $(2, 0)$. (See **Figure 30.1**.)

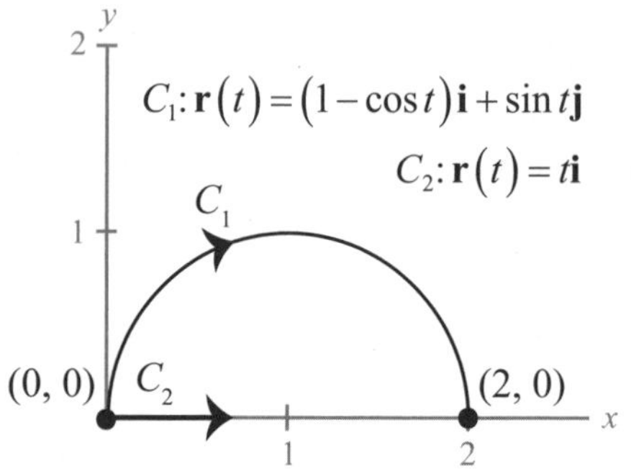

Solution

We will illustrate three possible solutions to this problem.

Solution 1

Parameterize the curve as $\mathbf{r}(t) = (1 - \cos t)\mathbf{i} + \sin t\mathbf{j}, 0 \le t \le \pi$.

Then, $\mathbf{r}'(t) = \sin t\mathbf{i} + \cos t\mathbf{j}$ and

$C_1 : \mathbf{r}(t) = (1 - \cos t)\mathbf{i} + \sin t\mathbf{j}$

$C_2 : \mathbf{r}(t) = t\mathbf{i}$

Figure 30.1

$$\int_C \mathbf{F} \cdot d\mathbf{r} = \int_0^\pi \left[(\sin^3 t + 1)\mathbf{i} + (3(1 - \cos t)\sin^2 t + 1)\mathbf{j}\right] \cdot [\sin t\mathbf{i} + \cos t\mathbf{j}] dt$$

$$= \int_0^\pi (\sin^4 t + \sin t + 3(1 - \cos t)\sin^2 t \cos t + \cos t) dt.$$

This is a very complicated integral. A calculator gives the answer of 2.

Solution 2

The vector field is conservative with potential $f(x, y) = xy^3 + x + y$. By the fundamental theorem of line integrals,

$$\int_C \mathbf{F} \cdot d\mathbf{r} = \int_C \nabla f \cdot d\mathbf{r} = f(2, 0) - f(0, 0) = 2 - 0 = 2.$$

Solution 3

Use a simpler path joining the points: C_2: $\mathbf{r}(t) = t\mathbf{i}$, $0 \le t \le 2$.

Then, the vector field is $\mathbf{F}(x, y) = (y^3 + 1)\mathbf{i} + (3xy^2 + 1)\mathbf{j} = \mathbf{i} + \mathbf{j}$. Because $\mathbf{r}'(t) = \mathbf{i}$, we have

$$\int_{C_2} \mathbf{F} \cdot d\mathbf{r} = \int_0^2 [\mathbf{i} + \mathbf{j}] \cdot \mathbf{i}\, dt = \int_0^2 1\, dt = [t]_0^2 = 2.$$

Notice that all three techniques give the same answer. Which method do you prefer?

Study Tips

- If a vector field is conservative, then the line integral between any two points is simply the difference of the potential function evaluated at those points. The line integral is independent of path. For example, the vector field in Example 1 is conservative, with potential $f(x, y) = x^2y$. By the fundamental theorem of line integrals,

$$\int_C \mathbf{F} \cdot d\mathbf{r} = \int_C \nabla f \cdot d\mathbf{r} = f(1, 1) - f(0, 0) = (1^2)(1) - 0 = 1 - 0 = 1.$$

- Note the similarities between the fundamental theorem of calculus and the fundamental theorem of line integrals:

$$\int_a^b f(x)\, dx = \int_a^b F'(x)\, dx = F(b) - F(a)$$

$$\int_C \mathbf{F} \cdot d\mathbf{r} = \int_C \nabla f \cdot d\mathbf{r} = f(x(b), y(b)) - f(x(a), y(a)).$$

You can use any potential you want in the fundamental theorem of line integrals. For instance, in Example 2, you could use $f(x, y) = x^2y - \dfrac{1}{2}y^2 + K$ for any constant K.

Pitfall

- When using the fundamental theorem of line integrals, you must make sure that the vector field is conservative.

Problems

1. Determine whether the vector field $\mathbf{F}(x, y) = e^x \sin y\mathbf{i} + e^x \cos y\mathbf{j}$ is conservative.

2. Determine whether the vector field $\mathbf{F}(x, y) = \dfrac{1}{y}\mathbf{i} + \dfrac{x}{y^2}\mathbf{j}$ is conservative.

3. Determine whether the vector field $\mathbf{F}(x, y, z) = y\ln z\mathbf{i} - x\ln z\mathbf{j} + \dfrac{xy}{z}\mathbf{k}$ is conservative.

4. Evaluate the line integral $\int_C 2xy\,dx + \left(x^2 + y^2\right)dy$, where C is the ellipse $\dfrac{x^2}{25} + \dfrac{y^2}{16} = 1$ from $(5, 0)$ to $(0, 4)$.

5. Evaluate the line integral $\int_C 2xy\,dx + \left(x^2 + y^2\right)dy$, where C is the parabola $y = 4 - x^2$ from $(2, 0)$ to $(0, 4)$.

6. Evaluate the line integral $\int_C yz\,dx + xz\,dy + xy\,dz$, where C is the curve $\mathbf{r}(t) = t\mathbf{i} + 2\mathbf{j} + t\mathbf{k}$, $0 \le t \le 4$.

7. Evaluate the line integral $\int_C yz\,dx + xz\,dy + xy\,dz$, where C is the curve $\mathbf{r}(t) = t^2\mathbf{i} + t\mathbf{j} + t^2\mathbf{k}$, $0 \le t \le 2$.

8. Evaluate the line integral $\int_C \cos x \sin y\,dx + \sin x \cos y\,dy$, where C is the line segment from $(0, -\pi)$ to $\left(\dfrac{3\pi}{2}, \dfrac{\pi}{2}\right)$.

9. Find the work done by the force field $\mathbf{F}(x, y) = \dfrac{2x}{y}\mathbf{i} - \dfrac{x^2}{y^2}\mathbf{j}$ in moving an object from the point $(-1, 1)$ to the point $(3, 2)$.

10. Verify that $\mathbf{F}(x, y) = \dfrac{y}{x^2 + y^2}\mathbf{i} - \dfrac{x}{x^2 + y^2}\mathbf{j}$ is conservative.

What is the value of the line integral $\int_C \mathbf{F}\cdot d\mathbf{r}$ if C is the circle $x^2 + (y - 4)^2 = 1$?

Green's Theorem—Boundaries and Regions
Lesson 31

Topics

- Green's theorem.

- Conservative vector fields and Green's theorem.

Definitions and Theorems

- **Green's theorem**: Let C be a piecewise smooth closed curve, oriented counterclockwise. The curve is traversed once with the simply connected region R on its left. Then,

$$\int_C M\, dx + N\, dy = \iint_R \left(\frac{\partial N}{\partial x} - \frac{\partial M}{\partial y} \right) dA.$$

Summary

Green's theorem relates a line integral around the boundary of a region with a double integral over the entire region. We begin by illustrating the theorem with an example, and then we state the general theorem. Green's theorem implies that for conservative vector fields, the line integral around any closed curve is zero. Finally, we show how Green's theorem is related to the rotational tendency of a velocity field.

Example 1

Let R be the region in the first quadrant bounded by the graphs of $y = x$ and $y = x^2$.

Let C be the boundary, oriented counterclockwise.

Calculate $\int_C y^2\, dx + x^2\, dy.$ (See **Figure 31.1**.)

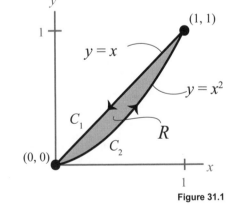

Figure 31.1

Solution

Notice that we are using differential notation here.

That is, $\int_C y^2\, dx + x^2\, dy = \int_C M\, dx + N\, dy,$ where $\mathbf{F}(x, y) = M\mathbf{i} + N\mathbf{j} = y^2\mathbf{i} + x^2\mathbf{j}.$

Also, the force field is not conservative because $\dfrac{\partial N}{\partial x} = 2x \neq \dfrac{\partial M}{\partial y} = 2y.$

We can parameterize the boundary as

$$\mathbf{r}(t) = \begin{cases} t\mathbf{i} + t^2\mathbf{j}, & 0 \le t \le 1 \\ (2-t)\mathbf{i} + (2-t)\mathbf{j}, & 1 \le t \le 2 \end{cases}.$$

Hence, there are two integrals to evaluate. The first one goes along the parabola C_1 from $(0, 0)$ to $(1, 1)$: $\mathbf{r}(t) = t\mathbf{i} + t^2\mathbf{j}, 0 \le t \le 1, \mathbf{r}'(t) = \mathbf{i} + 2t\mathbf{j}$.

Because $x = t, dx = dt, y = t^2, dy = 2t\,dt$, the line integral is

$$\int_{C_1} y^2 \, dx + x^2 \, dy = \int_0^1 \left[\left(t^2\right)^2 dt + t^2 \left(2t \, dt\right) \right]$$

$$= \int_0^1 \left(t^4 + 2t^3\right) dt$$

$$= \left[\frac{t^5}{5} + \frac{t^4}{2} \right]_0^1 = \frac{1}{5} + \frac{1}{2} = \frac{7}{10}.$$

The second path C_2 is the line from $(1, 1)$ to $(0, 0)$: $\mathbf{r}(t) = (2 - t)\mathbf{i} + (2 - t)\mathbf{j}, 1 \le t \le 2, \mathbf{r}'(t) = -\mathbf{i} - \mathbf{j}$.

Because $x = 2 - t, dx = -dt, y = 2 - t, dy = -dt$, we have

$$\int_{C_2} y^2 \, dx + x^2 \, dy = \int_1^2 \left[(2-t)^2 \left(-dt\right) + (2-t)^2 \left(-dt\right) \right]$$

$$= \int_1^2 2(2-t)^2 \left(-dt\right)$$

$$= \left[\frac{2(2-t)^3}{3} \right]_1^2 = 0 - \frac{2}{3} = -\frac{2}{3}.$$

Combining these results,

$$\int_C y^2 \, dx + x^2 \, dy = \frac{7}{10} - \frac{2}{3} = \frac{1}{30}.$$

Green's theorem says that the line integral around the boundary equals a certain double integral over the enclosed region.

$$\iint_R \left(\frac{\partial N}{\partial x} - \frac{\partial M}{\partial y} \right) dA.$$

Here, $M = y^2, \dfrac{\partial M}{\partial y} = 2y$, and $N = x^2, \dfrac{\partial N}{\partial x} = 2x$. So, we have

$$\iint_R \left(\frac{\partial N}{\partial x} - \frac{\partial M}{\partial y} \right) dA = \int_0^1 \int_{x^2}^{x} (2x - 2y)\, dy\, dx$$

$$= \int_0^1 \left[2xy - y^2 \right]_{x^2}^{x} dx$$

$$= \int_0^1 \left[\left(2x^2 - x^2 \right) - \left(2x^3 - x^4 \right) \right] dx$$

$$= \int_0^1 \left(x^2 - 2x^3 + x^4 \right) dx$$

$$= \left[\frac{x^3}{3} - \frac{x^4}{2} + \frac{x^5}{5} \right]_0^1 = \frac{1}{3} - \frac{1}{2} + \frac{1}{5} = \frac{1}{30}.$$

We have verified in this example that $\displaystyle \int_C M\, dx + N\, dy = \iint_R \left(\frac{\partial N}{\partial x} - \frac{\partial M}{\partial y} \right) dA.$

Example 2

A particle travels once counterclockwise around the circle of radius 3 centered at the origin, subject to the force $\mathbf{F}(x, y) = y^3 \mathbf{i} + (x^3 + 3xy^2)\mathbf{j}$. Use Green's theorem to find the work done by the force field.

Solution

Notice how we convert to polar coordinates.

$$W = \int_C y^3\, dx + \left(x^3 + 3xy^2 \right) dy$$

$$= \iint_R \left(\frac{\partial N}{\partial x} - \frac{\partial M}{\partial y} \right) dA$$

$$= \iint_R \left(3x^2 + 3y^2 - 3y^2 \right) dA = \iint_R 3x^2\, dA$$

$$= \int_0^{2\pi} \int_0^3 3\left(r\cos\theta \right)^2 r\, dr\, d\theta.$$

We can evaluate this integral using a half-angle formula:

$$W = \int_0^{2\pi} \int_0^3 3\left(r\cos\theta \right)^2 r\, dr\, d\theta = 3 \int_0^{2\pi} \left[\frac{r^4}{4} \cos^2 \theta \right]_0^3 d\theta$$

$$= 3\left(\frac{81}{4} \right) \int_0^{2\pi} \cos^2 \theta\, d\theta = \frac{243}{4} \int_0^{2\pi} \frac{1 + \cos 2\theta}{2}\, d\theta$$

$$= \frac{243}{8} \left[\theta + \frac{\sin 2\theta}{2} \right]_0^{2\pi} = \frac{243}{8}(2\pi) = \frac{243\pi}{4}.$$

Example 3

Calculate $\int_C y^3\,dx + 3xy^2\,dy$, where C is the curve in **Figure 31.2**.

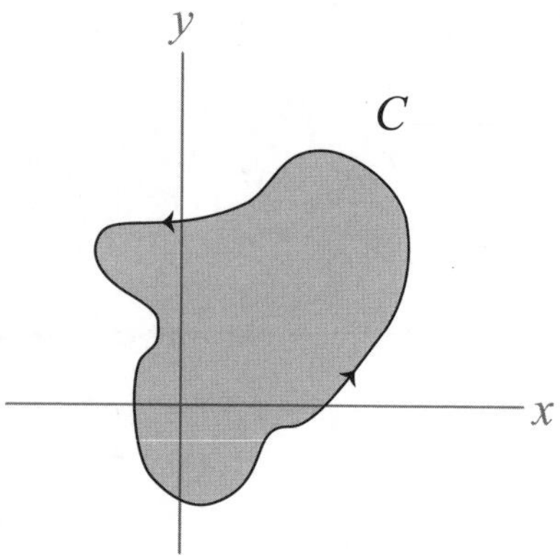

Solution

The vector field is conservative: $\dfrac{\partial M}{\partial y} = 3y^2 = \dfrac{\partial N}{\partial x}$.

Hence, the line integral is zero, $\int_C y^3\,dx + 3xy^2\,dy = 0$.

Figure 31.2

Study Tips

- Green's theorem can be extended to regions that are not necessarily simply connected.

- Green's theorem is a planar theorem. Generalizations to space will come in later lessons: the divergence theorem and Stokes's theorem.

- Some texts use the notation $\oint_C \mathbf{F} \cdot d\mathbf{r}$ for a line integral around a closed curve C.

- Recall that for conservative vector fields, $\dfrac{\partial N}{\partial x} = \dfrac{\partial M}{\partial y}$, the value of a line integral over a closed curve is zero. This is easily seen from Green's theorem:

$$\int_C M\,dx + N\,dy = \iint_R \left(\frac{\partial N}{\partial x} - \frac{\partial M}{\partial y} \right) dA = 0.$$

Pitfall

- When using Green's theorem, you must make sure that the boundary curve C is traversed once so that the region R is on the left.

Problems

1. Verify Green's theorem for the line integral $\int_C y^2\,dx + x^2\,dy$, where C is the boundary of the region lying between the graphs of $y = x$ and $y = \sqrt{x}$.

2. Use Green's theorem to evaluate the line integral $\int_C (y - x)\,dx + (2x - y)\,dy$, where C is the region lying inside the semicircle $y = \sqrt{25 - x^2}$ and outside the semicircle $y = \sqrt{9 - x^2}$.

3. Use Green's theorem to evaluate the line integral $\int_C (y - x)\,dx + (2x - y)\,dy$, where C is the ellipse $x = 2\cos\theta, y = \sin\theta$.

4. Use Green's theorem to evaluate the line integral $\int_C e^x \cos 2y \, dx - 2e^x \sin 2y \, dy$, where C is the circle $x^2 + y^2 = 9$.

5. Find the work done by the force $\mathbf{F}(x, y) = xy\mathbf{i} + (x + y)\mathbf{j}$ that is moving a particle counterclockwise once around the unit circle $x^2 + y^2 = 1$.

6. Find the work done by the force $\mathbf{F}(x, y) = \left(x^{3/2} - 3y\right)\mathbf{i} + \left(6x + 5\sqrt{y}\right)\mathbf{j}$ that is moving a particle counterclockwise once around the triangle with vertices $(0, 0)$, $(5, 0)$, and $(0, 5)$.

Applications of Green's Theorem
Lesson 32

Topics

- Green's theorem.

- Applications of Green's theorem to area.

- The area enclosed by a polygon.

- An alternate form of Green's theorem.

Definitions and Theorems

- **Green's theorem**: Let C be a piecewise smooth closed curve, oriented counterclockwise. The curve is traversed once with the simply connected region R on its left. Then,

$$\int_C M\,dx + N\,dy = \iint_R \left(\frac{\partial N}{\partial x} - \frac{\partial M}{\partial y} \right) dA.$$

- Green's theorem and area: Select functions M and N such that $\dfrac{\partial N}{\partial x} - \dfrac{\partial M}{\partial y} = 1$. Then,

$$\int_C M\,dx + N\,dy = \iint_R \left(\frac{\partial N}{\partial x} - \frac{\partial M}{\partial y} \right) dA = \iint_R 1\,dA = \text{area of } R.$$

- If R is a planar region bounded by the closed curve C, oriented counterclockwise, then the area enclosed is $A = \dfrac{1}{2} \displaystyle\int_C x\,dy - y\,dx$.

- The area of a polygon with vertices $(x_1, y_1), (x_2, y_2), \ldots, (x_n, y_n)$ is

$$A = \frac{1}{2}\left[\left(x_1 y_2 - x_2 y_1 \right) + \left(x_2 y_3 - x_3 y_2 \right) + \ldots + \left(x_{n-1} y_n - x_n y_{n-1} \right) + \left(x_n y_1 - x_1 y_n \right) \right].$$

- Alternate form of Green's theorem:

$$\int_C \mathbf{F} \cdot d\mathbf{r} = \int_C M\,dx + N\,dy = \iint_R \left(\frac{\partial N}{\partial x} - \frac{\partial M}{\partial y} \right) dA = \iint_R (\operatorname{curl} \mathbf{F}) \cdot \mathbf{k}\, dA.$$

Summary

In this lesson, we continue our study of Green's theorem. We begin with an example of how Green's theorem permits us to evaluate a line integral by calculating a corresponding double integral. We then show how Green's theorem can be used to calculate the area of a planar region. We end the lesson with a brief look at an alternate form of Green's theorem, one that we will later generalize to Stokes's theorem.

Example 1

Use Green's theorem to evaluate the integral $\int_C (y-x)\,dx + (2x-y)\,dy,$ where C is the boundary of the region between the graphs of $y = x$ and $y = x^2 - 2x.$

Solution

We can determine the region by finding the points where the graphs intersect.

$$x = x^2 - 2x \Rightarrow 3x - x^2 = 0 \Rightarrow x(3 - x) = 0 \Rightarrow x = 0, 3.$$

So, the graphs intersect at $(0, 0)$ and $(3, 3)$. (See **Figure 32.1**.)

You will need two line integrals: one from $(0, 0)$ to $(3, 3)$ along the parabola and one from $(3, 3)$ back to the origin along the line. The solution by Green's theorem is much easier.

We have $N = 2x - y \Rightarrow \dfrac{\partial N}{\partial x} = 2$ and $M = y - x \Rightarrow \dfrac{\partial M}{\partial y} = 1.$

Thus, the integrand for Green's theorem is $\dfrac{\partial N}{\partial x} - \dfrac{\partial M}{\partial y} = 2 - 1 = 1.$

Finally, the line integral is

$$\int_C (y-x)\,dx + (2x-y)\,dy = \iint_R 1\,dA$$

$$= \int_0^3 \int_{x^2-2x}^x dy\,dx = \int_0^3 [y]_{x^2-2x}^x dx$$

$$= \int_0^3 (x - x^2 + 2x)\,dx = \int_0^3 (3x - x^2)\,dx$$

$$= \left[\frac{3x^2}{2} - \frac{x^3}{3} \right]_0^3 = \frac{27}{2} - 9 = \frac{9}{2}.$$

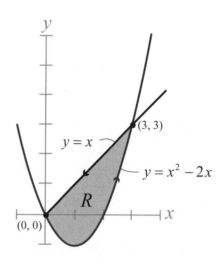

Figure 32.1

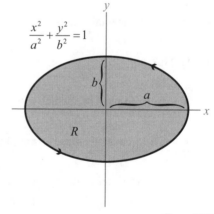

Figure 32.2

Example 2

Use a line integral to find the area enclosed by the ellipse $\dfrac{x^2}{a^2} + \dfrac{y^2}{b^2} = 1.$ (See **Figure 32.2**.)

Solution

We can parameterize the ellipse as $x = a\cos t,\ y = b\sin t,\ 0 \le t \le 2\pi.$ Then, $dx = -a\sin t\,dt$ and $dy = b\cos t\,dt.$

So, the area of the ellipse is

$$A = \frac{1}{2}\int_C x\,dy - y\,dx$$

$$= \frac{1}{2}\int_0^{2\pi}\left[(a\cos t)(b\cos t) - (b\sin t)(-a\sin t)\right]dt$$

$$= \frac{ab}{2}\int_0^{2\pi}\left(\cos^2 t + \sin^2 t\right)dt$$

$$= \frac{ab}{2}\int_0^{2\pi}(1)\,dt = \frac{ab}{2}[t]_0^{2\pi} = \pi ab.$$

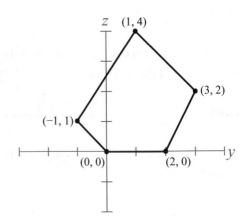

Figure 32.3

Example 3

Find the area of the pentagon with vertices $(0, 0)$, $(2, 0)$, $(3, 2)$, $(1, 4)$, $(-1, 1)$. (See **Figure 32.3**.)

Solution

Using the formula for area of a polygon, twice the area is

$$\left[0(0) - 0(2)\right] + \left[2(2) - 3(0)\right] + \left[3(4) - 1(2)\right] + \left[1(1) - (-1)(4)\right] + \left[(-1)(0) - 0(1)\right]$$
$$= 0 + 4 + 10 + 5 + 0 = 19.$$

Dividing by 2, the total area is $\frac{19}{2}$.

Study Tips

- In Example 1, we actually found the area of the region.

- The area of an ellipse is πab. If the ellipse is a circle, then $a = b$, and we get the area of a circle, πa^2.

- A planimeter is an engineering device for calculating the area of a region by tracing out its boundary. It is based on Green's theorem.

- The key to the formula for the area of a polygon is the value of the line integral

$$\int_C x\,dy - y\,dx = x_1 y_2 - x_2 y_1,$$

where C is the line segment joining (x_1, y_1) and (x_2, y_2). You are asked to derive this formula in Problem 5.

Pitfall

- When using Green's theorem, the curve must be oriented counterclockwise around the region.

Problems

1. Verify that the line integral $\int_C (y-x)dx + (2x-y)dy$ along the parabola $y = x^2 - 2x$, $0 \le x \le 3$ is 9.

2. Use a line integral to find the area of the circle $x^2 + y^2 = a^2$.

3. Use a line integral to find the area of the region bounded by the graphs of $y = 5x - 3$ and $y = x^2 + 1$.

4. Calculate $\int_C \dfrac{y\,dx - x\,dy}{x^2 + y^2}$ if C is a circle oriented counterclockwise that does not contain the origin.

5. Let C be the line segment joining the points (x_1, y_1) and (x_2, y_2).

   Verify the formula $\int_C x\,dy - y\,dx = x_1 y_2 - x_2 y_1$.

6. Find the area enclosed by the hexagon with vertices $(0, 0), (2, 0), (3, 2), (2, 4), (0, 3), (-1, 1)$.

7. Prove that $\int_C f(x)dx + g(y)dy = 0$ if f and g are differentiable functions and C is a piecewise smooth simple closed path.

Parametric Surfaces in Space
Lesson 33

Topics

- Parametric curves.

- Parametric surfaces in space.

- Normal vectors to parametric surfaces.

- Surface area and the differential of surface area.

Definitions and Theorems

- As the real numbers u and v vary across their domains, the function

$$\mathbf{r}(u, v) = x(u, v)\mathbf{i} + y(u, v)\mathbf{j} + z(u, v)\mathbf{k}$$

  traces out a **parametric surface**.

- Consider a parametric surface and its partial derivatives,

$$\mathbf{r}(u, v) = x(u, v)\mathbf{i} + y(u, v)\mathbf{j} + z(u, v)\mathbf{k}$$

$$\mathbf{r}_u(u, v) = \frac{\partial x}{\partial u}\mathbf{i} + \frac{\partial y}{\partial u}\mathbf{j} + \frac{\partial z}{\partial u}\mathbf{k}$$

$$\mathbf{r}_v(u, v) = \frac{\partial x}{\partial v}\mathbf{i} + \frac{\partial y}{\partial v}\mathbf{j} + \frac{\partial z}{\partial v}\mathbf{k}.$$

  A **normal vector** to the surface is the cross product $\mathbf{N} = \mathbf{r}_v \times \mathbf{r}_u$.

- The **surface area** of a parametric surface is $A = \iint\limits_{D} \|\mathbf{r}_u \times \mathbf{r}_v\| \, dA$.

- The **differential of surface area** is $dS = \|\mathbf{r}_u \times \mathbf{r}_v\| \, dA$.

Summary

In this lesson, we extend our knowledge of parametric curves to parametric surfaces. A parametric surface is given by a vector-valued function having two parameters. As the parameters vary over their domains, the function traces out a surface in space. We will use the cross product of partial derivatives to construct normal vectors to parametric surfaces. We close the lesson with the integral for surface area and the corresponding differential of surface area.

Example 1

Sketch the parametric surface given by

$$\mathbf{r}(u, v) = 3\cos u\,\mathbf{i} + 3\sin u\,\mathbf{j} + v\mathbf{k}, \text{ where } 0 \le u \le 2\pi, 0 \le v \le 4.$$

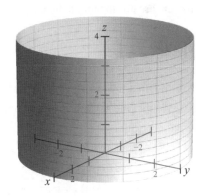

Figure 33.1

Solution

For each point (x, y, z) on the surface, we have $x = 3\cos u$, $y = 3\sin u$. This means that $x^2 + y^2 = 9$, which tells us that the surface is a right circular cylinder of radius 3 and height 4. (See **Figure 33.1**.)

Example 2

Describe the surface $\mathbf{r}(u, v) = u\mathbf{i} + v\mathbf{j} + \dfrac{v}{2}\mathbf{k}$.

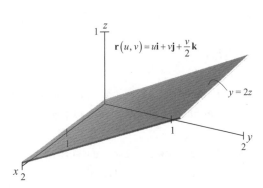

Solution

Because $y - 2z = 0$, this surface is a plane in space. (See **Figure 33.2**.)

Figure 33.2

Example 3

The paraboloid $z = x^2 + y^2$ can be described as a parametric surface $\mathbf{r}(u, v) = u\mathbf{i} + v\mathbf{j} + (u^2 + v^2)\mathbf{k}$. Find an equation of a normal vector to this surface at the point $(1, 2, 5)$. Then, find an equation of the tangent plane to the surface at the point.

Solution

The partial derivatives are $\mathbf{r}_u = \mathbf{i} + 2u\mathbf{k}$, $\mathbf{r}_v = \mathbf{j} + 2v\mathbf{k}$. Their cross product is $\mathbf{r}_v \times \mathbf{r}_u = 2u\mathbf{i} + 2v\mathbf{j} - \mathbf{k}$. At the point $(1, 2, 5)$, the normal vector is $\mathbf{N} = 2\mathbf{i} + 4\mathbf{j} - \mathbf{k}$.

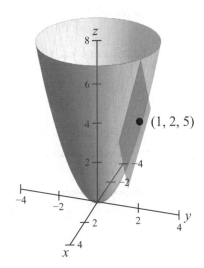

Notice that this vector is an outward normal vector because the third component is negative.

The tangent plane is $2(x - 1) + 4(y - 2) - (z - 5) = 0$, which simplifies to $2x + 4y - z = 5$. (See **Figure 33.3**.)

Figure 33.3

Example 4

Find the area of the unit sphere $\mathbf{r}(u, v) = \sin u \cos v \mathbf{i} + \sin u \sin v \mathbf{j} + \cos u \mathbf{k}$, where $0 \le u \le \pi$, $0 \le v \le 2\pi$.

Solution

We know that the answer should be $4\pi r^2 = 4\pi$. In Problem 9, you are asked to use trigonometric identities to verify that the surface is indeed a unit sphere. To use the formula for surface area, first calculate the partial derivatives.

$$\mathbf{r}_u = \cos u \cos v \mathbf{i} + \cos u \sin v \mathbf{j} - \sin u \mathbf{k}$$
$$\mathbf{r}_v = -\sin u \sin v \mathbf{i} + \sin u \cos v \mathbf{j}.$$

As shown in Problem 10, the magnitude of the cross product is $\|\mathbf{r}_u \times \mathbf{r}_v\| = \sin u$.

Finally, the surface area is $\displaystyle\iint_D \|\mathbf{r}_u \times \mathbf{r}_v\| \, dA = \int_0^{2\pi} \int_0^\pi \sin u \, du \, dv = 4\pi$.

Study Tips

- Parametric curves in the plane and space, such as $\mathbf{r}(t) = 3\cos t\mathbf{i} + 4\sin t\mathbf{j} + t\mathbf{k}$, have one parameter, t. Parametric surfaces, such as $\mathbf{r}(u, v) = u\mathbf{i} + v\mathbf{j} + (u^2 + v^2)\mathbf{k}$, have two parameters, u and v.

- You can always describe a surface $z = f(x, y)$ as a parametric surface by simply writing $\mathbf{r}(x, y) = x\mathbf{i} + y\mathbf{j} + f(x, y)\mathbf{k}$.

- If the surface is given by the function $z = f(x, y)$, then the surface can be described by the parametric equation $\mathbf{r}(x, y) = x\mathbf{i} + y\mathbf{j} + f(x, y)\mathbf{k}$.

  The partial derivatives are $\mathbf{r}_x = \mathbf{i} + \left(\dfrac{\partial f}{\partial x}\right)\mathbf{k}$ and $\mathbf{r}_y = \mathbf{j} + \left(\dfrac{\partial f}{\partial y}\right)\mathbf{k}$.

  The cross product is $\mathbf{r}_x \times \mathbf{r}_y = -\dfrac{\partial f}{\partial x}\mathbf{i} - \dfrac{\partial f}{\partial y}\mathbf{j} + \mathbf{k}$ and $\|\mathbf{r}_x \times \mathbf{r}_y\| = \sqrt{\left(\dfrac{\partial f}{\partial x}\right)^2 + \left(\dfrac{\partial f}{\partial y}\right)^2 + 1}$.

Pitfalls

- The Möbius strip is an example of a surface with only one side. We will see later that the Möbius strip is not orientable.

- Notice that the normal vectors to a surface, $\mathbf{N}_1 = \mathbf{r}_v \times \mathbf{r}_u$ and $\mathbf{N}_2 = \mathbf{r}_u \times \mathbf{r}_v = -\mathbf{N}_1$, point in opposite directions. For instance, in Example 3, the two normal vectors are $\mathbf{r}_v \times \mathbf{r}_u = 2u\mathbf{i} + 2v\mathbf{j} - \mathbf{k}$ and $\mathbf{r}_u \times \mathbf{r}_v = -2u\mathbf{i} - 2v\mathbf{j} + \mathbf{k}$.

Problems

1. Describe the parametric surface $\mathbf{r}(u, v) = u\mathbf{i} + (u + v)\mathbf{j} + v\mathbf{k}$.

2. Describe the parametric surface $\mathbf{r}(u, v) = u\cos v\mathbf{i} + u\sin v\mathbf{j} + u\mathbf{k}$.

3. Find an equation of the normal vector to the surface $\mathbf{r}(u, v) = (u + v)\mathbf{i} + (u - v)\mathbf{j} + v\mathbf{k}$ at the point $(1, -1, 1)$.

4. Find an equation of the normal vector to the surface $\mathbf{r}(u, v) = 2u\cos v\mathbf{i} + 3u\sin v\mathbf{j} + u^2\mathbf{k}$ at the point $(0, 6, 4)$.

5. Find an equation of the tangent plane to the surface in Exercise 3 at the same point. What do you observe?

6. Find an equation of the tangent plane to the surface in Exercise 4 at the same point.

7. Find the surface area of the portion of the plane $\mathbf{r}(u, v) = 4u\mathbf{i} - v\mathbf{j} + v\mathbf{k}$, where $0 \leq u \leq 2$ and $0 \leq v \leq 1$.

8. Find the surface area of the portion of the cylinder $\mathbf{r}(u, v) = 2\cos u\mathbf{i} + 2\sin u\mathbf{j} + v\mathbf{k}$, where $0 \leq u \leq 2\pi$ and $0 \leq v \leq 3$.

9. Verify that the surface $\mathbf{r}(u, v) = \sin u\cos v\mathbf{i} + \sin u\sin v\mathbf{j} + \cos u\mathbf{k}$, where $0 \leq u \leq \pi$ and $0 \leq v \leq 2\pi$, is a sphere of radius 1.

10. Verify that the magnitude of the cross product of the vectors

$$\mathbf{r}_u = \cos u\cos v\mathbf{i} + \cos u\sin v\mathbf{j} - \sin u\mathbf{k}$$
$$\mathbf{r}_v = -\sin u\sin v\mathbf{i} + \sin u\cos v\mathbf{j}$$

is $\|\mathbf{r}_u \times \mathbf{r}_v\| = \sin u$.

Surface Integrals and Flux Integrals
Lesson 34

Topics

- Surface integrals.

- Surface integrals and mass.

- Parametric surfaces and surface integrals.

- Orientable surfaces.

- Flux integrals.

Definitions and Theorems

- Let the surface S be given by $z = g(x, y)$, and let $f(x, y, z)$ be defined at all points on S. Let R be the projection of S onto the xy-plane. With suitable hypotheses on f and g, the **surface integral** is

$$\iint_S f(x, y, z)\, dS = \iint_R f\left(x, y, g(x, y)\right)\sqrt{1+\left(g_x\right)^2+\left(g_y\right)^2}\, dA.$$

  The **differential of surface area** is $dS = \sqrt{1+\left(g_x\right)^2+\left(g_y\right)^2}\, dA.$

- Consider the parametric surface $\mathbf{r}(u, v) = x(u, v)\mathbf{i} + y(u, v)\mathbf{j} + z(u, v)\mathbf{k}$. The **surface integral** is

$$\iint_S f(x, y, z)\, dS = \iint_S f\left(x(u, v), y(u, v), z(u, v)\right)\, dS,$$

  where $dS = \left\|\mathbf{r}_u(u, v)\times\mathbf{r}_v(u, v)\right\| dA$ is the **differential of surface area**.

- A surface S is **orientable** if a unit normal vector $\mathbf{N}$ can be defined at every nonboundary point on S such that the normal vectors vary continuously over the surface.

- Let $z = g(x, y)$ be an orientable surface, and let $G(x, y, z) = z - g(x, y)$. The gradient of G is normal to the surface.

  So, a **unit normal to the surface** is $\mathbf{N} = \dfrac{\nabla G(x, y, z)}{\left\|\nabla G(x, y, z)\right\|}$, or its negative.

- For a parametric surface $\mathbf{r}(u, v) = x(u, v)\mathbf{i} + y(u, v)\mathbf{j} + z(u, v)\mathbf{k}$, the cross product of the partial derivatives is normal to the surface.

  So, a **unit normal to the surface** is $\mathbf{N} = \dfrac{\mathbf{r}_v \times \mathbf{r}_u}{\|\mathbf{r}_v \times \mathbf{r}_u\|}$, or its negative.

- Let $\mathbf{F}(x, y, z) = M\mathbf{i} + N\mathbf{j} + P\mathbf{k}$ have continuous first partial derivatives on the surface S with unit normal $\mathbf{N}$. The **flux integral** of $\mathbf{F}$ across S is $\displaystyle\iint_S \mathbf{F} \cdot \mathbf{N}\, dS$. Notice that this is a surface integral.

- Evaluation of a flux integral: If the surface is $z = g(x, y)$, let $G(x, y, z) = z - g(x, y)$.

  The gradient of G is $\nabla G = (-g_x)\mathbf{i} + (-g_y)\mathbf{j} + \mathbf{k}$ and $\|\nabla G\| = \sqrt{(g_x)^2 + (g_y)^2 + 1}$.

  A unit normal is $\mathbf{N} = \dfrac{\nabla G(x, y, z)}{\|\nabla G(x, y, z)\|}$, and the differential of surface area is $dS = \sqrt{(g_x)^2 + (g_y)^2 + 1}\, dA$.

  Finally,

$$\mathbf{N}dS = \frac{\nabla G(x, y, z)}{\|\nabla G(x, y, z)\|} \sqrt{(g_x)^2 + (g_y)^2 + 1}\, dA = \nabla G(x, y, z)\, dA.$$

Summary

In this lesson, we study surface integrals and flux integrals. Surface integrals are integrals defined on surfaces in space, a generalization of line integrals defined on curves in space. We define surface integrals for surfaces of the form $z = g(x, y)$ and also for parametric surfaces. We then study flux integrals, which model the flow of a liquid through a surface. These topics lead to the major theorems in the final two lessons: the divergence theorem and Stokes's theorem.

Example 1

Evaluate the surface integral

$$\iint_S (y^2 + 2yz)\, dS,$$

where S is the first-octant portion of the plane $z = 3 - x - \dfrac{1}{2} y$.
(See **Figure 34.1**.)

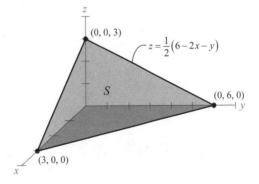

Figure 34.1

Solution

The partial derivatives are $g_x(x, y) = -1$, $g_y(x, y) = -\dfrac{1}{2}$.

The differential of surface area is

$$dS = \sqrt{1 + (g_x)^2 + (g_y)^2}\, dA = \sqrt{1 + 1 + \frac{1}{4}}\, dA = \sqrt{\frac{9}{4}}\, dA = \frac{3}{2} dA.$$

So, we have

$$\iint_S \left(y^2 + 2yz\right) dS = \iint_R \left[y^2 + 2y\left(3 - x - \frac{1}{2}y\right)\right]\left(\frac{3}{2}\right) dA$$

$$= \iint_R \left[y^2 + 6y - 2xy - y^2\right]\left(\frac{3}{2}\right) dA$$

$$= \iint_R \left[6y - 2xy\right]\left(\frac{3}{2}\right) dA = 3\iint_R y(3 - x) dA.$$

The region R is a triangle, so the integral becomes

$$3\iint_R y(3 - x) dA = 3\int_0^3 \int_0^{6-2x} y(3 - x) dy\, dx = \frac{243}{2}.$$

You are asked to evaluate this integral in Problem 3.

Example 2

Consider a cup given by the formula $S: z = \sqrt{9 - x^2 - y^2}$. Find the mass of the cup if the density is $\rho(x, y, z) = 2z$. (See **Figure 34.2**.)

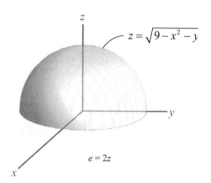

Figure 34.2

Solution

The partial derivatives are $g_x = \dfrac{-x}{\sqrt{9 - x^2 - y^2}}$ and $g_y = \dfrac{-y}{\sqrt{9 - x^2 - y^2}}$. The differential of surface area is

$$dS = \sqrt{1 + \left(g_x\right)^2 + \left(g_y\right)^2}\, dA$$

$$= \sqrt{1 + \frac{x^2}{9 - x^2 - y^2} + \frac{y^2}{9 - x^2 - y^2}}\, dA$$

$$= \sqrt{\frac{\left(9 - x^2 - y^2\right) + x^2 + y^2}{9 - x^2 - y^2}}\, dA = \frac{3}{\sqrt{9 - x^2 - y^2}}\, dA.$$

Therefore, the mass is

$$\text{mass} = \iint_S \rho(x, y, z) dS = \iint_R 2z\left(\frac{3}{\sqrt{9 - x^2 - y^2}}\right) dA$$

$$= \iint_R 2\sqrt{9 - x^2 - y^2}\left(\frac{3}{\sqrt{9 - x^2 - y^2}}\right) dA = \iint_R 6\, dA.$$

Because R is a circle of radius 3, $m = 6\iint_R dA = 6\left(\pi 3^2\right) = 54\pi$.

Example 3

Set up the surface integral $\iint\limits_S (y^2 + 2yz)\, dS$, where S is the first-octant portion of the plane

$$\mathbf{r}(u, v) = u\mathbf{i} + v\mathbf{j} + \left(3 - u - \frac{1}{2}v\right)\mathbf{k}.$$

Solution

This is the same problem as Example 1, but now we are using parametric equations. The partial derivatives are $\mathbf{r}_u = \mathbf{i} - \mathbf{k}$ and $\mathbf{r}_v = \mathbf{j} - \frac{1}{2}\mathbf{k}$.

Their cross product is $\mathbf{r}_u \times \mathbf{r}_v = \mathbf{i} + \frac{1}{2}\mathbf{j} + \mathbf{k}$, which implies that $\|\mathbf{r}_u \times \mathbf{r}_v\| = \frac{3}{2}$.

Finally, the surface integral is $\iint\limits_S (y^2 + 2yz)\, dS = \iint\limits_R \left[v^2 + 2v\left(3 - u - \frac{1}{2}v\right)\right]\left(\frac{3}{2}\right) dA = \frac{243}{2}.$

This is the same integral as Example 1, but using different letters for the variables.

Example 4

Let S be the portion of the paraboloid $z = g(x, y) = 4 - x^2 - y^2$ lying above the xy-plane and oriented by an upward unit normal.

A fluid is flowing through the surface according to the vector field $\mathbf{F}(x, y, z) = x\mathbf{i} + y\mathbf{j} + z\mathbf{k}$.

Find $\iint\limits_S \mathbf{F} \cdot \mathbf{N}\, dS$, the rate of mass flow through the surface. (See **Figure 34.3**.)

Solution

We have $G(x, y, z) = z - g(x, y) = z - (4 - x^2 - y^2)$ and, hence,

$$\mathbf{N}dS = \nabla G(x, y, z)\, dA = (2x\mathbf{i} + 2y\mathbf{j} + \mathbf{k})\, dA.$$

The rate of mass flow is the flux integral:

$$\iint\limits_S \mathbf{F} \cdot \mathbf{N}\, dS = \iint\limits_R \left[x\mathbf{i} + y\mathbf{j} + \left(4 - x^2 - y^2\right)\mathbf{k}\right] \cdot \left[2x\mathbf{i} + 2y\mathbf{j} + \mathbf{k}\right] dA$$

$$= \iint\limits_R \left(2x^2 + 2y^2 + 4 - x^2 - y^2\right) dA$$

$$= \iint\limits_R \left(4 + x^2 + y^2\right) dA.$$

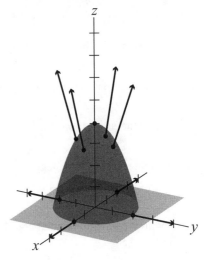

Figure 34.3

Next, convert to polar coordinates to obtain

$$\iint_R \left(4 + x^2 + y^2\right) dA = \int_0^{2\pi} \int_0^2 \left(4 + r^2\right) r\, dr\, d\theta$$

$$= \int_0^{2\pi} \int_0^2 \left(4r + r^3\right) dr\, d\theta$$

$$= \int_0^{2\pi} \left[2r^2 + \frac{r^4}{4} \right]_0^2 d\theta$$

$$= \int_0^{2\pi} (8 + 4)\, d\theta = 24\pi.$$

Study Tips

- An orientable surface has two distinct sides, such as spheres, paraboloids, and planes. The Möbius strip is not orientable.

- Flux integrals are motivated by fluid flow through an orientable surface.

- A flux integral is a surface integral over S of the normal component of the vector field $\mathbf{F} \cdot \mathbf{N}$. It represents the amount of liquid crossing the surface per unit of time.

Pitfall

- Flux integrals are only defined for orientable surfaces. For example, the Möbius strip is not orientable.

Problems

1. Evaluate the surface integral $\iint_S (x - 2y + z)\, dS$, where S is the surface $z = 4 - x$, $0 \le x \le 4$, and $0 \le y \le 3$.

2. Evaluate the surface integral $\iint_S xy\, dS$, where S is the surface $z = h$, $0 \le x \le 2$ and $0 \le y \le \sqrt{4 - x^2}$.

3. Verify the integration $3 \int_0^3 \int_0^{2(3-x)} y(3 - x)\, dy\, dx = \frac{243}{2}$.

4. Evaluate the surface integral $\iint_S (y + 5)\, dS$, where S is the parametric surface $\mathbf{r}(u, v) = u\mathbf{i} + v\mathbf{j} + 2v\mathbf{k}$, $0 \le u \le 1$ and $0 \le v \le 2$.

5. Set up the integral in polar coordinates for the surface integral $\iint_S \frac{xy}{z}\, dS$, where S is the surface $z = x^2 + y^2$, $4 \le x^2 + y^2 \le 16$.

6. Set up the flux integral $\iint\limits_S \mathbf{F} \cdot \mathbf{N} \, dS$, where $\mathbf{F}(x, y, z) = 3z\mathbf{i} - 4\mathbf{j} + y\mathbf{k}$ and S is the surface $z = 1 - x - y$ in the first octant.

7. Use polar coordinates to set up the flux integral $\iint\limits_S \mathbf{F} \cdot \mathbf{N} \, dS$, where $\mathbf{F}(x, y, z) = x\mathbf{i} + y\mathbf{j} + z\mathbf{k}$ and S is the surface $x^2 + y^2 + z^2 = 36$ in the first octant.

Divergence Theorem—Boundaries and Solids
Lesson 35

Topics

- The divergence theorem.

- The divergence theorem and Green's theorem.

- Sources and sinks.

- Gauss's law.

Definitions and Theorems

- Let Q be a solid region in space bounded by the surface S oriented outward by a unit normal $\mathbf{N}$. Let $\mathbf{F}(x, y, z)$ be a vector field whose component functions have continuous first partial derivatives. The **divergence theorem** states that

$$\iint_S \mathbf{F} \cdot \mathbf{N} \, dS = \iiint_Q \text{div}\mathbf{F} \, dV.$$

- If $\text{div}\mathbf{F} > 0$, we say that we have a **source**. If $\text{div}\mathbf{F} < 0$, we have a **sink**.

- **Gauss's law** relates the flux out of a surface to the total charge inside the surface.

  In particular, if E is an electric field, then $\iint_S \mathbf{E} \cdot \mathbf{N} \, dS = \dfrac{Q}{\varepsilon_0}$.

  Here, Q is the electric charge inside a sphere, and ε_0 is the permittivity of space, or the electric constant.

Summary

The divergence theorem relates a flux integral over the boundary of a solid with a triple integral over the entire solid. After stating the theorem, we verify both sides of the equation with a simple example. We then show how the divergence theorem is the three-dimensional analog of Green's theorem. We discuss how the concept of divergence is related to fluid flow. The divergence theorem is similar to Gauss's law of electrostatics, which relates the flux out of a surface with the total charge inside the surface.

Example 1

Let Q be the solid region between the paraboloid $z = 4 - x^2 - y^2$ and the xy-plane. Verify the divergence theorem for the function $\mathbf{F}(x, y, z) = 2z\mathbf{i} + x\mathbf{j} + y^2\mathbf{k}$. (See **Figure 35.1**.)

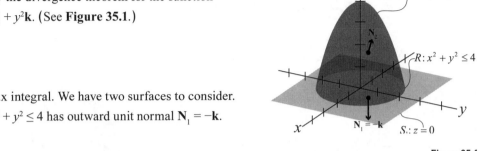

Figure 35.1

Solution

Let's first do the flux integral. We have two surfaces to consider. The flat plane $S_1 : x^2 + y^2 \leq 4$ has outward unit normal $\mathbf{N}_1 = -\mathbf{k}$.

So, for this surface,

$$\iint_{S_1} \mathbf{F} \cdot \mathbf{N}_1 \, dS = \iint_{S_1} \mathbf{F} \cdot (-\mathbf{k}) \, dS = \iint_R \left[2z\mathbf{i} + x\mathbf{j} + y^2\mathbf{k} \right] \cdot (-\mathbf{k}) \, dA = \iint_R (-y^2) \, dA.$$

Next, use polar coordinates:

$$\iint_R (-y^2) \, dA = \int_0^{2\pi} \int_0^2 -(r\sin\theta)^2 \, r \, dr \, d\theta$$

$$= -\int_0^{2\pi} \int_0^2 r^3 \sin^2\theta \, dr \, d\theta = -\int_0^{2\pi} \left[\frac{r^4}{4} \sin^2\theta \right]_0^2 d\theta$$

$$= -\int_0^{2\pi} 4\sin^2\theta \, d\theta = -4 \int_0^{2\pi} \frac{1 - \cos 2\theta}{2} \, d\theta$$

$$= -2 \left[\theta - \frac{\sin 2\theta}{2} \right]_0^{2\pi} = -2(2\pi) = -4\pi.$$

The paraboloid forms the second surface: $S_2 : z = 4 - x^2 - y^2$. If $G = z - (4 - x^2 - y^2)$, the outward unit normal is

$$\mathbf{N}_2 = \frac{\nabla G(x, y, z)}{\left\| \nabla G(x, y, z) \right\|} = \frac{2x\mathbf{i} + 2y\mathbf{j} + \mathbf{k}}{\sqrt{4x^2 + 4y^2 + 1}}.$$

So, we have

$$\mathbf{N}_2 dS = \frac{\nabla G(x, y, z)}{\left\| \nabla G(x, y, z) \right\|} \sqrt{(g_x)^2 + (g_y)^2 + 1} \, dA$$

$$= \frac{2x\mathbf{i} + 2y\mathbf{j} + \mathbf{k}}{\sqrt{4x^2 + 4y^2 + 1}} \sqrt{4x^2 + 4y^2 + 1} \, dA = (2x\mathbf{i} + 2y\mathbf{j} + \mathbf{k}) \, dA.$$

So, $\displaystyle \iint_{S_2} \mathbf{F} \cdot \mathbf{N}_2 \, dS = \iint_R (2z\mathbf{i} + x\mathbf{j} + y^2\mathbf{k}) \cdot (2x\mathbf{i} + 2y\mathbf{j} + \mathbf{k}) \, dA = \iint_R (4xz + 2xy + y^2) \, dA.$

This integral becomes $\int_{-2}^{2}\int_{-\sqrt{4-y^2}}^{\sqrt{4-y^2}}\left(4xz+2xy+y^2\right)dx\,dy = 4\pi$. You are asked to verify this computation in Problem 3. The total flux is

$$\iint_S \mathbf{F} \cdot \mathbf{N}\, dS = \iint_{S_1} \mathbf{F} \cdot \mathbf{N}_1\, dS + \iint_{S_2} \mathbf{F} \cdot \mathbf{N}_2\, dS = -4\pi + 4\pi = 0.$$

The divergence theorem makes this problem much easier.

First of all, the divergence of $\mathbf{F}$ is

$$\text{div}\,\mathbf{F} = \frac{\partial}{\partial x}\left[2z\right]+\frac{\partial}{\partial y}\left[x\right]+\frac{\partial}{\partial z}\left[y^2\right] = 0.$$

So, the triple integral is zero, and we have verified that

$$\iint_S \mathbf{F} \cdot \mathbf{N}\, dS = \iiint_Q \text{div}\,\mathbf{F}\, dV = \iiint_Q 0\, dV = 0.$$

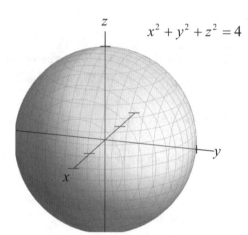

$x^2 + y^2 + z^2 = 4$

Figure 35.2

Example 2

Find the flux integral $\iint_S \mathbf{F} \cdot \mathbf{N}\, dS$ given the vector field $\mathbf{F}(x, y, z) = x\mathbf{i} + y\mathbf{j} + z\mathbf{k}$ and the sphere $x^2 + y^2 + z^2 = 4$. (See **Figure 35.2**.)

Solution

Because $\text{div}\,\mathbf{F} = 1 + 1 + 1 = 3$, the divergence theorem says that

$$\iint_S \mathbf{F} \cdot \mathbf{N}\, dS = \iiint_Q \text{div}\,\mathbf{F}\, dV = 3\iiint_Q dV = 3\left(\text{volume of sphere}\right) = 3\left(\frac{4}{3}\pi(2)^3\right) = 32\pi.$$

Study Tips

- The divergence theorem is often written using the del notation: $\iint_S \mathbf{F} \cdot \mathbf{N}\, dS = \iiint_Q \text{div}\,\mathbf{F}\, dV = \iiint_Q \nabla \cdot \mathbf{F}\, dV$.

- The divergence theorem is the three-dimensional analog of Green's theorem.

- You can think of Example 2 as computing fluid flow out of a sphere, or electric current.

- Loosely speaking, divergence measures the outward flux per unit volume.

- Gauss's law is one of Maxwell's equations and is valid for more general closed surfaces.

Pitfall

- Make sure to use the outward unit normal vector. For instance, in Example 1, the outward unit normal to the xy-plane was $-\mathbf{k}$, not $\mathbf{k}$.

Problems

1. Verify the divergence theorem for $\mathbf{F}(x, y, z) = 2x\mathbf{i} - 2y\mathbf{j} + z^2\mathbf{k}$ and the cube bounded by $x = 0$, $x = 2$, $y = 0$, $y = 2$, $z = 0$, $z = 2$. That is, calculate the flux integral $\iint_S \mathbf{F} \cdot \mathbf{N}\, dS$ and the corresponding triple integral $\iiint_Q \mathrm{div}\,\mathbf{F}\, dV$.

2. Verify the divergence theorem for $\mathbf{F}(x, y, z) = xz\mathbf{i} + zy\mathbf{j} + 2z^2\mathbf{k}$ and the surface bounded by $z = 1 - x^2 - y^2$ and $z = 0$. That is, calculate the flux integral $\iint_S \mathbf{F} \cdot \mathbf{N}\, dS$ and the corresponding triple integral $\iiint_Q \mathrm{div}\,\mathbf{F}\, dV$.

3. Use a graphing utility to verify the integration $\int_{-2}^{2} \int_{-\sqrt{4-y^2}}^{\sqrt{4-y^2}} \left(4xz + 2xy + y^2\right) dx\, dy = 4\pi$, where $z = 4 - x^2 - y^2$.

4. Use the divergence theorem to evaluate the flux integral $\iint_S \mathbf{F} \cdot \mathbf{N}\, dS$, where $\mathbf{F}(x, y, z) = x^2\mathbf{i} + y^2\mathbf{j} + z^2\mathbf{k}$ and S is the cube bounded by the planes $x = 0$, $x = 1$, $y = 0$, $y = 1$, $z = 0$, $z = 1$.

5. Use the divergence theorem to evaluate the flux integral $\iint_S \mathbf{F} \cdot \mathbf{N}\, dS$, where $\mathbf{F}(x, y, z) = x\mathbf{i} + y^2\mathbf{j} - z\mathbf{k}$ and S is the surface bounded by $x^2 + y^2 = 25$, $z = 0$, and $z = 7$.

6. For the constant vector field $\mathbf{F}(x, y, z) = a\mathbf{i} + b\mathbf{j} + c\mathbf{k}$, verify that $\iint_S \mathbf{F} \cdot \mathbf{N}\, dS = 0$, where V is the volume of the closed surface S.

Stokes's Theorem and Maxwell's Equations
Lesson 36

Topics

- Summary of fundamental theorems in calculus.

- Stokes's theorem.

- Maxwell's equations.

Definitions and Theorems

- The fundamental theorem of calculus: $\int_a^b F'(x)\,dx = F(b) - F(a)$.

- The fundamental theorem of line integrals: If $\mathbf{F}$ is conservative with potential f, then

$$\int_C \mathbf{F} \cdot d\mathbf{r} = \int_C \nabla f \cdot d\mathbf{r} = f\big(x(b), y(b), z(b)\big) - f\big(x(a), y(a), z(a)\big).$$

- Green's theorem: $\displaystyle \int_C \mathbf{F} \cdot d\mathbf{r} = \int_C M\,dx + N\,dy = \iint_R \left(\frac{\partial N}{\partial x} - \frac{\partial M}{\partial y} \right) dA$.

- The divergence theorem: $\displaystyle \iint_S \mathbf{F} \cdot \mathbf{N}\,dS = \iiint_Q \operatorname{div} \mathbf{F}\,dV = \iiint_Q \nabla \cdot \mathbf{F}\,dV$.

- Let S be an oriented surface with unit normal $\mathbf{N}$, and let C be a closed curve bounding the surface. Let $\mathbf{F}(x, y, z)$ be a vector field whose component functions have continuous first partial derivatives. Then, **Stokes's theorem** states that

$$\int_C \mathbf{F} \cdot d\mathbf{r} = \iint_S (\operatorname{curl} \mathbf{F}) \cdot \mathbf{N}\,dS.$$

- Maxwell's first equation: Let $\mathbf{E}$ be an electric field, and let S be a surface enclosing a charge Q.

  The flux of the electric field across S is $\displaystyle \iint_S \mathbf{E} \cdot \mathbf{N}\,dS = \frac{Q}{\varepsilon_0}$, where ε_0 is the permittivity of free space.

  The differential form is $\nabla \cdot \mathbf{E} = \dfrac{\rho}{\varepsilon_0}$, where ρ is the charge density.

- Maxwell's second equation: If $\mathbf{B}$ is a magnetic field, $\nabla \cdot \mathbf{B} = 0$.

- Maxwell's third equation: If $\mathbf{E}$ is an electric field and $\mathbf{B}$ is a magnetic field, $\nabla \times \mathbf{E} + \dfrac{\partial \mathbf{B}}{\partial t} = 0$.

- Maxwell's fourth equation: If $\mathbf{E}$ is an electric field, $\mathbf{B}$ is a magnetic field, and $\mathbf{J}$ is the current density, $\nabla \times \mathbf{B} = \dfrac{\partial \mathbf{E}}{\partial t} + \mathbf{J}$.

Summary

Stokes's theorem relates a line integral around a closed curve C to a surface integral for which C is the boundary. However, before we present the theorem, we take a moment to review the various calculus theorems relating integration and differentiation. We illustrate Stokes's theorem with an example similar to one from the previous lesson. We end the lesson with a brief look at Maxwell's famous partial differential equations, which describe the interaction of electric and magnetic fields.

Example 1

Let S be the portion of the paraboloid $z = 4 - x^2 - y^2$ above the xy-plane. Let C be its boundary, oriented counterclockwise. Verify Stokes's theorem for the function $\mathbf{F}(x, y, z) = 2z\mathbf{i} + x\mathbf{j} + y^2\mathbf{k}$. (See **Figure 36.1**.)

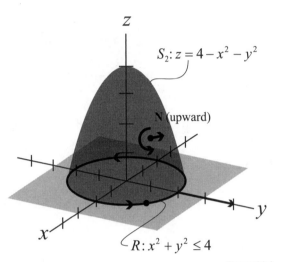

Figure 36.1

Solution

Note that this is the same paraboloid from Example 1 in the previous lesson. However, now it is not closed but, rather, bounded by the curve $x^2 + y^2 = 4$. We want to verify that $\int_C \mathbf{F} \cdot d\mathbf{r} = \iint_S (\text{curl } \mathbf{F}) \cdot \mathbf{N} \, dS$.

Let's first calculate the double integral.

If we let $G(x, y, z) = z - g(x, y) = z - (4 - x^2 - y^2)$, then $\nabla G(x, y, z) \, dA = (2x\mathbf{i} + 2y\mathbf{j} + \mathbf{k}) \, dA$. So,

$$\mathbf{N} \, dS = \frac{\nabla G(x, y, z)}{\|\nabla G(x, y, z)\|} \sqrt{(g_x)^2 + (g_y)^2 + 1} \, dA = \nabla G(x, y, z) \, dA.$$

Next, we calculate the curl of $\mathbf{F}(x, y, z) = 2z\mathbf{i} + x\mathbf{j} + y^2\mathbf{k}$.

$$\text{curl } \mathbf{F} = \begin{vmatrix} \mathbf{i} & \mathbf{j} & \mathbf{k} \\ \dfrac{\partial}{\partial x} & \dfrac{\partial}{\partial y} & \dfrac{\partial}{\partial z} \\ 2z & x & y^2 \end{vmatrix} = 2y\mathbf{i} + 2\mathbf{j} + \mathbf{k}.$$

Finally,

$$\iint_S (\text{curl } \mathbf{F}) \cdot \mathbf{N} \, dS = \iint_R (2y\mathbf{i} + 2\mathbf{j} + \mathbf{k}) \cdot (2x\mathbf{i} + 2y\mathbf{j} + \mathbf{k}) \, dA$$

$$= \iint_R (4xy + 4y + 1) \, dA = 4\pi.$$

141

We next calculate the line integral.

The boundary C can be parameterized as $\mathbf{r}(t) = 2\cos t\mathbf{i} + 2\sin t\mathbf{j} + 0\mathbf{k}, 0 \le t \le 2\pi$. So, $\mathbf{r}'(t) = -2\sin t\mathbf{i} + 2\cos t\mathbf{j}$.

We have $x = 2\cos t$, $dx = -2\sin t\, dt$, $y = 2\sin t$, $dy = 2\cos t\, dt$, and $z = 0$. Because $\mathbf{F}(x, y, z) = 2z\mathbf{i} + x\mathbf{j} + y^2\mathbf{k}$,

$$\int_C \mathbf{F}\cdot d\mathbf{r} = \int_C M\, dx + N\, dy + P\, dz$$

$$= \int_C 2z\, dx + x\, dy + y^2\, dz$$

$$= \int_0^{2\pi} \left[0 + 2\cos t(2\cos t) + 0\right] dt$$

$$= \int_0^{2\pi} 4\cos^2 t\, dt = 4\pi.$$

Therefore, we have verified Stokes's theorem, $\displaystyle\int_C \mathbf{F}\cdot d\mathbf{r} = \iint_S (\text{curl } \mathbf{F})\cdot \mathbf{N}\, dS = 4\pi$.

Example 2

Let $\mathbf{F}(x, y, z) = yze^x\mathbf{i} + ze^x\mathbf{j} + ye^x\mathbf{k}$, and consider a surface with boundary C. Show that $\displaystyle\int_C \mathbf{F}\cdot d\mathbf{r} = 0$.

Solution

We see that the curl of $\mathbf{F}$ is zero: $\text{curl } \mathbf{F} = \begin{vmatrix} \mathbf{i} & \mathbf{j} & \mathbf{k} \\ \dfrac{\partial}{\partial x} & \dfrac{\partial}{\partial y} & \dfrac{\partial}{\partial z} \\ yze^x & ze^x & ye^x \end{vmatrix} = 0$. Therefore, $\displaystyle\iint_S (\text{curl } \mathbf{F})\cdot \mathbf{N}\, dS = \int_C \mathbf{F}\cdot d\mathbf{r} = 0$.

Example 3

Show that the integral and differential forms of Gauss's law are equivalent.

Solution

Using the divergence theorem,

$$\iint_S \mathbf{E}\cdot\mathbf{N}\, dS = \iiint_D \text{div}\mathbf{E}\, dV = \iiint_D \frac{\rho}{\varepsilon_0}\, dV = \frac{1}{\varepsilon_0}\iiint_D \rho\, dV = \frac{1}{\varepsilon_0}Q.$$

Study Tips

- In Example 1, the value $\mathbf{N}\, dS = \nabla G(x, y, z)\, dA = (2x\mathbf{i} + 2y\mathbf{j} + \mathbf{k})\, dA$ is the same as in Lesson 35.

- In Example 1, we used a half-angle formula to calculate the final integral:

$$\int_0^{2\pi} 4\cos^2 t\, dt = 4\int_0^{2\pi} \frac{1 + \cos 2t}{2}\, dt = 2\left[t + \frac{\sin 2t}{2}\right]_0^{2\pi} = 4\pi.$$

- Stokes's theorem relates the circulation around the boundary of a surface to the surface integral of the curl of the vector field.

- Recall that if the curl of a vector field is zero, then the vector field is conservative. Furthermore, line integrals on closed curves equal zero. Stokes's theorem reflects this property:
$$\int_C \mathbf{F} \cdot d\mathbf{r} = \iint_S (\operatorname{curl} \mathbf{F}) \cdot \mathbf{N} \, dS = 0.$$

- Notice that the surface integral in Stokes's theorem only depends on the values of the vector field on the boundary C. Thus, if two surfaces have the same boundary, the corresponding surface integrals will be the same.

- All of Maxwell's equations have corresponding integral forms.

- Maxwell's third equation is often called Faraday's law.

Pitfall

- Make sure that the surface and boundary are oriented correctly. For instance, in Example 1, the normal is upward (outward), and the boundary is oriented counterclockwise.

Problems

1. Verify Stokes's theorem for $\mathbf{F}(x, y, z) = (-y + z)\mathbf{i} + (x - z)\mathbf{j} + (x - y)\mathbf{k}$, where S is the surface $z = 9 - x^2 - y^2$, $z \geq 0$. That is, calculate $\iint_S (\operatorname{curl} \mathbf{F}) \cdot \mathbf{N} \, dS$ and the corresponding line integral.

2. Use Stokes's theorem to evaluate the line integral $\int_C \mathbf{F} \cdot d\mathbf{r}$, where $\mathbf{F}(x, y, z) = \arctan \frac{x}{y} \mathbf{i} + \ln \sqrt{x^2 + y^2} \mathbf{j} + \mathbf{k}$ and C is the triangle with vertices $(0, 0, 0)$, $(1, 1, 1)$, and $(0, 0, 2)$.

3. Use Stokes's theorem to evaluate the line integral $\int_C \mathbf{F} \cdot d\mathbf{r}$, where $\mathbf{F}(x, y, z) = xyz\mathbf{i} + y\mathbf{j} + z\mathbf{k}$ and S is the surface $z = x^2$, $0 \leq x \leq 3$, $0 \leq y \leq 3$. Assume that $\mathbf{N}$ is the downward unit normal to the surface.

4. Assume that the motion of a liquid in a cylindrical container of radius 1 is described by the velocity field $\mathbf{F}(x, y, z) = \mathbf{i} + \mathbf{j} - 2\mathbf{k}$. Find $\iint_S (\operatorname{curl} \mathbf{F}) \cdot \mathbf{N} \, dS$, where S is the upper surface of the cylindrical container.

5. Assume that the motion of a liquid in a cylindrical container of radius 2 is described by the velocity field $\mathbf{F}(x, y, z) = -y\sqrt{x^2 + y^2}\mathbf{i} + x\sqrt{x^2 + y^2}\mathbf{j}$. Find $\iint_S (\operatorname{curl} \mathbf{F}) \cdot \mathbf{N} \, dS$, where S is the upper surface of the cylindrical container.

Solutions

Lesson 1

1. By the chain rule, $f'(x) = \frac{1}{2x}(2) + e^{3x}(3) = \frac{1}{x} + 3e^{3x}$.

2. $\int_0^{\pi/2} \cos x \, dx = [\sin x]_0^{\pi/2} = \sin\frac{\pi}{2} - \sin 0 = 1$.

3. $\mathbf{v} = \langle -4-1, 0-2 \rangle = \langle -5, -2 \rangle = -5\mathbf{i} - 2\mathbf{j}$.

4. $x = 3\cos t$ and $y = 3\sin t$ implies $\cos t = \frac{x}{3}$ and $\sin t = \frac{y}{3}$.

By the fundamental trigonometric identity, we have $\cos^2 t + \sin^2 t = \frac{x^2}{9} + \frac{y^2}{9} = 1 \Rightarrow x^2 + y^2 = 9$. This is the equation of a circle of radius 3 centered at the origin.

5. $f'(x) = 6x^2 + 6x - 12 = 6(x^2 + x - 2) = 6(x+2)(x-1)$. Setting this derivative equal to zero yields the critical numbers $x = 1$ and $x = -2$. Analyzing the derivative in the open intervals determined by the critical numbers, we see that the graph is increasing on $(-\infty, -2)$ and $(1, \infty)$ and decreasing on $(-2, 1)$. Hence, there is a relative maximum at $(-2, 20)$ and a relative minimum at $(1, -7)$.

6. The distance is $\sqrt{(6-1)^2 + (-2-(-2))^2 + (-2-4)^2} = \sqrt{25+0+36} = \sqrt{61}$.

7. The midpoint is $\left(\frac{4+8}{2}, \frac{0+8}{2}, \frac{-6+20}{2} \right) = (6, 4, 7)$.

8. $(x-0)^2 + (y-2)^2 + (z-5)^2 = 2^2 \Rightarrow x^2 + (y-2)^2 + (z-5)^2 = 4$.

9. $f(1, 3) = \ln 3 + e^{1+3} = \ln 3 + e^4$.

10. $g(\pi, 0) = 3\cos(\pi + 0) - \sin(\pi - 0) = 3(-1) + 0 = -3$.

Lesson 2

1. $f(0, 5, 4) = \sqrt{0+5+4} = \sqrt{9} = 3$.

2. The domain is $\{(x, y): x \neq 0 \text{ and } y \neq 0\}$. That is, the domain consists of all points in the plane that do not lie on either axis.

3. We must have $4 - x - y > 0 \Rightarrow x + y < 4$. So, the domain is the set $\{(x, y): y < -x + 4\}$.

4. The graph is a plane 4 units above, and parallel to, the xy-plane.

5. The graph is a hemisphere of radius 1 above the xy-plane.

6. Setting $6 - 2x - 3y = c$, we see that $2x + 3y = 6 - c$. Hence, the level curves are lines of slope $-\frac{2}{3}$.

7. The level curves are hyperbolas of the form $xy = c$.

8. The level surface is the sphere of radius 3, $x^2 + y^2 + z^2 = 9$.

9. We complete the square as follows:

    $$z = 2x + 4y - x^2 - y^2 = -\left(x^2 - 2x + 1\right) - \left(y^2 - 4y + 4\right) + 5 = 5 - \left(x-1\right)^2 - \left(y-2\right)^2.$$

    Hence, the largest value of z is 5, when $x = 1$ and $y = 2$.

10. The volume consists of the cylinder and two hemispheres. Hence, we have

    $$V = \pi r^2 x + \frac{4}{3}\pi r^3 = \frac{\pi r^2}{3}\left(3x + 4r\right).$$

Lesson 3

1. $\lim\limits_{(x,y)\to(2,1)}\left(2x^2+y\right)=2(2)^2+1=9.$

2. $\lim\limits_{(x,y)\to(1,2)}e^{xy}=e^{1(2)}=e^2.$

3. $\lim\limits_{(x,y)\to(1,1)}\dfrac{xy-1}{1+xy}=\dfrac{1(1)-1}{1+1(1)}=\dfrac{0}{2}=0.$

4. The function is continuous except at the point $(0,0)$. This point is not in the domain of the function.

5. The continuous for all (x,y) satisfying $x^2+y^2\neq4$. These points are not in the domain of the function.

6. Approaching the origin along the path $y=0$, the function equals 0.

   Approaching the origin along the path $y=x$, the function equals $\dfrac{x^2}{x^2+x^2}=\dfrac{1}{2}.$

   For any open disk about the origin, there are values of the function equal to 0 and other values equal to $\dfrac{1}{2}$. Hence, the limit does not exist.

7. Approaching the origin along the path $x=y^2$, the function equals $\dfrac{-xy^2}{x^2+y^4}=\dfrac{-y^2y^2}{y^4+y^4}=-\dfrac{1}{2}.$

   Approaching the origin along the path $x=-y^2$, the function equals $\dfrac{-xy^2}{x^2+y^4}=\dfrac{y^2y^2}{y^4+y^4}=\dfrac{1}{2}.$

   For any open disk about the origin, there are values of the function equal to $-\dfrac{1}{2}$ and other values equal to $\dfrac{1}{2}$. Hence, the limit does not exist.

8. $\dfrac{\partial f}{\partial x}=2,\ \dfrac{\partial f}{\partial y}=-5.$

9. $\dfrac{\partial f}{\partial x}=\sqrt{y},\ \dfrac{\partial f}{\partial y}=\dfrac{1}{2}xy^{-\frac{1}{2}}=\dfrac{x}{2\sqrt{y}}.$

10. $\dfrac{\partial f}{\partial x}=-\sin xy(y)=-y\sin xy,\ \dfrac{\partial f}{\partial y}=-\sin xy(x)=-x\sin xy.$

Lesson 4

1. $f_x = 5\cos 5x \cos 5y, f_y = -5\sin 5x \sin 5y$.

2. $f_x = ye^{y/x}\left(-yx^{-2}\right) = \dfrac{-y^2}{x^2}e^{y/x}, f_y = e^{y/x} + \dfrac{1}{x}ye^{y/x} = e^{y/x}\left(1 + \dfrac{y}{x}\right)$.

3. $g_x = -2x, g_y = -2y$. At the given point, the slope in the x-direction is $-2(1) = -2$, and the slope in the y-direction is $-2(1) = -2$.

4. $f_x = 3x^2yz^2, f_x(1,1,1) = 3, f_y = x^3z^2, f_y(1,1,1) = 1, f_z = 2x^3yz, f_z(1,1,1) = 2$.

5. The first partial derivatives are $f_x = 2x - 2y, f_y = -2x + 6y$. Differentiating again, $f_{xx} = 2, f_{yy} = 6, f_{xy} = -2, f_{yx} = -2$.

6. The first partial derivatives are $f_x = e^x \tan y, f_y = e^x \sec^2 y$. Differentiating again, $f_{xx} = e^x \tan x, f_{yy} = 2e^x \sec^2 y \tan y, f_{xy} = e^x \sec^2 y, f_{yx} = e^x \sec^2 y$.

7. We have $f_x = 2x - y - 5 = 0 \Rightarrow y = 2x - 5$. Next, substitute into the partial with respect to y:
   $f_y = -x + 2y + 1 = -x + 2(2x - 5) + 1 = 3x - 9 = 0$. Hence, $x = 3$ and $y = 1$.

8. $f_x = -\dfrac{1}{x^2} + y, f_y = -\dfrac{1}{y^2} + x$. Setting these partial derivatives equal to zero gives $y = \dfrac{1}{x^2}$ and $x = \dfrac{1}{y^2}$.

   Hence, $y = y^4 \Rightarrow y = 1$ and $x = 1$. Notice that $x \neq 0$ and $y \neq 0$.

9. We first calculate the second partial derivatives.

   $$z_x = \frac{-y}{x^2 + y^2}, z_{xx} = \frac{2xy}{\left(x^2 + y^2\right)^2}, z_y = \frac{x}{x^2 + y^2}, z_{yy} = \frac{-2xy}{\left(x^2 + y^2\right)^2}.$$

   Hence, $\dfrac{\partial^2 z}{\partial x^2} + \dfrac{\partial^2 z}{\partial y^2} = \dfrac{2xy}{\left(x^2 + y^2\right)^2} + \dfrac{-2xy}{\left(x^2 + y^2\right)^2} = 0$.

10. We first calculate the second partial derivatives.

$$z_t = -c\cos(x-ct),\; z_{tt} = -c^2\sin(x-ct),\; z_x = \cos(x-ct),\; z_{xx} = -\sin(x-ct).$$

Hence, $\dfrac{\partial^2 z}{\partial t^2} = -c^2\sin(x-ct) = c^2\dfrac{\partial^2 z}{\partial x^2}.$

Lesson 5

1. $dz = 4xy^3\,dx + 6x^2y^2\,dy.$

2. $dz = e^x\sin y\,dx + e^x\cos y\,dy.$

3. $dw = \dfrac{1}{z-3y}\,dx + \dfrac{3x+z}{(z-3y)^2}\,dy - \dfrac{x+y}{(z-3y)^2}\,dz.$

4. Let $z = x^2 y$, $x = 2$, $y = 9$, $dx = 0.01$, $dy = 0.02$.

Then, $dz = 2xy\,dx + x^2\,dy$ and $(2.01)^2(9.02) - 2^2(9) \approx 2(2)(9)(0.01) + 2^2(0.02) = 0.44.$

5. Let $z = \sin(x^2 + y^2)$, $x = y = 1$, $dx = 0.05$, $dy = -0.05$. Then, $dz = 2x\cos(x^2 + y^2)\,dx + 2y\cos(x^2 + y^2)\,dy$, and we have $\sin\big[(1.05)^2 + (0.95)^2\big] - \sin(1^2 + 1^2) \approx 2(1)\cos(1^2 + 1^2)(0.05) + 2(1)\cos(1^2 + 1^2)(-0.05) = 0.$

6. The volume is $V = \pi r^2 h$, which implies that $dV = (2\pi rh)\,dr + (\pi r^2)\,dh$. Hence,

$$\frac{dV}{V} = \frac{2\pi rh\,dr + \pi r^2\,dh}{\pi r^2 h} = 2\frac{dr}{r} + \frac{dh}{h} = 2(0.04) + 0.02 = 0.10.$$

So, the percentage error is $\pm 10\%$.

7. $h'(x) = \cos\!\left(e^{3x^2}\right)\dfrac{d}{dx}\!\left(e^{3x^2}\right) = \cos\!\left(e^{3x^2}\right)e^{3x^2}(6x) = 6xe^{3x^2}\cos\!\left(e^{3x^2}\right).$

8. $\dfrac{dw}{dt} = \dfrac{\partial w}{\partial x}\dfrac{dx}{dt} + \dfrac{\partial w}{\partial y}\dfrac{dy}{dt} = y(e^t) + x(-2e^{-2t}) = e^{-2t}e^t + e^t(-2e^{-2t}) = -e^{-t}.$

9. $\dfrac{dw}{dt} = \dfrac{\partial w}{\partial x}\dfrac{dx}{dt} + \dfrac{\partial w}{\partial y}\dfrac{dy}{dt} = -\sin(x-y)(2t) + \sin(x-y)(0) = -2t\sin(t^2 - 1).$

10. $\dfrac{dw}{dt} = \dfrac{\partial w}{\partial x}\dfrac{dx}{dt} + \dfrac{\partial w}{\partial y}\dfrac{dy}{dt} = ye^{xy}(2t) + xe^{xy}(1).$ At $t = 1$, $x = 1$ and $y = 1$. Hence, $\dfrac{dw}{dt} = e(2) + e = 3e.$

Lesson 6

1. $f_x = \dfrac{x}{\sqrt{x^2 + y^2 + 1}} = 0 \Rightarrow x = 0,\ f_y = \dfrac{y}{\sqrt{x^2 + y^2 + 1}} = 0 \Rightarrow y = 0.$ The critical point is $(0, 0).$

2. $f_x = -2x + 10 = 0 \Rightarrow x = 5,\ f_y = -2y + 12 = 0 \Rightarrow y = 6.$ The critical point is $(5, 6).$

3. The partial derivatives $f_x = \dfrac{4x}{3(x^2 + y^2)^{1/3}},\ f_y = \dfrac{4y}{3(x^2 + y^2)^{1/3}}$ are not defined at $x = y = 0$. The critical point is $(0, 0).$

4. $2x^2 + y^2 + 8x - 6y + 20 = 2(x^2 + 4x + 4) + (y^2 - 6y + 9) + 20 - 8 - 9 \Rightarrow f(x,y) = 2(x+2)^2 + (y-3)^2 + 3$ has a relative minimum at $(-2, 3, 3).$

5. $f_x = y,\ f_y = x \Rightarrow (0,0)$ is the only critical point. $f_{xx} = f_{yy} = 0,\ f_{xy} = 1.$

By the second partials test, $d = f_{xx}f_{yy} - (f_{xy})^2 = 0 - 1 < 0,$ and hence, $(0, 0, 0)$ is a saddle point.

6. $f_x = 6x - 6,\ f_y = 4y - 4 \Rightarrow (1, 1)$ is the only critical point. $f_{xx} = 6,\ f_{yy} = 4,\ f_{xy} = 0.$

Hence, $d = f_{xx}f_{yy} - (f_{xy})^2 = 6(4) - 0 > 0,$ and by the second partials test, $(1, 1, 11)$ is a relative minimum.

7. $f_x = -10x + 4y + 16 = 0,\ f_y = 4x - 2y = 0.$ Solving these equations, we see that $(8, 16)$ is the only critical point. $f_{xx} = -10,\ f_{yy} = -2,\ f_{xy} = 4.$

Hence, $d = f_{xx}f_{yy} - (f_{xy})^2 = (-10)(-2) - 4^2 > 0,$ and by the second partials test, $(8, 16, 71)$ is a relative maximum.

8. $f_x = 2y - 2x^3 = 0, f_y = 2x - 2y^3 = 0$. Solving these equations, we see that there are three critical points: $(0, 0), (1, 1)$, and $(-1, -1)$. $f_{xx} = -6x^2, f_{yy} = -6y^2, f_{xy} = 2$.

At $(0, 0)$, $d = f_{xx}f_{yy} - (f_{xy})^2 < 0 \Rightarrow (0, 0, 1)$ is a saddle point.

At $(1, 1)$, $d = f_{xx}f_{yy} - (f_{xy})^2 > 0$ and $f_{xx} < 0$, so $(1, 1, 2)$ is a relative maximum.

Finally, at $(-1, -1)$, $d = f_{xx}f_{yy} - (f_{xy})^2 > 0$ and $f_{xx} < 0$, so $(-1, -1, 2)$ is a relative maximum.

9. $f_x = \dfrac{2}{3x^{1/3}}, f_y = \dfrac{2}{3y^{1/3}}$, which implies that $(0, 0)$ is the only critical point.

Clearly, $f(x, y) \geq 0$, so $(0, 0, 0)$ is a relative minimum.

10. Let x and y be the dimensions of the base and z the height.

The amount of material is $2 = xy + 2xz + 2yz \Rightarrow z = \dfrac{2 - xy}{2x + 2y}$.

The volume of the box is therefore $V = xyz = xy\left(\dfrac{2 - xy}{2x + 2y}\right)$.

Setting the partial derivatives equal to zero, you obtain $x = y$ and the nontrivial critical point

$(x, y) = \left(\dfrac{\sqrt{6}}{3}, \dfrac{\sqrt{6}}{3}\right)$.

By the second partials test, this is a maximum. The corresponding z value is $\dfrac{\sqrt{6}}{6}$, and the maximum volume is $\dfrac{\sqrt{6}}{9}$.

11. We have $V = xy\dfrac{C - 3xy}{4(x + y)} = \dfrac{Cxy - 3x^2y^2}{4(x + y)}$ So, by the quotient rule,

$$V_x = \frac{4(x + y)(Cy - 6xy^2) - (Cxy - 3x^2y^2)(4)}{[4(x + y)]^2} = \frac{Cxy - 6x^2y^2 + Cy^2 - 6xy^3 - Cxy + 3x^2y^2}{4(x + y)^2}.$$

This simplifies to $V_x = \dfrac{y^2(C - 3x^2 - 6xy)}{4(x + y)^2}$.

12. The numerators both equal zero: $C - 3x^2 - 6xy = C - 3y^2 - 6xy$, which implies that $x = y$. Using the value $C = 1296$, $1296 - 3x^2 - 6x^2 = 0 \Rightarrow 9x^2 = 1296 \Rightarrow x = 12$. Hence, the solution is $x = y = 12$.

Lesson 7

1. $f_x = 2x - 4y = 0$, $f_y = -4x = 0 \Rightarrow (0, 0)$ is the only critical point, and it lies outside the rectangular region. We now analyze the function along its boundaries.

   Along $y = 0, 1 \leq x \leq 4$: $f = x^2 + 5$, $f(1, 0) = 6$, $f(4, 0) = 21$.

   Along $y = 2, 1 \leq x \leq 4$, $f = x^2 - 8x + 5$, $f' = 2x - 8 = 0$, $f(1, 2) = -2$, $f(4, 2) = -11$.

   Along $x = 1, 0 \leq y \leq 2$, $f = -4y + 6$, $f(1, 0) = 6$, $f(1, 2) = -2$.

   Along $x = 4, 0 \leq y \leq 2$, $f = 21 - 16y$, $f(4, 0) = 21$, $f(4, 2) = -11$.

   Summarizing, the maximum is $(4, 0, 21)$, and the minimum is $(4, 2, -11)$.

2. The function has no critical points. We analyze the function along its boundary.

   Along the line $y = x + 1, 0 \leq x \leq 1$, $f = 12 - 3x - 2(x + 1) = -5x + 10$. The maximum is 10, and the minimum is 5.

   Along $y = -2x + 4, 1 \leq x \leq 2$, $f = 12 - 3x - 2(-2x + 4) = x + 4$. The maximum is 6, and the minimum is 5.

   Along $y = -\dfrac{1}{2}x + 1, 0 \leq x \leq 2$, $f = -2x + 10$. The maximum is 10, and the minimum is 6.

   Finally, the absolute maximum is $(0, 1, 10)$, and the absolute minimum is $(1, 2, 5)$.

3. A point on the plane is given by $(x, y, z) = (x, y, 3 - x + y)$.

   The square of the distance from $(0, 0, 0)$ to this point is $S = x^2 + y^2 + (3 - x + y)^2$.

   The partial derivatives are $S_x = 2x - 2(3 - x + y)$, $S_y = 2y + 2(3 - x + y)$.

   From the equations $S_x = S_y = 0$, we obtain the critical point $(1, -1)$.

   The corresponding z-value is 1, and the minimum distance is $\sqrt{1^2 + (-1)^2 + 1^2} = \sqrt{3}$.

4. Let x, y, and z be the three numbers. Because $xyz = 27$, $z = \dfrac{27}{xy}$.

The sum is $S = x + y + \dfrac{27}{xy}$, and the partial derivatives are $S_x = 1 - \dfrac{27}{x^2 y}$, $S_y = 1 - \dfrac{27}{xy^2}$.

Setting the partial derivatives equal to zero yields $x = 3$, $y = 3$.

Finally, we have $z = 3$, and the three numbers are equal, $x = y = z = 3$.

5. Let x, y, and z be the length, width, and height, respectively, and let V be the fixed volume.

Hence, $V = xyz \Rightarrow z = \dfrac{V}{xy}$. The surface area is given by $S = 2xy + 2yz + 2xz = 2\left(xy + \dfrac{V}{x} + \dfrac{V}{y}\right)$.

Setting the partial derivatives equal to zero, $S_x = 2\left(y - \dfrac{V}{x^2}\right) = 0$, $S_y = 2\left(x - \dfrac{V}{y^2}\right) = 0$, you obtain $x = y = z = \sqrt[3]{V}$.

6. We have

$$108y - 4xy - 2y^2 = y(108 - 4x - 2y) = 0 \Rightarrow 108 - 4x - 2y = 0$$

and

$$108x - 2x^2 - 4xy = x(108 - 2x - 4y) = 0 \Rightarrow 108 - 2x - 4y = 0.$$

Setting these two equations equal to each other, you have $4x + 2y = 2x + 4y$, which implies that $x = y$.

Finally, $108 - 4x - 2y = 108 - 4x - 2x = 0 \Rightarrow x = y = 18$.

7. Because $C_y = \dfrac{2(y-x)}{\sqrt{(y-x)^2 + 1}} - 1 = 0$, $\dfrac{2(y-x)}{\sqrt{(y-x)^2 + 1}} = 1$. So, $C_x = \dfrac{3x}{\sqrt{x^2+4}} - 1 = 0$.

Solving this equation for x, $3x = \sqrt{x^2 + 4} \Rightarrow 9x^2 = x^2 + 4 \Rightarrow x^2 = \dfrac{1}{2} \Rightarrow x = \dfrac{\sqrt{2}}{2}$.

Knowing this value, you obtain $y = \dfrac{\sqrt{3}}{3} + \dfrac{\sqrt{2}}{2}$.

Lesson 8

1. $n = 3,\ \sum x_i = 9, \sum y_i = 9, \sum x_i y_i = 39, \sum x_i^2 = 35.$

$$a = \frac{n\sum x_i y_i - \sum x_i \sum y_i}{n \sum x_i^2 - \left(\sum x_i\right)^2} = \frac{3(39) - 9(9)}{3(35) - (9)^2} = \frac{36}{24} = \frac{3}{2}.$$

$$b = \frac{1}{n}\left(\sum y_i - a\sum x_i\right) = \frac{1}{3}\left(9 - \frac{3}{2}(9)\right) = -\frac{9}{6} = -\frac{3}{2}.$$

The least squares regression line is $y = \frac{3}{2}x - \frac{3}{2}.$

2. $n = 5,\ \sum x_i = 13, \sum y_i = 12, \sum x_i y_i = 46, \sum x_i^2 = 51.$

$$a = \frac{n\sum x_i y_i - \sum x_i \sum y_i}{n \sum x_i^2 - \left(\sum x_i\right)^2} = \frac{5(46) - 13(12)}{5(51) - (13)^2} = \frac{74}{86} = \frac{37}{43}.$$

$$b = \frac{1}{n}\left(\sum y_i - a\sum x_i\right) = \frac{1}{5}\left(12 - \frac{37}{43}(13)\right) = \frac{7}{43}.$$

The least squares regression line is $y = \frac{37}{43}x + \frac{7}{43}.$

3. You obtain $y = -\frac{175}{148}x + \frac{945}{148} \approx -1.1824x + 6.3851.$

4. You obtain $y = \frac{29}{53}x + \frac{425}{318} \approx 0.5472x + 1.3365.$

5. You obtain $y = 14x + 19.$ When $x = 1.6, y = 14(1.6) + 19 = 41.4$ bushels per acre.

6. You obtain $y = -300x + 832.$ When $x = 1.59, y = -300(1.59) + 832 = 355.$

Lesson 9

1. The component form is $\langle 4-3, 1-2, 6-0 \rangle = \langle 1, -1, 6 \rangle$. The magnitude is
    $\| \langle 1, -1, 6 \rangle \| = \sqrt{1^2 + (-1)^2 + 6^2} = \sqrt{38}$.

2. The length is $\sqrt{1^2 + 3^2 + 4^2} = \sqrt{26}$.

3. The vector joining the first two points is $\langle 1, 3, -4 \rangle$, and the vector joining the first and third points is $\langle -1, -1, 1 \rangle$. Because these vectors are not parallel, the points are not collinear.

4. $\mathbf{u} \cdot \mathbf{v} = \langle 2, -1, 1 \rangle \cdot \langle 1, 0, -1 \rangle = 2(1) + (-1)(0) + 1(-1) = 1$.

5. The length of the vector is $\sqrt{4+1+4} = 3$.

    The unit vector in the same direction is $\frac{1}{3}\mathbf{v} = \frac{1}{3}\langle 2, 1, -2 \rangle = \left\langle \frac{2}{3}, \frac{1}{3}, -\frac{2}{3} \right\rangle$.

6. $\cos\theta = \dfrac{\mathbf{u} \cdot \mathbf{v}}{\|\mathbf{u}\|\|\mathbf{v}\|} = \dfrac{3(2) + 2(-3) + 1(0)}{\|\mathbf{u}\|\|\mathbf{v}\|} = 0$, which implies that the angle is $\dfrac{\pi}{2} = 90°$.

    The vectors are orthogonal.

7. $\cos\theta = \dfrac{\mathbf{u} \cdot \mathbf{v}}{\|\mathbf{u}\|\|\mathbf{v}\|} = \dfrac{3(0) + 4(2) + 0(3)}{\|\sqrt{9+16}\|\|\sqrt{4+9}\|} = \dfrac{8}{5\sqrt{13}}$.

    Using a calculator, we have $\theta = \arccos\left(\dfrac{8}{5\sqrt{13}}\right) \approx 1.111 \approx 63.7°$.

8. The point is $P(0, 0, 0)$, and the direction vector is $\mathbf{v} = \langle 3, 1, 5 \rangle$. The parametric equations are
    $x = 0 + 3t, \, y = 0 + t, \, z = 0 + 5t \Rightarrow x = 3t, \, y = t, \, z = 5t$.

9. $x = -3 + 0t, \, y = 0 + 6t, \, z = 2 + 3t \Rightarrow x = -3, \, y = 6t, \, z = 2 + 3t$.

10. The direction vector is $\mathbf{v} = \langle -3-7, 0-(-2), 6-6 \rangle = \langle -10, 2, 0 \rangle$. Using the first point, we obtain
    $x = 7 - 10t, \, y = -2 + 2t, \, z = 6$.

Lesson 10

1. $\mathbf{k} \times \mathbf{i} = \begin{vmatrix} \mathbf{i} & \mathbf{j} & \mathbf{k} \\ 0 & 0 & 1 \\ 1 & 0 & 0 \end{vmatrix} = 0\mathbf{i} - (-\mathbf{j}) + 0\mathbf{k} = \mathbf{j}$ and $\mathbf{i} \times \mathbf{k} = \begin{vmatrix} \mathbf{i} & \mathbf{j} & \mathbf{k} \\ 1 & 0 & 0 \\ 0 & 0 & 1 \end{vmatrix} = 0\mathbf{i} - (\mathbf{j}) + 0\mathbf{k} = -\mathbf{j}.$

The vectors i and k are orthogonal, and $\mathbf{k} \times \mathbf{i} = -(\mathbf{i} \times \mathbf{k})$.

2. $\mathbf{u} \times \mathbf{v} = \begin{vmatrix} \mathbf{i} & \mathbf{j} & \mathbf{k} \\ 7 & 3 & 2 \\ 1 & -1 & 5 \end{vmatrix} = \begin{vmatrix} 3 & 2 \\ -1 & 5 \end{vmatrix}\mathbf{i} - \begin{vmatrix} 7 & 2 \\ 1 & 5 \end{vmatrix}\mathbf{j} + \begin{vmatrix} 7 & 3 \\ 1 & -1 \end{vmatrix}\mathbf{k} = 17\mathbf{i} - 33\mathbf{j} - 10\mathbf{k}.$

3. $\mathbf{u} \times \mathbf{v} = \begin{vmatrix} \mathbf{i} & \mathbf{j} & \mathbf{k} \\ 3 & 1 & -2 \\ 1 & -2 & 1 \end{vmatrix} = \begin{vmatrix} 1 & -2 \\ -2 & 1 \end{vmatrix}\mathbf{i} - \begin{vmatrix} 3 & -2 \\ 1 & 1 \end{vmatrix}\mathbf{j} + \begin{vmatrix} 3 & 1 \\ 1 & -2 \end{vmatrix}\mathbf{k} = -3\mathbf{i} - 5\mathbf{j} - 7\mathbf{k}.$

4. $\mathbf{u} \times \mathbf{v} = \begin{vmatrix} \mathbf{i} & \mathbf{j} & \mathbf{k} \\ 1 & 1 & 1 \\ 0 & 1 & 1 \end{vmatrix} = \begin{vmatrix} 1 & 1 \\ 1 & 1 \end{vmatrix}\mathbf{i} - \begin{vmatrix} 1 & 1 \\ 0 & 1 \end{vmatrix}\mathbf{j} + \begin{vmatrix} 1 & 1 \\ 0 & 1 \end{vmatrix}\mathbf{k} = -\mathbf{j} + \mathbf{k}.$

The dot product of this vector with the original vectors is zero, showing orthogonality.

$$(\mathbf{i} + \mathbf{j} + \mathbf{k}) \cdot (-\mathbf{j} + \mathbf{k}) = -1 + 1 = 0, (\mathbf{j} + \mathbf{k}) \cdot (-\mathbf{j} + \mathbf{k}) = -1 + 1 = 0.$$

5. The cross product of the given vectors will be orthogonal to the two vectors.

$$\mathbf{i} \times (2\mathbf{j} + \mathbf{k}) = \begin{vmatrix} \mathbf{i} & \mathbf{j} & \mathbf{k} \\ 1 & 0 & 0 \\ 0 & 2 & 1 \end{vmatrix} = \begin{vmatrix} 0 & 0 \\ 2 & 1 \end{vmatrix}\mathbf{i} - \begin{vmatrix} 1 & 0 \\ 0 & 1 \end{vmatrix}\mathbf{j} + \begin{vmatrix} 1 & 0 \\ 0 & 2 \end{vmatrix}\mathbf{k} = -\mathbf{j} + 2\mathbf{k}.$$

6. $\mathbf{v} \times \mathbf{v} = \begin{vmatrix} \mathbf{i} & \mathbf{j} & \mathbf{k} \\ 1 & 0 & -2 \\ 1 & 0 & -2 \end{vmatrix} = \begin{vmatrix} 0 & -2 \\ 0 & -2 \end{vmatrix}\mathbf{i} - \begin{vmatrix} 1 & -2 \\ 1 & -2 \end{vmatrix}\mathbf{j} + \begin{vmatrix} 1 & 0 \\ 1 & 0 \end{vmatrix}\mathbf{k} = 0.$

The cross product of a vector with itself is always the zero vector.

7. One way to solve this problem is to find the cross product and then divide by its length to generate a unit vector. Another way is to observe that these vectors lie in the xy-plane, so an orthogonal unit vector is k (or $-k$).

8. The area is the magnitude of the cross product.

$$\langle 3, 2, -1 \rangle \times \langle 1, 2, 3 \rangle = \begin{vmatrix} \mathbf{i} & \mathbf{j} & \mathbf{k} \\ 3 & 2 & -1 \\ 1 & 2 & 3 \end{vmatrix} = \begin{vmatrix} 2 & -1 \\ 2 & 3 \end{vmatrix} \mathbf{i} - \begin{vmatrix} 3 & -1 \\ 1 & 3 \end{vmatrix} \mathbf{j} + \begin{vmatrix} 3 & 2 \\ 1 & 2 \end{vmatrix} \mathbf{k} = 8\mathbf{i} - 10\mathbf{j} + 4\mathbf{k}.$$

$$\text{Area} = \|8\mathbf{i} - 10\mathbf{j} + 4\mathbf{k}\| = \sqrt{64 + 100 + 16} = \sqrt{180} = 6\sqrt{5}.$$

9. The volume is the absolute value of the triple scalar product.

$$\mathbf{u} \cdot (\mathbf{v} \times \mathbf{w}) = \begin{vmatrix} 1 & 3 & 1 \\ 0 & 6 & 6 \\ -4 & 0 & -4 \end{vmatrix} = \begin{vmatrix} 6 & 6 \\ 0 & -4 \end{vmatrix}(1) - \begin{vmatrix} 0 & 6 \\ -4 & -4 \end{vmatrix}(3) + \begin{vmatrix} 0 & 6 \\ -4 & 0 \end{vmatrix}(1) = -24 - 24(3) + 24 = -72.$$

Hence, the volume is 72.

10. The following three vectors form adjacent sides of the parallelepiped:

$$\langle 3-0, 0-0, 0-0 \rangle = \langle 3, 0, 0 \rangle, \langle 0-0, 5-0, 1-0 \rangle = \langle 0, 5, 1 \rangle, \langle 2-0, 0-0, 5-0 \rangle = \langle 2, 0, 5 \rangle.$$

We next form the triple scalar product of these three vectors:

$$\begin{vmatrix} 3 & 0 & 0 \\ 0 & 5 & 1 \\ 2 & 0 & 5 \end{vmatrix} = \begin{vmatrix} 5 & 1 \\ 0 & 5 \end{vmatrix}(3) - \begin{vmatrix} 0 & 1 \\ 2 & 5 \end{vmatrix}(0) + \begin{vmatrix} 0 & 5 \\ 2 & 0 \end{vmatrix}(0) = 75.$$

Hence, the volume is 75.

11. Form the vectors $\overline{AC} = \langle 3, -8, -2 \rangle$ and $\overline{AB} = \langle 1, -1, -3 \rangle$. Their cross product $\langle 22, 7, 5 \rangle$ is orthogonal to the triangle.

Lesson 11

1. The normal vector is $\mathbf{n} = \mathbf{j} = 0\mathbf{i} + \mathbf{j} + 0\mathbf{k}$.

   So, an equation of the plane is $0(x-1) + 1(y-3) + 0(z-(-7)) = 0 \Rightarrow y - 3 = 0$.

2. The normal vector is $\mathbf{n} = 2\mathbf{i} - \mathbf{j} - 2\mathbf{k}$.

   So, an equation of the plane is $2(x+1) - 1(y-4) - 2(z-0) = 0 \Rightarrow 2x - y - 2z + 6 = 0$.

3. Let $\mathbf{u} = \langle 2, 0, 3 \rangle$ be the vector from the point $(0, 0, 0)$ to $(2, 0, 3)$, and let $\mathbf{v} = \langle -3, -1, 5 \rangle$ be the vector from the point $(0, 0, 0)$ to $(-3, -1, 5)$.

   The normal vector to the plane is their cross product, $\mathbf{n} = \mathbf{u} \times \mathbf{v} = \langle 3, -19, -2 \rangle$.

   So, the equation of the plane is $3(x-0) - 19(y-0) - 2(z-0) = 0 \Rightarrow 3x - 19y - 2z = 0$.

4. The angle between the two planes is the angle between their normal vectors, $\mathbf{n}_1 = \langle 3, 2, -1 \rangle$ and $\mathbf{n}_2 = \langle 1, -4, 2 \rangle$.
$$\cos\theta = \frac{|\mathbf{n}_1 \cdot \mathbf{n}_2|}{\|\mathbf{n}_1\| \|\mathbf{n}_2\|} = \frac{|3 - 8 - 2|}{\sqrt{14}\sqrt{21}} = \frac{7}{7\sqrt{6}} = \frac{\sqrt{6}}{6} \Rightarrow \theta \approx 1.1503 \approx 65.91°.$$

5. The dot product of the normal vectors $\mathbf{n}_1 = \langle 5, -3, 1 \rangle$ and $\mathbf{n}_2 = \langle 1, 4, 7 \rangle$ is zero, so the planes are orthogonal.

6. The normal vectors $\mathbf{n}_1 = \langle 3, 1, -4 \rangle$ and $\mathbf{n}_2 = \langle -9, -3, 12 \rangle$ are parallel (multiples of each other), so the planes are parallel.

7. The direction vector of the line is $\mathbf{v} = 3\mathbf{i} + 2\mathbf{j} - \mathbf{k}$. The parametric equations of the line are $x = 2 + 3t$, $y = 3 + 2t$, $z = 4 - t$.

8. The direction vector of the line is $\mathbf{v} = \mathbf{k}$. The parametric equations of the line are $x = 2, y = 3, z = 4 + t$.

9. The normal to the plane is $\mathbf{n} = \langle 5, 1, -1 \rangle$. The given point is $Q(0, 0, 0)$, a point in the plane is $P(0, 9, 0)$, and the vector $\overrightarrow{PQ}$ is $\langle 0, -9, 0 \rangle$.

Therefore, the distance is $D = \dfrac{\left| \overrightarrow{PQ} \cdot \mathbf{n} \right|}{\|\mathbf{n}\|} = \dfrac{|-9|}{\sqrt{27}} = \dfrac{9}{3\sqrt{3}} = \sqrt{3}$.

10. The normal to the plane is $\mathbf{n} = \langle 3, -4, 5 \rangle$. The given point is $Q(1, 3, -1)$, a point in the plane is $P(2, 0, 0)$, and the vector $\overrightarrow{PQ}$ is $\langle -1, 3, -1 \rangle$.

Therefore, the distance is $D = \dfrac{\left| \overrightarrow{PQ} \cdot \mathbf{n} \right|}{\|\mathbf{n}\|} = \dfrac{|-20|}{\sqrt{50}} = \dfrac{20}{5\sqrt{2}} = 2\sqrt{2}$.

Lesson 12

1. The surface is a plane parallel to the xz-plane.

2. The x-coordinate is missing, so you have a right circular cylinder with rulings parallel to the x-axis. The radius of the cylinder is 3.

3. The surface is an ellipsoid centered at the origin.

4. Rewriting the equation, $4x^2 - \dfrac{y^2}{4} + 4z^2 = 1$, we see that this is a hyperboloid of one sheet centered at the origin.

5. The surface is a hyperboloid of two sheets centered at the origin.

6. We have $y = x^2 + z^2$, so the surface is an elliptic paraboloid.

7. By completing the square, we see that the surface is an ellipsoid with center at $(1, 2, 0)$.

$$16\left(x^2 - 2x + 1\right) + 9\left(y^2 - 4y + 4\right) + 16z^2 = -36 + 16 + 36$$
$$16(x-1)^2 + 9(y-2)^2 + 16z^2 = 16$$
$$\dfrac{(x-1)^2}{1} + \dfrac{(y-2)^2}{16/9} + z^2 = 1.$$

Solutions

158

8. By completing the square, we see that the surface is an elliptic cone with center at $(3, 2, -3)$.

$$9(x^2 - 6x + 9) + (y^2 - 4y + 4) - 9(z^2 + 6z + 9) = -4 + 81 + 4 - 81$$
$$9(x-3)^2 + (y-2)^2 - 9(z+3)^2 = 0.$$

9. One equation is $x^2 + z^2 = 4y$.

10. One equation is $x^2 + y^2 = \left(\dfrac{z}{2}\right)^2$, or $4x^2 + 4y^2 = z^2$.

Lesson 13

1. $\mathbf{r}'(t) = \dfrac{-1}{t^2}\mathbf{i} + 16\mathbf{j} + t\mathbf{k}.$

2. $\mathbf{r}'(t) = \langle 3t^2, -3\sin 3t, 3\cos 3t \rangle.$

3. $\mathbf{r}'(t) = \left\langle t, -1, \dfrac{1}{2}t^2 \right\rangle, \mathbf{r}''(t) = \langle 1, 0, t \rangle \Rightarrow \mathbf{r}'(t) \cdot \mathbf{r}''(t) = t(1) + (-1)0 + \dfrac{1}{2}t^2(t) = t + \dfrac{t^3}{2}.$

4. $\int (2t\mathbf{i} + \mathbf{j} + \mathbf{k})\, dt = t^2\mathbf{i} + t\mathbf{j} + t\mathbf{k} + \mathbf{C}.$

5. $\int_0^{\pi/4} \left[(\sec t \tan t)\mathbf{i} + (\tan t)\mathbf{j} + (2\sin t \cos t)\mathbf{k} \right] dt = \left[\sec t\mathbf{i} - \ln|\cos t|\mathbf{j} + \sin^2 t\mathbf{k} \right]_0^{\pi/4}$

$= (\sqrt{2} - 1)\mathbf{i} - \left(\ln \dfrac{\sqrt{2}}{2} - 0 \right)\mathbf{j} + \left(\dfrac{1}{2} - 0 \right)\mathbf{k} = (\sqrt{2} - 1)\mathbf{i} + \ln\sqrt{2}\,\mathbf{j} + \dfrac{1}{2}\mathbf{k}.$

6. $\mathbf{r}(t) = 4t\mathbf{i} + 4t\mathbf{j} + 2t\mathbf{k}, \mathbf{v}(t) = \mathbf{r}'(t) = 4\mathbf{i} + 4\mathbf{j} + 2\mathbf{k}, \mathbf{a}(t) = \mathbf{v}'(t) = \mathbf{0},$ and the speed is $\|\mathbf{v}(t)\| = \sqrt{4^2 + 4^2 + 2^2} = \sqrt{36} = 6.$

7. We calculate the derivative and then divide by its length, as follows:

$$\mathbf{r}'(t) = \langle -2\sin t, 2\cos t, 0 \rangle \Rightarrow \mathbf{T}(t) = \dfrac{\mathbf{r}'(t)}{\|\mathbf{r}'(t)\|} = \dfrac{\langle -2\sin t, 2\cos t, 0 \rangle}{2} = \langle -\sin t, \cos t, 0 \rangle.$$

8. At the point $(0, 0, 0)$, $t = 0$. Hence, $\mathbf{r}'(t) = \mathbf{i} + 2t\mathbf{j} + \mathbf{k}$, $\mathbf{r}'(0) = \mathbf{i} + \mathbf{k}$, $\|\mathbf{r}'(0)\| = \sqrt{2}$.

The unit tangent is $\mathbf{T}(0) = \dfrac{\mathbf{r}'(0)}{\|\mathbf{r}'(0)\|} = \dfrac{\mathbf{i} + \mathbf{k}}{\sqrt{2}} = \dfrac{\sqrt{2}}{2}\mathbf{i} + \dfrac{\sqrt{2}}{2}\mathbf{k}$.

9. $x'(t) = -1$, $y'(t) = 4$, $z'(t) = 3$. Hence, the arc length is given by

$$s = \int_a^b \sqrt{\left[x'(t)\right]^2 + \left[y'(t)\right]^2 + \left[z'(t)\right]^2}\, dt = \int_0^1 \sqrt{1 + 16 + 9}\, dt = \left[\sqrt{26}\,t\right]_0^1 = \sqrt{26}.$$

10. $x'(t) = 2\cos t$, $y'(t) = 5$, $z'(t) = -2\sin t$. Hence, the arc length is given by

$$s = \int_a^b \sqrt{\left[x'(t)\right]^2 + \left[y'(t)\right]^2 + \left[z'(t)\right]^2}\, dt = \int_0^\pi \sqrt{4\cos^2 t + 25 + 4\sin^2 t}\, dt$$

$$= \int_0^\pi \sqrt{4 + 25}\, dt = \left[\sqrt{29}\,t\right]_0^\pi = \sqrt{29}\,\pi.$$

Lesson 14

1. The vertices of the ellipse occur when $\theta = \dfrac{\pi}{2}$ and $\theta = \dfrac{3\pi}{2}$. So, the length of the major axis is

$$2a = 35.88 = \frac{0.967d}{1 + 0.967} + \frac{0.967d}{1 - 0.967} \approx 29.79d.$$

So, $d \approx 1.204$ and $ed \approx (0.967)(1.204) \approx 1.164$. The equation for the orbit is now

$$r = \frac{1.164}{1 + 0.967\sin\theta}.$$

To find the closest point to the Sun (the focus), use $c = ea = (0.967)(17.94) = 17.35$. The closest point is therefore $a - c \approx 17.94 - 17.35 \approx 0.59$ AU, or $55{,}000{,}000$ miles.

2. The area swept out from $\theta = -\dfrac{\pi}{2}$ to $\theta = \dfrac{\pi}{2}$ is given by the integral

$$A = \frac{1}{2}\int_\alpha^\beta r^2\, d\theta = \frac{1}{2}\int_{-\pi/2}^{\pi/2}\left(\frac{9}{9 + 5\cos\theta}\right)^2 d\theta \approx 0.90429.$$

We next apply Kepler's second law. The time t required to move from position $\theta = -\dfrac{\pi}{2}$ to position $\theta = \dfrac{\pi}{2}$ is given by

$$\frac{t}{661} = \frac{\text{area of elliptical segment}}{\text{area of ellipse}} = \frac{0.90429}{5.46507} \Rightarrow t \approx 109 \text{ days.}$$

Lesson 15

1. $\nabla f(x, y) = (3 - 4y)\mathbf{i} + (9 - 4x)\mathbf{j} \Rightarrow \nabla f(1, 2) = -5\mathbf{i} + 5\mathbf{j}$.

   The vector v is a unit vector, so $D_{\mathbf{u}} f(1, 2) = \nabla f(1, 2) \cdot \mathbf{v} = (-5\mathbf{i} + 5\mathbf{j}) \cdot \left(\frac{3}{5}\mathbf{i} + \frac{4}{5}\mathbf{j} \right) = -3 + 4 = 1$.

2. $\nabla f(x, y) = e^x \sin y \, \mathbf{i} + e^x \cos y \, \mathbf{j} \Rightarrow \nabla f\left(1, \frac{\pi}{2} \right) = e\mathbf{i}$.

   The vector v is a unit vector, so $D_{\mathbf{u}} f\left(1, \frac{\pi}{2} \right) = \nabla f\left(1, \frac{\pi}{2} \right) \cdot \mathbf{v} = e\mathbf{i} \cdot (-\mathbf{i}) = -e$.

3. $\nabla f(x, y, z) = 2x\mathbf{i} + 2y\mathbf{j} + 2z\mathbf{k} \Rightarrow \nabla f(1, 1, 1) = 2\mathbf{i} + 2\mathbf{j} + 2\mathbf{k}$.

   The vector v is a not a unit vector, so $\mathbf{u} = \dfrac{\mathbf{v}}{\|\mathbf{v}\|} = \dfrac{\sqrt{3}}{3}\mathbf{i} - \dfrac{\sqrt{3}}{3}\mathbf{j} + \dfrac{\sqrt{3}}{3}\mathbf{k}$.

   Finally, the directional derivative is

   $$D_{\mathbf{u}} f(1, 1, 1) = \nabla f(1, 1, 1) \cdot \mathbf{u} = (2\mathbf{i} + 2\mathbf{j} + 2\mathbf{k}) \cdot \left(\frac{\sqrt{3}}{3}\mathbf{i} - \frac{\sqrt{3}}{3}\mathbf{j} + \frac{\sqrt{3}}{3}\mathbf{k} \right) = \frac{2\sqrt{3}}{3}.$$

4. $\nabla f(x, y) = 3\mathbf{i} + 10y\mathbf{j} \Rightarrow \nabla f(2, 1) = 3\mathbf{i} + 10\mathbf{j}$.

5. $\nabla f(x, y) = \dfrac{2x}{x^2 - y}\mathbf{i} - \dfrac{1}{x^2 - y}\mathbf{j} \Rightarrow \nabla f(2, 3) = 4\mathbf{i} - \mathbf{j}$.

6. $\nabla f(x, y, z) = 6x\mathbf{i} - 10y\mathbf{j} + 4z\mathbf{k} \Rightarrow \nabla f(1, 1, -2) = 6\mathbf{i} - 10\mathbf{j} - 8\mathbf{k}$.

7. The maximum value is the magnitude of the gradient. So, we have

   $$\nabla f(x, y) = (2x + 2y)\mathbf{i} + 2x\mathbf{j} \Rightarrow \nabla f(1, 0) = 2\mathbf{i} + 2\mathbf{j} \text{ and } \|\nabla f(1, 0)\| = \sqrt{4 + 4} = 2\sqrt{2}.$$

8. The maximum value is the magnitude of the gradient. So, we have

   $$\nabla f(x, y, z) = y^2 z^2 \mathbf{i} + 2xyz^2 \mathbf{j} + 2xy^2 z \mathbf{k} \Rightarrow \nabla f(2, 1, 1) = \mathbf{i} + 4\mathbf{j} + 4\mathbf{k}$$

   and, thus,

   $$\|\nabla f(2, 1, 1)\| = \sqrt{1 + 16 + 16} = \sqrt{33}.$$

9. The gradient is $\nabla f(x, y) = -2\mathbf{i} - 3\mathbf{j}$. The level curve is $2x + 3y = 0$. At $(0, 0)$, the gradient $\nabla f(0, 0) = -2\mathbf{i} - 3\mathbf{j}$ is normal to this line.

10. The gradient points in the direction of maximum increase in heat.

Therefore, $\nabla T = \dfrac{y^2 - x^2}{\left(x^2 + y^2\right)^2}\mathbf{i} - \dfrac{2xy}{\left(x^2 + y^2\right)^2}\mathbf{j} \Rightarrow \nabla T(3, 4) = \dfrac{7}{625}\mathbf{i} - \dfrac{24}{625}\mathbf{j}$ is the direction.

Lesson 16

1. Let $F(x, y, z) = 3x + 4y + 12z$ and, hence, $\nabla F = 3\mathbf{i} + 4\mathbf{j} + 12\mathbf{k}$.

We have $\|\nabla F\| = \sqrt{9 + 16 + 144} = \sqrt{169} = 13$.

So, a unit normal vector to this plane is $\mathbf{n} = \dfrac{\nabla F}{\|\nabla F\|} = \dfrac{3}{13}\mathbf{i} + \dfrac{4}{13}\mathbf{j} + \dfrac{12}{13}\mathbf{k}$.

2. Let $F(x, y, z) = x^2 + y^2 + z^2 - 6$ and, hence, $\nabla F = 2x\mathbf{i} + 2y\mathbf{j} + 2z\mathbf{k}$.

We have $\nabla F(1, 1, 2) = 2\mathbf{i} + 2\mathbf{j} + 4\mathbf{k}$ and $\|\nabla F(1, 1, 2)\| = \sqrt{4 + 4 + 16} = \sqrt{24} = 2\sqrt{6}$.

So, a unit normal vector to this surface is $\mathbf{n} = \dfrac{\nabla F}{\|\nabla F\|} = \dfrac{1}{\sqrt{6}}\mathbf{i} + \dfrac{1}{\sqrt{6}}\mathbf{j} + \dfrac{2}{\sqrt{6}}\mathbf{k}$.

3. Let $F(x, y, z) = -x\sin y + z - 4$ and, hence, $\nabla F = -\sin y\mathbf{i} - x\cos y\mathbf{j} + \mathbf{k}$.

A normal vector to the surface at the point $\left(6, \dfrac{\pi}{6}, 7\right)$ is $\nabla F\left(6, \dfrac{\pi}{6}, 7\right) = -\dfrac{1}{2}\mathbf{i} - 3\sqrt{3}\mathbf{j} + \mathbf{k}$.

4. Let $F(x, y, z) = x^3 - z$ and, hence, $\nabla F = 3x^2\mathbf{i} - \mathbf{k}$.

Hence, a normal vector to the surface at the point $(2, -1, 8)$ is $\nabla F(2, -1, 8) = 12\mathbf{i} - \mathbf{k}$.

5. Let $F(x, y, z) = x^2 + y^2 + 3 - z$. We have $F_x = 2x, F_y = 2y, F_z = -1$.

At the point $(2, 1, 8)$, $F_y(2, 1, 8) = 2$, $F_y(2, 1, 8) = 2$, and $F_z(2, 1, 8) = -1$.

So, the tangent plane is $4(x - 2) + 2(y - 1) - 1(z - 8) = 0$, which simplifies to $4x + 2y - z = 2$.

6. Let $F(x, y, z) = \dfrac{y}{x} - z$. We have $F_x = -\dfrac{y}{x^2}, F_y = \dfrac{1}{x}, F_z = -1$.

At the point $(1, 2, 2)$, $F_x(1, 2, 2) = -2$, $F_y(1, 2, 2) = 1$, and $F_z(1, 2, 2) = -1$.

So, the tangent plane is $-2(x-1) + (y-2) - 1(z-2) = 0$, which simplifies to $2x - y + z = 2$.

7. Let $F(x, y, z) = x^2 - y^2 + 2z^2$. We have $F_x = 2x, F_y = -2y, F_z = 4z$.

At the point $(1, 3, -2)$, $F_x(1, 3, -2) = 2$, $F_y(1, 3, -2) = -6$, and $F_z(1, 3, -2) = -8$.

So, the tangent plane is $2(x-1) - 6(y-3) - 8(z+2) = 0$, which simplifies to $x - 3y - 4z = 0$.

8. Let $F(x, y, z) = x^2 + 4y^2 + z^2 - 36$. We have $F_x = 2x, F_y = 8y, F_z = 2z$.

At the point $(2, -2, 4)$, $F_x(2, -2, 4) = 4$, $F_y(2, -2, 4) = -16$, and $F_z(2, -2, 4) = 8$.

So, the tangent plane is $4(x-2) - 16(y+2) + 8(z-4) = 0$, which simplifies to $x - 4y + 2z = 18$.

9. Let $F(x, y, z) = 3 - x^2 - y^2 + 6y - z$. We have $\nabla F = -2x\mathbf{i} + (-2y+6)\mathbf{j} - \mathbf{k}$.

The tangent plane will be horizontal if $-2x = 0$ and $-2y + 6 = 0$. Thus, $x = 0, y = 3$, and $z = 3 - 0^2 - 3^2 + 6(3) = 12$. The point is $(0, 3, 12)$, which is the vertex of the paraboloid.

10. Let $F(x, y, z) = xy + \dfrac{1}{x} + \dfrac{1}{y} - z$. We have $\nabla F = \left(y - \dfrac{1}{x^2}\right)\mathbf{i} + \left(x - \dfrac{1}{y^2}\right)\mathbf{j} - \mathbf{k}$.

The tangent plane will be horizontal if $y = \dfrac{1}{x^2}$ and $x = \dfrac{1}{y^2}$. Thus, $x = \dfrac{1}{y^2} = x^4 \Rightarrow x = 1, y = 1, z = 3$.
The point is $(1, 1, 3)$.

Lesson 17

1. The constraint is $g(x, y) = x + 2y - 5 = 0$. $\nabla f = \lambda \nabla g \Rightarrow 2x\mathbf{i} + 2y\mathbf{j} = \lambda(\mathbf{i} + 2\mathbf{j})$.

We solve the equations $2x = \lambda, 2y = 2\lambda, x + 2y - 5 = 0$ and obtain $\lambda = 2, x = 1, y = 2$. The minimum value is $f(1, 2) = 1^2 + 2^2 = 5$.

2. The constraint is $g(x, y) = 2y - x^2 = 0$. $\nabla f = \lambda \nabla g \Rightarrow 2x\mathbf{i} - 2y\mathbf{j} = \lambda(-2x\mathbf{i} + 2\mathbf{j})$.

We solve the equations $2x = -2\lambda x, -2y = 2\lambda, 2y - x^2 = 0$ and obtain $\lambda = -1, x = \sqrt{2}, y = 1$. The maximum value is $f(\sqrt{2}, 1) = 2 - 1 = 1$.

3. $g(x, y) = 2x + y = 100$. $\nabla f = \lambda \nabla g \Rightarrow (2 + 2y)\mathbf{i} + (2x + 1)\mathbf{j} = \lambda(2\mathbf{i} + \mathbf{j})$.

We solve the equations $2 + 2y = 2\lambda, 2x + 1 = \lambda, 2x + y = 100$ and obtain $\lambda = 51, x = 25, y = 50$. The maximum value is $f(25, 50) = 2(25) + 2(25)(50) + 50 = 2600$.

4. $g(x, y) = x + y + z = 9$. $\nabla f = \lambda \nabla g$ gives rise to the equations $2x = \lambda, 2y = \lambda, 2z = \lambda, x + y + z = 9$.

Solving these equations, we obtain $\lambda = 6, x = 3, y = 3, z = 3$. The minimum value is $f(3, 3, 3) = 27$.

5. $g(x, y) = x + y + z = 3$. $\nabla f = \lambda \nabla g$ gives rise to the equations $yz = \lambda, xz = \lambda, xy = \lambda, x + y + z = 3$.

Solving these equations, we obtain $\lambda = 1, x = 1, y = 1, z = 1$. The maximum value is $f(1, 1, 1) = 1$.

6. We minimize the square of the distance. $f(x, y) = x^2 + y^2$ with the constraint $g(x, y) = x + y - 1 = 0$. $\nabla f = \lambda \nabla g$ gives rise to the equations $2x = \lambda, 2y = \lambda, x + y = 1$.

Solving these equations, $\lambda = 1, x = \dfrac{1}{2}, y = \dfrac{1}{2}$. The minimum distance is therefore $\sqrt{\left(\dfrac{1}{2}\right)^2 + \left(\dfrac{1}{2}\right)^2} = \dfrac{\sqrt{2}}{2}$.

7. We minimize the square of the distance. $f(x, y) = x^2 + (y - 3)^2$ with the constraint $g(x, y) = y - x^2 = 0$. $\nabla f = \lambda \nabla g$ gives rise to the equations $2x = \lambda(-2x), 2(y - 3) = \lambda, y = x^2$.

If $x = 0, y = 0$, then $f(0, 0) = 9$. If $x \neq 0, \lambda = -1, y = \dfrac{5}{2}, x = \pm\sqrt{\dfrac{5}{2}}$. $f\left(\pm\sqrt{\dfrac{5}{2}}, \dfrac{5}{2}\right) = \dfrac{5}{2} + \left(\dfrac{-1}{2}\right)^2 = \dfrac{11}{4}$.

The minimum distance is therefore $\dfrac{\sqrt{11}}{2}$.

8. Minimize $C(x, y, z) = 5xy + 3(2xz + 2yz + xy)$ subject to the constraint $g(x, y, z) = xyz = 480$. $\nabla C = \lambda \nabla g$ gives rise to the equations $8y + 6z = \lambda yz, 8x + 6z = \lambda xz, 6x + 6y = \lambda xy, xyz = 480$.

Solving these equations, you obtain $x = y = \sqrt[3]{360}, z = \dfrac{4}{3}\sqrt[3]{360}$.

The dimensions are $\sqrt[3]{360} \times \sqrt[3]{360} \times \dfrac{4}{3}\sqrt[3]{360}$ feet.

Lesson 18

1. The gradient is $\nabla f(x, y) = 75x^{-\frac{1}{4}}y^{\frac{1}{4}}\mathbf{i} + 25x^{\frac{3}{4}}y^{-\frac{3}{4}}\mathbf{j}$. The constraint is $g(x, y) = 150x + 250y = 500,000$.
    So, $\nabla g(x, y) = 150\mathbf{i} + 250\mathbf{j}$. Setting $\nabla f = \lambda \nabla g$ produces the system of equations

    $$75x^{-\frac{1}{4}}y^{\frac{1}{4}} = 150\lambda$$
    $$25x^{\frac{3}{4}}y^{-\frac{3}{4}} = 250\lambda$$
    $$150x + 250y = 50,000.$$

    Solving these equations, you obtain $x = 250$, $y = 50$, and $\lambda = \dfrac{5^{\frac{3}{4}}}{10} \approx 0.334$. The maximum production
    level is therefore

    $$f(250, 50) = 100(250)^{\frac{3}{4}}(50)^{\frac{1}{4}} = 5000(5)^{\frac{3}{4}} \approx 16,719 \text{ units.}$$

2. There are two cases. For points *on the circle* $x^2 + y^2 = 10$, you can use Lagrange multipliers to find the
    maximum and minimum values. If $y \neq 0$, then you obtain $x = -1$, $y = \pm 3$, and $\lambda = 2$. Hence, the maximum
    value of f is 24, which occurs at $(-1, 3)$ and $(-1, -3)$. If $y = 0$, you obtain the minimum value of f,
    approximately 6.675, and this value occurs at $\left(\sqrt{10}, 0\right)$. For points *inside the circle*, you can use partial
    derivatives to conclude that the function has a relative minimum of 2 at the point $(1, 0)$. Combining these
    results, f has a maximum of 24 at $(-1, \pm 3)$ and a minimum of 2 at $(1, 0)$.

3. We want to maximize $f(a, b, c) = \dfrac{4\pi}{3}abc$ subject to the constraint $g(a, b, c) = a + b + c = K$.
    Setting $\nabla f = \lambda \nabla g$ produces the equations

    $$\frac{4\pi bc}{3} = \lambda, \frac{4\pi ac}{3} = \lambda, \frac{4\pi ab}{3} = \lambda, a + b + c = K.$$

    Solving these equations, you obtain $a = b = c = \dfrac{K}{3}$. So, the ellipse is a sphere.

4. We want to minimize $A(h, r) = 2\pi rh + 2\pi r^2$ subject to the constraint $g(h, r) = \pi r^2 h = V_0$. Setting
    $\nabla A = \lambda \nabla g$ produces the equations

    $$2\pi h + 4\pi r = \lambda 2\pi rh, 2\pi r = \lambda \pi r^2, \pi r^2 h = V_0.$$

    Solving these equations, you obtain $h = 2r$ and $V_0 = 2\pi r^3$. The dimensions are $r = \sqrt[3]{\dfrac{V_0}{2\pi}}$ and $h = 2\sqrt[3]{\dfrac{V_0}{2\pi}}$.

5. Minimize the square of the distance $f(x, y, z) = (x-2)^2 + (y-1)^2 + (z-1)^2$ subject to the constraint $g(x, y, z) = x + y + z = 1$. Setting $\nabla f = \lambda \nabla g$ produces

$$2(x-2) = \lambda, 2(y-1) = \lambda, 2(z-1) = \lambda, x + y + z = 1.$$

Solving these equations, you obtain $x = 1$, $y = z = 0$, and $\lambda = -2$. The point on the plane is $(1, 0, 0)$, and the desired distance is $d = \sqrt{(1-2)^2 + (0-1)^2 + (0-1)^2} = \sqrt{3}$.

Lesson 19

1. $\int_0^x (x+2y)\,dy = \left[xy + y^2\right]_0^x = x^2 + x^2 - 0 = 2x^2$.

2. $\int_1^{2y} \dfrac{y}{x}\,dx = \left[y \ln|x|\right]_1^{2y} = y\ln|2y| - 0 = y\ln 2y, \; y > 0$.

3. $\int_0^1 \int_0^2 (x+y)\,dy\,dx = \int_0^1 \left[xy + \dfrac{1}{2}y^2\right]_0^2 dx = \int_0^1 (2x+2)\,dx = \left[x^2 + 2x\right]_0^1 = 1 + 2 = 3$.

4. $\int_0^{\pi/2} \int_0^1 y\cos x\,dy\,dx = \int_0^{\pi/2} \left[\dfrac{y^2}{2}\cos x\right]_0^1 dx = \int_0^{\pi/2} \dfrac{1}{2}\cos x\,dx = \left[\dfrac{1}{2}\sin x\right]_0^{\pi/2} = \dfrac{1}{2}$.

5. $\int_1^3 \int_0^y \dfrac{4}{x^2+y^2}\,dx\,dy = \int_1^3 \left[\dfrac{4}{y}\arctan\left(\dfrac{x}{y}\right)\right]_0^y dy = \int_1^3 \dfrac{4}{y}\left(\dfrac{\pi}{4}\right)dy = \int_1^3 \dfrac{\pi}{y}\,dy = \left[\pi \ln y\right]_1^3 = \pi \ln 3$.

6. $A = \int_0^4 \int_0^{(2-\sqrt{x})^2} dy\,dx = \int_0^4 \left[y\right]_0^{(2-\sqrt{x})^2} dx = \int_0^4 (4 - 4\sqrt{x} + x)\,dx = \left[4x - \dfrac{8}{3}x\sqrt{x} + \dfrac{x^2}{2}\right]_0^4 = \dfrac{8}{3}$.

7. $\int_0^1 \int_{-\sqrt{1-y^2}}^{\sqrt{1-y^2}} dx\,dy = \int_0^1 \left(2\sqrt{1-y^2}\right)dy = \dfrac{\pi}{2}$ (area of semicircle).

Reversing the order of integration, $\int_0^1 \int_{-\sqrt{1-y^2}}^{\sqrt{1-y^2}} dx\,dy = \int_{-1}^1 \int_0^{\sqrt{1-x^2}} dy\,dx = \int_{-1}^1 \sqrt{1-x^2}\,dx = \dfrac{\pi}{2}$.

8. $\int_0^2 \int_{x/2}^1 dy\,dx = \int_0^2 \left(1 - \dfrac{x}{2}\right)dx = \left[x - \dfrac{x^2}{4}\right]_0^2 = 1$.

Reversing the order of integration, $\int_0^1 \int_0^{2y} dx\,dy = \int_0^1 2y\,dy = \left[y^2\right]_0^1 = 1$.

9. We must reverse the order of integration.

$$\int_0^1 \int_{2x}^2 4e^{y^2}\,dy\,dx = \int_0^2 \int_0^{y/2} 4e^{y^2}\,dx\,dy = \int_0^2 \left[4xe^{y^2}\right]_0^{y/2} dy = \int_0^2 2ye^{y^2}\,dy = \left[e^{y^2}\right]_0^2 = e^4 - 1.$$

10. We must reverse the order of integration.

$$\int_0^2 \int_{y^2}^4 \sqrt{x}\,\sin x\,dx\,dy = \int_0^4 \int_0^{\sqrt{x}} \sqrt{x}\,\sin x\,dy\,dx = \int_0^4 \left[y\sqrt{x}\,\sin x \right]_0^{\sqrt{x}} dx = \int_0^4 x\sin x\,dx.$$

Next, use integration by parts to obtain $\left[\sin x - x\cos x \right]_0^4 = \sin 4 - 4\cos 4 \approx 1.858.$

Lesson 20

1. $V = \int_0^4 \int_0^2 \dfrac{y}{2}\,dy\,dx = \int_0^4 \left[\dfrac{y^2}{4} \right]_0^2 dx = \int_0^4 dx = 4.$

2. $V = \int_0^1 \int_0^y \left(1 - xy\right) dx\,dy = \int_0^1 \left[x - \dfrac{x^2 y}{2} \right]_0^y dy = \int_0^1 \left(y - \dfrac{y^3}{2} \right) dy = \left[\dfrac{y^2}{2} - \dfrac{y^4}{8} \right]_0^1 = \dfrac{3}{8}.$

3. $V = \int_0^1 \int_0^x xy\,dy\,dx \ \left(= \dfrac{1}{8} \right).$

4. We calculate the volume of the sphere in the first octant and multiply the answer by 8:

$$V = 8 \int_0^r \int_0^{\sqrt{r^2 - x^2}} \sqrt{r^2 - x^2 - y^2}\,dy\,dx \ \left(= \dfrac{4}{3}\pi r^3 \right).$$

5. $V = \int_0^2 \int_0^{4 - x^2} \left(4 - x^2\right) dy\,dx \ \left(= \dfrac{256}{15} \right).$

6. Notice that we use integration by parts in the solution.

$$\int_0^1 \int_{y/2}^{1/2} e^{-x^2}\,dx\,dy = \int_0^{1/2} \int_0^{2x} e^{-x^2}\,dy\,dx = \int_0^{1/2} 2x e^{-x^2}\,dx = \left[-e^{-x^2} \right]_0^{1/2} = 1 - e^{-1/4}.$$

7. $\int_0^2 \int_{x^2/2}^2 \sqrt{y}\,\cos y\,dy\,dx = \int_0^2 \int_0^{\sqrt{2y}} \sqrt{y}\,\cos y\,dx\,dy = \int_0^2 \sqrt{2y}\,\sqrt{y}\,\cos y\,dy = \sqrt{2}\int_0^2 y\cos y\,dy$

$= \sqrt{2}\left[\cos y + y\sin y \right]_0^2 = \sqrt{2}\left[\cos 2 + 2\sin 2 - 1 \right].$

8. The area of the region is 8. The average value is therefore

$$\text{Average} = \dfrac{1}{8} \int_0^4 \int_0^2 x\,dy\,dx = \dfrac{1}{8} \int_0^4 2x\,dx = \dfrac{1}{8}\left[x^2 \right]_0^4 = 2.$$

9. The area of the region is π^2. The average value is

$$\text{Average} = \frac{1}{\pi^2} \int_0^\pi \int_0^\pi \sin(x+y)\,dy\,dx = \frac{1}{\pi^2} \int_0^\pi \left[-\cos(x+y)\right]_0^\pi dx$$

$$= \frac{1}{\pi^2} \int_0^\pi \left(-\cos(x+\pi) + \cos x\right) dx = \frac{1}{\pi^2} \int_0^\pi 2\cos x\,dx = \frac{1}{\pi^2}\left[2\sin x\right]_0^\pi = 0.$$

10. The limits of integration for the inside integral cannot contain the variable of integration, in this case, y.

Lesson 21

1. $\displaystyle\int_0^3 \int_0^{\sqrt{9-x^2}} x\,dy\,dx = \int_0^{\pi/2} \int_0^3 (r\cos\theta)r\,dr\,d\theta = \int_0^{\pi/2}\left[\frac{r^3}{3}\cos\theta\right]_0^3 d\theta = 9\left[\sin\theta\right]_0^{\pi/2} = 9.$

2. $\displaystyle\int_{-2}^2 \int_0^{\sqrt{4-x^2}} \left(x^2+y^2\right) dy\,dx = \int_0^\pi \int_0^2 r^2 r\,dr\,d\theta = \int_0^\pi \left[\frac{r^4}{4}\right]_0^2 d\theta = \int_0^\pi 4\,d\theta = 4\pi.$

3. Note that $y = \sqrt{2x - x^2} = \sqrt{1-(x-1)^2} \Rightarrow (x-1)^2 + y^2 = 1.$

The region is the semicircle given by $r = 2\cos\theta, 0 \le \theta \le \frac{\pi}{2}$. So, we have

$$\int_0^2 \int_0^{\sqrt{2x-x^2}} xy\,dy\,dx = \int_0^{\pi/2} \int_0^{2\cos\theta} (r\cos\theta)(r\sin\theta)r\,dr\,d\theta$$

$$= \int_0^{\pi/2} \int_0^{2\cos\theta} r^3 \cos\theta \sin\theta\,dr\,d\theta$$

$$= \int_0^{\pi/2} \left[\frac{r^4}{4}\cos\theta\sin\theta\right]_0^{2\cos\theta} d\theta$$

$$= 4\int_0^{\pi/2} \cos^5\theta \sin\theta\,d\theta$$

$$= \left[-\frac{4}{6}\cos^6\theta\right]_0^{\pi/2} = \frac{2}{3}.$$

4. The graph is a circle of radius 3. We have

$$A = \int_0^\pi \int_0^{6\cos\theta} r\,dr\,d\theta = \int_0^\pi 18\cos^2\theta\,d\theta = 9\int_0^\pi (1+\cos 2\theta)\,d\theta = 9\left[\theta + \frac{\sin 2\theta}{2}\right]_0^\pi = 9\pi.$$

5. $A = \int_0^{2\pi} \int_2^4 r \, dr \, d\theta = \int_0^{2\pi} \left[\frac{r^2}{2} \right]_2^4 d\theta = \int_0^{2\pi} 6 \, d\theta = 12\pi.$

6. We will calculate the area of one leaf and multiply the answer by 3.

$$A = 3 \int_0^{\pi/3} \int_0^{2\sin 3\theta} r \, dr \, d\theta = \frac{3}{2} \int_0^{\pi/3} 4 \sin^2 3\theta \, d\theta = 3 \int_0^{\pi/3} (1 - \cos 6\theta) \, d\theta = 3 \left[\theta - \frac{\sin 6\theta}{6} \right]_0^{\pi/3} = \pi.$$

7. The volume is

$$V = \int_0^{\pi/2} \int_0^1 (r\cos\theta)(r\sin\theta) r \, dr \, d\theta = \frac{1}{2} \int_0^{\pi/2} \int_0^1 r^3 \sin 2\theta \, dr \, d\theta$$

$$= \frac{1}{8} \int_0^{\pi/2} \sin 2\theta \, d\theta = \left[-\frac{\cos 2\theta}{16} \right]_0^{\pi/2} = \frac{1}{8}.$$

8. $V = \int_0^{2\pi} \int_0^5 r^2 \, dr \, d\theta = \int_0^{2\pi} \frac{125}{3} d\theta = \frac{250\pi}{3}.$

9. $V = \int_0^{2\pi} \int_1^4 \sqrt{16 - r^2} \, r \, dr \, d\theta = \int_0^{2\pi} \left[-\frac{\left(16 - r^2\right)^{3/2}}{3} \right]_1^4 d\theta = \int_0^{2\pi} 5\sqrt{15} \, d\theta = 10\sqrt{15}\pi.$

10. $r = 1 = 2\cos\theta \Rightarrow \theta = \pm\frac{\pi}{3}.$ We double the integral for the area in the first quadrant:

$$A = 2 \int_0^{\pi/3} \int_1^{2\cos\theta} r \, dr \, d\theta \left(= \frac{\pi}{3} + \frac{\sqrt{3}}{2} \right).$$

Lesson 22

1. $m = \int_0^2 \int_0^2 xy \, dy \, dx = \int_0^2 \left[\frac{xy^2}{2} \right]_0^2 dx = \int_0^2 2x \, dx = \left[x^2 \right]_0^2 = 4.$

2. $m = \int_0^{\pi/2} \int_0^1 (r\cos\theta)(r\sin\theta) r \, dr \, d\theta = \int_0^{\pi/2} \left[\cos\theta \sin\theta \frac{r^4}{4} \right]_0^1 d\theta = \left[\frac{1}{4} \frac{\sin^2\theta}{2} \right]_0^{\pi/2} = \frac{1}{8}.$

3. We have the following results:

$$m = \int_0^3 \int_0^y 4y \, dx \, dy = 36$$

$$M_x = \int_0^3 \int_0^y 4y^2 \, dx \, dy = 81$$

$$M_y = \int_0^3 \int_0^y 4xy \, dx \, dy = \frac{81}{2}$$

$$\bar{x} = \frac{M_y}{m} = \frac{9}{8}, \ \bar{y} = \frac{M_x}{m} = \frac{9}{4}, \ (\bar{x}, \bar{y}) = \left(\frac{9}{8}, \frac{9}{4}\right).$$

4. We have the following results:

$$m = \int_0^3 \int_0^y 4x \, dx \, dy = 18$$

$$M_x = \int_0^3 \int_0^y 4xy \, dx \, dy = \frac{81}{2}$$

$$M_y = \int_0^3 \int_0^y 4x^2 \, dx \, dy = 27$$

$$\bar{x} = \frac{M_y}{m} = \frac{3}{2}, \ \bar{y} = \frac{M_x}{m} = \frac{9}{4}, \ (\bar{x}, \bar{y}) = \left(\frac{3}{2}, \frac{9}{4}\right).$$

5. We have the following results:

$$m = \int_0^1 \int_0^{\sqrt{x}} 5y \, dy \, dx = \frac{5}{4}$$

$$M_x = \int_0^1 \int_0^{\sqrt{x}} 5y^2 \, dy \, dx = \frac{2}{3}$$

$$M_y = \int_0^1 \int_0^{\sqrt{x}} 5xy \, dy \, dx = \frac{5}{6}$$

$$\bar{x} = \frac{M_y}{m} = \frac{2}{3}, \ \bar{y} = \frac{M_x}{m} = \frac{8}{15}, \ (\bar{x}, \bar{y}) = \left(\frac{2}{3}, \frac{8}{15}\right).$$

6. We have the following results:

$$m = \int_0^2 \int_0^{x^2} 3xy \, dy \, dx = 16$$

$$M_x = \int_0^2 \int_0^{x^2} 3xy^2 \, dy \, dx = 32$$

$$M_y = \int_0^2 \int_0^{x^2} 3x^2 y \, dy \, dx = \frac{192}{7}$$

$$\bar{x} = \frac{M_y}{m} = \frac{12}{7}, \ \bar{y} = \frac{M_x}{m} = 2, \ (\bar{x}, \bar{y}) = \left(\frac{12}{7}, 2\right).$$

7. We use polar coordinates, as follows:

$$m = \int_0^4 \int_0^{\sqrt{16-x^2}} 3\left(x^2+y^2\right) dy\, dx = \int_0^{\pi/2} \int_0^4 3r^3\, dr\, d\theta = 96\pi$$

$$M_x = \int_0^4 \int_0^{\sqrt{16-x^2}} 3\left(x^2+y^2\right) y\, dy\, dx = \int_0^{\pi/2} \int_0^4 3r^4 \sin\theta\, dr\, d\theta = \frac{3072}{5}$$

$M_y = M_x$ by symmetry

$$\overline{x} = \overline{y} = \frac{M_x}{m} = \frac{32}{5\pi}, \left(\overline{x}, \overline{y}\right) = \left(\frac{32}{5\pi}, \frac{32}{5\pi}\right).$$

Lesson 23

1. $f_x = 2, f_y = 2, \sqrt{1+\left(f_x\right)^2+\left(f_y\right)^2} = \sqrt{1+4+4} = 3.$

The surface area is $S = \int_0^4 \int_0^{4-x} 3\, dy\, dx = 3\int_0^4 (4-x)\, dx = 3\left[4x - \frac{x^2}{2}\right]_0^4 = 24.$

2. $f_x = 2, f_y = -3, \sqrt{1+\left(f_x\right)^2+\left(f_y\right)^2} = \sqrt{1+4+9} = \sqrt{14}.$

The surface area is $S = \int_0^3 \int_0^3 \sqrt{14}\, dy\, dx = 3\int_0^3 \sqrt{14}\, dx = 9\sqrt{14}.$

3. $f_x = 2, f_y = -3, \sqrt{1+\left(f_x\right)^2+\left(f_y\right)^2} = \sqrt{1+4+9} = \sqrt{14}.$

We use polar coordinates. $S = \int_0^{2\pi} \int_0^3 \sqrt{14}\, r\, dr\, d\theta = \int_0^{2\pi} \frac{9\sqrt{14}}{2}\, d\theta = 9\sqrt{14}\pi.$

4. $f_x = -3, f_y = -2, \sqrt{1+\left(f_x\right)^2+\left(f_y\right)^2} = \sqrt{1+9+4} = \sqrt{14}.$

The surface area is $S = \int_0^8 \int_0^{12-3x/2} \sqrt{14}\, dy\, dx = 48\sqrt{14}.$

5. $f_x = -2x, f_y = -2y, \sqrt{1+\left(f_x\right)^2+\left(f_y\right)^2} = \sqrt{1+4x^2+4y^2}.$

In polar coordinates, $S = \int_0^{\pi/2} \int_0^4 \sqrt{1+4r^2}\, r\, dr\, d\theta \left(= \frac{\pi}{24}\left(65\sqrt{65}-1\right)\right).$

6. $f_x = 2x, f_y = 2, \sqrt{1+\left(f_x\right)^2+\left(f_y\right)^2} = \sqrt{1+4x^2+4} = \sqrt{5+4x^2}.$

We have $S = \int_0^1 \int_0^x \sqrt{5+4x^2}\, dy\, dx \left(= \frac{1}{12}\left(27-5\sqrt{5}\right)\right).$

7. $f_x = -2x$, $f_y = -2y$, $\sqrt{1+\left(f_x\right)^2+\left(f_y\right)^2} = \sqrt{1+4x^2+4y^2}$.

In polar coordinates, $S = \int_0^{2\pi}\int_0^3 \sqrt{1+4r^2}\; r\,dr\,d\theta\left(=\dfrac{\pi}{6}\left(37\sqrt{37}-1\right)\right)$.

8. $f_x = e^x$, $f_y = 0$, $\sqrt{1+\left(f_x\right)^2+\left(f_y\right)^2} = \sqrt{1+e^{2x}}$.

The surface area is given by $S = \int_0^1\int_0^1 \sqrt{1+e^{2x}}\; dy\,dx\; (\approx 2.0035)$.

9. We calculate the surface area as follows.

$$f_x = \frac{kx}{\sqrt{x^2+y^2}},\; f_y = \frac{ky}{\sqrt{x^2+y^2}},\; \sqrt{1+\left(f_x\right)^2+\left(f_y\right)^2} = \sqrt{1+\frac{k^2x^2}{x^2+y^2}+\frac{k^2y^2}{x^2+y^2}} = \sqrt{1+k^2}.$$

$$S = \iint_R \sqrt{1+k^2}\; dA = \sqrt{1+k^2}\iint_R dA = \sqrt{1+k^2}\,(\text{area of circle}) = \sqrt{1+k^2}\,\pi r^2 = \pi r^2\sqrt{1+k^2}.$$

Lesson 24

1. $\int_0^5\int_0^2\int_0^1 dy\,dx\,dz = \int_0^5\int_0^2 \left[y\right]_0^1 dx\,dz = \int_0^5\int_0^2 dx\,dz = \int_0^5 \left[x\right]_0^2 dz = \int_0^5 2\,dz = \left[2z\right]_0^5 = 10$.

This is the volume of the box of dimensions $1 \times 2 \times 5$.

2. We have the following:

$$\int_0^3\int_0^2\int_0^1 (x+y+z)\,dx\,dz\,dy = \int_0^3\int_0^2 \left[\frac{x^2}{2}+yx+zx\right]_0^1 dz\,dy = \int_0^3\int_0^2 \left(\frac{1}{2}+y+z\right)dz\,dy$$

$$= \int_0^3\left[\frac{z}{2}+yz+\frac{z^2}{2}\right]_0^2 dy = \int_0^3 (1+2y+2)\,dy = \left[3y+y^2\right]_0^3 = 18.$$

3. We have the following:

$$\int_{-1}^1\int_{-1}^1\int_{-1}^1 x^2y^2z^2\,dx\,dy\,dz = \frac{1}{3}\int_{-1}^1\int_{-1}^1 \left[x^3y^2z^2\right]_{-1}^1 dy\,dz = \frac{2}{3}\int_{-1}^1\int_{-1}^1 y^2z^2\,dy\,dz$$

$$= \frac{2}{9}\int_{-1}^1 \left[y^3z^2\right]_{-1}^1 dz = \frac{4}{9}\int_{-1}^1 z^2\,dz = \frac{4}{27}\left[z^3\right]_{-1}^1 = \frac{8}{27}.$$

4. $V = \int_0^5\int_0^{5-x}\int_0^{5-x-y} dz\,dy\,dx\;\left(=\dfrac{125}{6}\right)$. Note: Other orders of integration are possible.

5. $V = \int_0^3 \int_0^{2x} \int_0^{9-x^2} dz\, dy\, dx \left(= \frac{81}{2} \right)$. Note: Other orders of integration are possible.

6. $V = \int_{-\sqrt{6}}^{\sqrt{6}} \int_{-\sqrt{6-x^2}}^{\sqrt{6-x^2}} \int_0^{6-x^2-y^2} dz\, dy\, dx \left(= 18\pi \right)$. Note: Other orders of integration are possible.

7. $m = \int_0^6 \int_0^{4-(2x/3)} \int_0^{2-(y/2)-(x/3)} 3\, dz\, dy\, dx \left(= 24 \right)$.

8. $m = \int_0^5 \int_0^{5-x} \int_0^{(15-3x-3y)/5} 3y\, dz\, dy\, dx \left(= \frac{375}{8} \right)$.

9. $\int_0^1 \int_{-1}^0 \int_0^{y^2} dz\, dy\, dx = \int_0^1 \int_0^1 \int_{-1}^{-\sqrt{z}} dy\, dz\, dx \left(= \frac{1}{3} \right)$.

10. $\int_0^4 \int_0^{(4-x)/2} \int_0^{(12-3x-6y)/4} dz\, dy\, dx = \int_0^3 \int_0^{(12-4z)/3} \int_0^{(12-4z-3x)/6} dy\, dx\, dz \left(= 4 \right)$.

Lesson 25

1. $x = r\cos\theta = 1\cos(-\pi) = -1$, $y = r\sin\theta = 1\sin(-\pi) = 0$, $z = -4$.

   The rectangular coordinates are $(x, y, z) = (-1, 0, -4)$.

2. $x = r\cos\theta = 3\cos\left(\frac{\pi}{4}\right) = \frac{3\sqrt{2}}{2}$, $y = r\sin\theta = 3\sin\left(\frac{\pi}{4}\right) = \frac{3\sqrt{2}}{2}$, $z = 1$.

   The rectangular coordinates are $(x, y, z) = \left(\frac{3\sqrt{2}}{2}, \frac{3\sqrt{2}}{2}, 1 \right)$.

3. $r^2 = \left(2\sqrt{2}\right)^2 + \left(-2\sqrt{2}\right)^2 = 8 + 8 = 16 \Rightarrow r = 4$. $\tan\theta = \frac{y}{x} = \frac{-2\sqrt{2}}{2\sqrt{2}} = -1$.

   Hence, $\theta = -\frac{\pi}{4}$ and the cylindrical coordinates are $(r, \theta, z) = \left(4, -\frac{\pi}{4}, 4 \right)$.

4. $x = r\cos\theta = 9 \Rightarrow r = 9\sec\theta$.

5. $r^2 + z^2 = x^2 + y^2 + z^2 = 5$, a sphere of radius $\sqrt{5}$.

6. $r = 2\sin\theta \Rightarrow r^2 = 2r\sin\theta \Rightarrow x^2 + y^2 = 2y.$ Completing the square, you obtain the cylinder $x^2 + (y-1)^2 = 1.$

7. We have the following:

$$2\int_0^{2\pi}\int_{R_2}^{R_1}\int_0^{\sqrt{R_1^2-r^2}} r\,dz\,dr\,d\theta = 2\int_0^{2\pi}\int_{R_2}^{R_1}\left[rz\right]_0^{\sqrt{R_1^2-r^2}}dr\,d\theta$$

$$= 2\int_0^{2\pi}\int_{R_2}^{R_1} r\sqrt{R_1^2-r^2}\,dr\,d\theta$$

$$= -\frac{2}{3}\int_0^{2\pi}\left[\left(R_1^2-r^2\right)^{3/2}\right]_{R_2}^{R_1}d\theta$$

$$= \frac{2}{3}\int_0^{2\pi}\left(R_1^2-R_2^2\right)^{3/2}d\theta$$

$$= \frac{4\pi}{3}\left(R_1^2-R_2^2\right)^{3/2}.$$

8. $\displaystyle\int_{-2}^{2}\int_{-\sqrt{4-x^2}}^{\sqrt{4-x^2}}\int_{x^2+y^2}^{4} x\,dz\,dy\,dx = \int_0^{2\pi}\int_0^{2}\int_{r^2}^{4}(r\cos\theta)r\,dz\,dr\,d\theta = \int_0^{2\pi}\int_0^{2}\int_{r^2}^{4} r^2\cos\theta\,dz\,dr\,d\theta.$

9. In the xy-plane, $2x = 2x^2 + 2y^2 \Rightarrow x^2 - x + y^2 = 0.$

Completing the square, you have the circle $\left(x-\frac{1}{2}\right)^2 + y^2 = \left(\frac{1}{2}\right)^2.$

In polar coordinates, the circle is $r = \cos\theta.$ Hence, $V = \displaystyle\int_0^{\pi}\int_0^{\cos\theta}\int_{2r^2}^{2r\cos\theta} r\,dz\,dr\,d\theta.$

10. The two surfaces intersect when $x^2 + y^2 + z^2 = x^2 + y^2 + (x^2 + y^2) = 4.$

Hence, $x^2 + y^2 = 2,$ and the integral is $V = \displaystyle\int_0^{2\pi}\int_0^{\sqrt{2}}\int_r^{\sqrt{4-r^2}} r\,dz\,dr\,d\theta.$

Lesson 26

1. $x = 12\sin 0\cos\left(-\frac{\pi}{4}\right) = 0,\ y = 12\sin 0\sin\left(-\frac{\pi}{4}\right) = 0,\ z = 12\cos 0 = 12.$

The rectangular coordinates are $(x, y, z) = (0, 0, 12).$

2. $x = 5\sin\left(\dfrac{3\pi}{4}\right)\cos\left(\dfrac{\pi}{4}\right) = \dfrac{5}{2}$, $y = 5\sin\left(\dfrac{3\pi}{4}\right)\sin\left(\dfrac{\pi}{4}\right) = \dfrac{5}{2}$, $z = 5\cos\left(\dfrac{3\pi}{4}\right) = -\dfrac{5\sqrt{2}}{2}$.

The rectangular coordinates are $(x, y, z) = \left(\dfrac{5}{2}, \dfrac{5}{2}, -\dfrac{5\sqrt{2}}{2}\right)$.

3. $\rho = \sqrt{(-2)^2 + \left(2\sqrt{3}\right)^2 + 4^2} = \sqrt{32} = 4\sqrt{2}$. $\tan\theta = \dfrac{y}{x} = \dfrac{2\sqrt{3}}{-2} = -\sqrt{3}$.

So, $\theta = \dfrac{2\pi}{3}$. Finally, $\cos\phi = \dfrac{z}{\rho} = \dfrac{4}{4\sqrt{2}} = \dfrac{\sqrt{2}}{2} \Rightarrow \phi = \dfrac{\pi}{4}$.

The spherical coordinates are $(\rho, \theta, \phi) = \left(4\sqrt{2}, \dfrac{2\pi}{2}, \dfrac{\pi}{4}\right)$.

4. $z = \rho\cos\phi = 6 \Rightarrow \rho = 6\sec\phi$.

5. $\cos\phi = \cos\left(\dfrac{\pi}{6}\right) = \dfrac{\sqrt{3}}{2} = \dfrac{z}{\sqrt{x^2 + y^2 + z^2}}$.

Squaring both sides, we have $\dfrac{3}{4} = \dfrac{z^2}{x^2 + y^2 + z^2} \Rightarrow 3x^2 + 3y^2 - z^2 = 0$, $z \geq 0$, which is the upper nappe of a cone.

6. By sketching the solid, you see that $0 \leq \phi \leq \dfrac{\pi}{4}$ and $0 \leq \theta \leq 2\pi$.

For $z = 2$, we have $2 = \rho\cos\phi \Rightarrow \rho = 2\sec\phi$. Finally, for $z = 2 + \sqrt{4 - x^2 - y^2}$, $(z-2)^2 = 4 - x^2 - y^2$.

So, $x^2 + y^2 + z^2 = 4z \Rightarrow \rho^2 = 4\rho\cos\phi$, and the upper limit is $\rho = 4\cos\phi$. The integral is

$$\int_{-2}^{2}\int_{-\sqrt{4-x^2}}^{\sqrt{4-x^2}}\int_{2}^{2+\sqrt{4-x^2-y^2}} x\,dz\,dy\,dx = \int_{0}^{\pi/4}\int_{0}^{2\pi}\int_{2\sec\phi}^{4\cos\phi} (\rho\sin\phi\cos\theta)\rho^2\sin\phi\,d\rho\,d\theta\,d\phi,$$

which simplifies to $\displaystyle\int_{0}^{\pi/4}\int_{0}^{2\pi}\int_{2\sec\phi}^{4\cos\phi} \rho^3\sin^2\phi\cos\theta\,d\rho\,d\theta\,d\phi$.

7. We have the following:

$$\iiint_{Q} dV = \int_{0}^{2\pi}\int_{0}^{\pi/4}\int_{0}^{\sqrt{2}} \rho^2\sin\phi\,d\rho\,d\phi\,d\theta = \int_{0}^{2\pi}\int_{0}^{\pi/4}\left[\dfrac{\rho^3}{3}\sin\phi\right]_{0}^{\sqrt{2}} d\phi\,d\theta$$

$$= \int_{0}^{2\pi}\int_{0}^{\pi/4}\dfrac{2\sqrt{2}}{3}\sin\phi\,d\phi\,d\theta = \int_{0}^{2\pi}\left[\dfrac{2\sqrt{2}}{3}(-\cos\phi)\right]_{0}^{\pi/4} d\theta$$

$$= \int_{0}^{2\pi}\dfrac{2\sqrt{2}}{3}\left(-\dfrac{\sqrt{2}}{2} + 1\right)d\theta = \left(-\dfrac{2}{3} + \dfrac{2\sqrt{2}}{3}\right)(2\pi) = \dfrac{4\pi}{3}\left(\sqrt{2} - 1\right).$$

8. $V = \int_0^{2\pi} \int_{\pi/4}^{\pi/2} \int_0^3 \rho^2 \sin\phi \, d\rho \, d\phi \, d\theta.$

9. $V = \int_0^{2\pi} \int_0^{\pi} \int_0^{4\sin\phi} \rho^2 \sin\phi \, d\rho \, d\phi \, d\theta \left(= 16\pi^2\right).$

10. The distance from a point to the z-axis is $r = \sqrt{x^2 + y^2} = \rho\sin\phi.$ We set up the integral for the mass in the first octant and multiply by 8:

$$m = 8k \int_0^{\pi/2} \int_0^{\pi/2} \int_0^3 (\rho\sin\phi)\rho^2 \sin\phi \, d\rho \, d\phi \, d\theta = 8k \int_0^{\pi/2} \int_0^{\pi/2} \int_0^3 \rho^3 \sin^2\phi \, d\rho \, d\phi \, d\theta.$$

Lesson 27

1. The vectors make a 45° angle with the x-axis. They have constant length $\|\mathbf{F}\| = \sqrt{1^2 + 1^2} = \sqrt{2}.$

2. The vectors point in the direction from the origin to the point $(1, 1, 1)$. They have constant length $\|\mathbf{F}\| = \sqrt{1^2 + 1^2 + 1^2} = \sqrt{3}.$

3. $M = 5y^3, \; N = 15xy^2 \Rightarrow \dfrac{\partial N}{\partial x} = 15y^2 = \dfrac{\partial M}{\partial y}.$

Hence, the vector field is conservative.

4. $M = \dfrac{1}{\sqrt{x^2 + y^2}}, \; N = \dfrac{1}{\sqrt{x^2 + y^2}} \Rightarrow \dfrac{\partial N}{\partial x} = \dfrac{-x}{\left(x^2 + y^2\right)^{3/2}} \neq \dfrac{\partial M}{\partial y} = \dfrac{-y}{\left(x^2 + y^2\right)^{3/2}}.$

Hence, the vector field is not conservative.

5. $f_x = 2x, \; f_y = -\dfrac{1}{2}y \Rightarrow \mathbf{F}(x, y) = 2x\mathbf{i} - \dfrac{1}{2}y\mathbf{j}.$ Note that $\nabla f = \mathbf{F}.$

6. $f_x = 6yz, \; f_y = 6xz, \; f_z = 6xy \Rightarrow \mathbf{F}(x, y, z) = 6yz\mathbf{i} + +6xz\mathbf{j} + 6xy\mathbf{k}.$ Note that $\nabla f = \mathbf{F}.$

7. $f_x = 2xye^{x^2}, \; f_y = e^{x^2}, \; f_z = 1 \Rightarrow \mathbf{F}(x, y, z) = 2xye^{x^2}\mathbf{i} + e^{x^2}\mathbf{j} + \mathbf{k}.$ Note that $\nabla f = \mathbf{F}.$

8. $f_x(x,y) = y \Rightarrow f(x,y) = xy + g(y)$. $f_y(x,y) = x \Rightarrow f(x,y) = xy + h(x)$.

Hence, $f(x,y) = xy + K$ is the potential function.

9. We have

$$f_x(x,y) = \frac{x}{x^2 + y^2} \Rightarrow f(x,y) = \frac{1}{2}\ln(x^2 + y^2) + g(y)$$

$$f_y(x,y) = \frac{y}{x^2 + y^2} \Rightarrow f(x,y) = \frac{1}{2}\ln(x^2 + y^2) + h(x).$$

Hence, $f(x,y) = \frac{1}{2}\ln(x^2 + y^2) + K$ is the potential function.

10. We have

$$f_x(x,y) = 3x^2y^2 \Rightarrow f(x,y) = x^3y^2 + g(y)$$
$$f_y(x,y) = 2x^3y \Rightarrow f(x,y) = x^3y^2 + h(x).$$

Hence, $f(x,y) = x^3y^2 + K$ is the potential function.

Lesson 28

1. $\operatorname{curl} \mathbf{F} = \begin{vmatrix} \mathbf{i} & \mathbf{j} & \mathbf{k} \\ \dfrac{\partial}{\partial x} & \dfrac{\partial}{\partial y} & \dfrac{\partial}{\partial z} \\ xyz & xyz & xyz \end{vmatrix} = (xz - xy)\mathbf{i} - (yz - xy)\mathbf{j} + (yz - xz)\mathbf{k}.$

2. $\operatorname{curl} \mathbf{F} = \begin{vmatrix} \mathbf{i} & \mathbf{j} & \mathbf{k} \\ \dfrac{\partial}{\partial x} & \dfrac{\partial}{\partial y} & \dfrac{\partial}{\partial z} \\ e^x \sin y & -e^x \cos y & 0 \end{vmatrix} = (-e^x \cos y - e^x \cos y)\mathbf{k} = -2e^x \cos y\mathbf{k}.$

3. $\operatorname{curl} \mathbf{F} = \begin{vmatrix} \mathbf{i} & \mathbf{j} & \mathbf{k} \\ \dfrac{\partial}{\partial x} & \dfrac{\partial}{\partial y} & \dfrac{\partial}{\partial z} \\ -y & x & 0 \end{vmatrix} = (1 - (-1))\mathbf{k} = 2\mathbf{k}.$

4. The vector field is not conservative because its curl is nonzero:

$$\text{curl}\,\mathbf{F} = \begin{vmatrix} \mathbf{i} & \mathbf{j} & \mathbf{k} \\ \dfrac{\partial}{\partial x} & \dfrac{\partial}{\partial y} & \dfrac{\partial}{\partial z} \\ \sin z & \sin x & \sin y \end{vmatrix} = (\cos y)\mathbf{i} - (-\cos z)\mathbf{j} + \cos x\,\mathbf{k} \neq 0.$$

5. The vector field is conservative because the curl is zero.

$$f_x = xy^2z^2 \Rightarrow f = \frac{1}{2}x^2y^2z^2 + g(y, z)$$

$$f_y = x^2yz^2 \Rightarrow f = \frac{1}{2}x^2y^2z^2 + h(x, z)$$

$$f_z = x^2y^2z \Rightarrow f = \frac{1}{2}x^2y^2z^2 + k(x, y).$$

Hence, the potential function is $f(x, y, z) = \dfrac{1}{2}x^2y^2z^2 + K.$

6. $\text{div}\,\mathbf{F}(x, y) = \dfrac{\partial M}{\partial x} + \dfrac{\partial N}{\partial y} = 2x + 4y.$

7. $\text{div}\,\mathbf{F}(x, y, z) = \dfrac{\partial M}{\partial x} + \dfrac{\partial N}{\partial y} + \dfrac{\partial P}{\partial z} = \cos x - \sin y + 2z.$

8. $\mathbf{r}'(t) = 4\mathbf{i} + 3\mathbf{j} \Rightarrow ds = \sqrt{4^2 + 3^2}\, dt = 5\, dt.$

So, the line integral becomes $\displaystyle\int_C xy\, ds = \int_0^1 (4t)(3t)5\, dt = \int_0^1 60t^2\, dt = \left[20t^3\right]_0^1 = 20.$

9. $\mathbf{r}'(t) = \cos t\,\mathbf{i} - \sin t\,\mathbf{j} \Rightarrow ds = \sqrt{\cos^2 t + \sin^2 t}\, dt = dt.$

So, the line integral becomes $\displaystyle\int_C (x^2 + y^2 + z^2)\, ds = \int_0^{\pi/2} (\sin^2 t + \cos^2 t + 4)\, dt = \int_0^{\pi/2} 5\, dt = [5t]_0^{\pi/2} = \frac{5\pi}{2}.$

10. $\displaystyle\int_0^{6\pi} (1+t)\sqrt{2}\, dt = \sqrt{2}\left[t + \frac{t^2}{2}\right]_0^{6\pi} = \sqrt{2}\left(6\pi + 18\pi^2\right) = 6\pi\sqrt{2}\,(3\pi + 1).$

Lesson 29

1. $\mathbf{F}(x, y) = x\mathbf{i} + y\mathbf{j} = t\mathbf{i} + t\mathbf{j}, \mathbf{r}'(t) = \mathbf{i} + \mathbf{j}$.

   So, the line integral becomes $\int_C \mathbf{F} \cdot d\mathbf{r} = \int_0^1 (t\mathbf{i} + t\mathbf{j}) \cdot (\mathbf{i} + \mathbf{j}) dt = \int_0^1 2t \, dt = \left[t^2 \right]_0^1 = 1$.

2. $\mathbf{F}(x, y) = 3x\mathbf{i} + 4y\mathbf{j} = 3t\mathbf{i} + 4\sqrt{4 - t^2}\,\mathbf{j}, \mathbf{r}'(t) = \mathbf{i} - \dfrac{t}{\sqrt{4 - t^2}}\,\mathbf{j}$. So, the line integral is

   $\int_C \mathbf{F} \cdot d\mathbf{r} = \int_{-2}^2 \left(3t\mathbf{i} + 4\sqrt{4 - t^2}\,\mathbf{j} \right) \cdot \left(\mathbf{i} - \dfrac{t}{\sqrt{4 - t^2}}\,\mathbf{j} \right) dt = \int_{-2}^2 (3t - 4t) \, dt = \int_{-2}^2 (-t) \, dt \left[-\dfrac{t^2}{2} \right]_{-2}^2 = 0$.

3. $\mathbf{F}(x, y, z) = xy\mathbf{i} + xz\mathbf{j} + yz\mathbf{k} = t^3\mathbf{i} + 2t^2\mathbf{j} + 2t^3\mathbf{k}, \mathbf{r}'(t) = \mathbf{i} + 2t\mathbf{j} + 2\mathbf{k}$.

   We have $\int_C \mathbf{F} \cdot d\mathbf{r} = \int_0^1 (t^3\mathbf{i} + 2t^2\mathbf{j} + 2t^3\mathbf{k}) \cdot (\mathbf{i} + 2t\mathbf{j} + 2\mathbf{k}) dt = \int_0^1 (t^3 + 4t^3 + 4t^3) \, dt = \int_0^1 (9t^3) \, dt = \left[\dfrac{9t^4}{4} \right]_0^1 = \dfrac{9}{4}$.

4. $\mathbf{F}(x, y, z) = x\mathbf{i} + y\mathbf{j} - 5z\mathbf{k} = 2\cos t\mathbf{i} + 2\sin t\mathbf{j} - 5t\mathbf{k}, \mathbf{r}'(t) = -2\sin t\mathbf{i} + 2\cos t\mathbf{j} + \mathbf{k}$.

   $\int_C \mathbf{F} \cdot d\mathbf{r} = \int_0^{2\pi} (2\cos t\mathbf{i} + 2\sin t\mathbf{j} - 5t\mathbf{k}) \cdot (-2\sin t\mathbf{i} + 2\cos t\mathbf{j} + \mathbf{k}) dt = \int_0^{2\pi} (-5t) \, dt = \left[-\dfrac{5t^2}{2} \right]_0^{2\pi} = -10\pi^2$.

5. $\mathbf{F}(x, y) = x\mathbf{i} + 2y\mathbf{j} = t\mathbf{i} + 2t^3\mathbf{j}, \mathbf{r}'(t) = \mathbf{i} + 3t^2\mathbf{j}$.

   So, the work done is $W = \int_C \mathbf{F} \cdot d\mathbf{r} = \int_0^2 (t\mathbf{i} + 2t^3\mathbf{j}) \cdot (\mathbf{i} + 3t^2\mathbf{j}) dt = \int_0^2 (t + 6t^5) \, dt = \left[\dfrac{t^2}{2} + t^6 \right]_0^2 = 2 + 64 = 66$.

6. The line joining the two points is $\mathbf{r}(t) = 5t\mathbf{i} + 3t\mathbf{j} + 2t\mathbf{k}, 0 \le t \le 1$.

   Hence, $\mathbf{F}(x, y, z) = yz\mathbf{i} + xz\mathbf{j} + xy\mathbf{k} = 6t^2\mathbf{i} + 10t^2\mathbf{j} + 15t^2\mathbf{k}, \mathbf{r}'(t) = 5\mathbf{i} + 3\mathbf{j} + 2\mathbf{k}$.

   The work done is $W = \int_C \mathbf{F} \cdot d\mathbf{r} = \int_0^1 (6t^2\mathbf{i} + 10t^2\mathbf{j} + 15t^2\mathbf{k}) \cdot (5\mathbf{i} + 3\mathbf{j} + 2\mathbf{k}) dt = \int_0^1 (90t^2) \, dt = \left[30t^3 \right]_0^1 \, dt = 30$.

7. $y = 5x, dy = 5 \, dx, 0 \le x \le 2$. So, we have

   $$\int_C (3y - x) \, dx + y^2 \, dy = \int_0^2 \left[(15x - x) \, dx + (5x)^2 (5 \, dx) \right]$$

   $$= \int_0^2 (14x + 125x^2) \, dx$$

   $$= \left[7x^2 + 125\dfrac{x^3}{3} \right]_0^2 = 28 + 125\dfrac{8}{3} = \dfrac{1084}{3}.$$

8. $y = 5x, dy = 5\,dx, 0 \le x \le 2$. So, we have

$$\int_C \left(x + 3y^2\right)dy = \int_0^2 \left(x + 3(5x)^2\right)5\,dx$$

$$= \int_0^2 \left(5x + 375x^2\right)dx$$

$$= \left[5\frac{x^2}{2} + 125x^3\right]_0^2 = 10 + 125(8) = 1010.$$

9. $\mathbf{F}(x, y) = x^2\mathbf{i} + xy\mathbf{j} = 4t^2\mathbf{i} + 2t(t-1)\mathbf{j}, \mathbf{r}'(t) = 2\mathbf{i} + \mathbf{j}$.

So, we have $\int_C \mathbf{F} \cdot d\mathbf{r} = \int_1^3 \left(4t^2\mathbf{i} + 2t(t-1)\mathbf{j}\right) \cdot (2\mathbf{i} + \mathbf{j})\,dt = \int_1^3 \left(8t^2 + 2t^2 - 2t\right)dt = \left[\frac{10t^3}{3} - t^2\right]_1^3 = \frac{236}{3}$.

10. $\mathbf{F}(x, y) = x^2\mathbf{i} + xy\mathbf{j} = 4(3-t)^2\,\mathbf{i} + 2(3-t)(2-t)\mathbf{j}, \mathbf{r}'(t) = -2\mathbf{i} - \mathbf{j}$.

So, we have $\int_C \mathbf{F} \cdot d\mathbf{r} = \int_0^2 \left(4(3-t)^2\,\mathbf{i} + 2(3-t)(2-t)\mathbf{j}\right) \cdot (-2\mathbf{i} - \mathbf{j})\,dt = \int_0^2 \left[-8(3-t)^2 - 2(3-t)(2-t)\right]dt$.

This integral simplifies to the negative of the answer to Problem 9:

$$\int_C \mathbf{F} \cdot d\mathbf{r} = \int_0^2 \left(-84 + 58t - 10t^2\right)dt = \left[-84t + 29t^2 - 10\frac{t^3}{3}\right]_0^2 = -168 + 116 - \frac{80}{3} = -\frac{236}{3}.$$

Lesson 30

1. $M = e^x \sin y, N = e^x \cos y \Rightarrow \dfrac{\partial N}{\partial x} = e^x \cos y = \dfrac{\partial M}{\partial y}$. The vector field is conservative.

2. $M = \dfrac{1}{y}, N = \dfrac{x}{y^2} \Rightarrow \dfrac{\partial N}{\partial x} = \dfrac{1}{y^2} \ne -\dfrac{1}{y^2} = \dfrac{\partial M}{\partial y}$. The vector field is not conservative.

3. The vector field is not conservative because the curl is nonzero:

$$\text{curl}\,\mathbf{F} = \begin{vmatrix} \mathbf{i} & \mathbf{j} & \mathbf{k} \\ \dfrac{\partial}{\partial x} & \dfrac{\partial}{\partial y} & \dfrac{\partial}{\partial z} \\ y\ln z & -x\ln z & \dfrac{xy}{z} \end{vmatrix} = \left(\dfrac{x}{z} - \left(-\dfrac{x}{z}\right)\right)\mathbf{i} - \left(\dfrac{y}{z} - \dfrac{y}{z}\right)\mathbf{j} + \left(-\ln z - \ln z\right)\mathbf{k} \ne 0.$$

4. Because $\dfrac{\partial N}{\partial x} = 2x = \dfrac{\partial M}{\partial y}$, the vector field $\mathbf{F}(x, y) = 2xy\mathbf{i} + (x^2 + y^2)\mathbf{j}$ is conservative.

The potential function is $f(x, y) = x^2 y + \dfrac{y^3}{3} + K$.

Hence, we have $\displaystyle\int_C 2xy\,dx + (x^2 + y^2)\,dy = \left[x^2 y + \dfrac{y^3}{3} \right]_{(5,0)}^{(0,4)} = \dfrac{64}{3}$.

5. Because $\dfrac{\partial N}{\partial x} = 2x = \dfrac{\partial M}{\partial y}$, the vector field $\mathbf{F}(x, y) = 2xy\mathbf{i} + (x^2 + y^2)\mathbf{j}$ is conservative.

The potential function is $f(x, y) = x^2 y + \dfrac{y^3}{3} + K$.

Hence, we have $\displaystyle\int_C 2xy\,dx + (x^2 + y^2)\,dy = \left[x^2 y + \dfrac{y^3}{3} \right]_{(2,0)}^{(0,4)} = \dfrac{64}{3}$.

6. Because the curl is zero, the vector field is conservative.

The potential function is $f(x, y, z) = xyz + K$. Hence, $\displaystyle\int_C yz\,dx + xz\,dy + xy\,dz = \left[xyz \right]_{(0,2,0)}^{(4,2,4)} = 32$.

7. Because the curl is zero, the vector field is conservative.

The potential is $f(x, y, z) = xyz + K$. Hence, $\displaystyle\int_C yz\,dx + xz\,dy + xy\,dz = \left[xyz \right]_{(0,0,0)}^{(4,2,4)} = 32$.

8. A potential function is $f(x, y) = \sin x \sin y$.

Hence, the line integral is $\displaystyle\int_C \cos x \sin y\,dx + \sin x \cos y\,dy = \left[\sin x \sin y \right]_{(0,-\pi)}^{(3\pi/2, \pi/2)} = -1$.

9. The vector field is conservative with potential $f(x, y) = \dfrac{x^2}{y} + K$.

The work is therefore $W = \left[\dfrac{x^2}{y} \right]_{(-1,1)}^{(3,2)} = \dfrac{9}{2} - 1 = \dfrac{7}{2}$.

10. The vector field is conservative because $\dfrac{\partial N}{\partial x} = \dfrac{x^2 - y^2}{(x^2 + y^2)^2} = \dfrac{\partial M}{\partial y}$.

Because the curve does not contain the origin, the line integral is zero.

Lesson 31

1. We first calculate the line integral. For the path C_1 from $(0, 0)$ to $(1, 1)$, we have $\mathbf{r}(t) = t\mathbf{i} + t\mathbf{j}, 0 \leq t \leq 1$.

Because $x = y = t$, $\int_{C_1} y^2 dx + x^2 dy = \int_0^1 (t^2) dt + (t^2) dt = \int_0^1 2t^2 \, dt = \left[2\frac{t^3}{3} \right]_0^1 = \frac{2}{3}$.

For the path C_2 from $(1, 1)$ to $(0, 0)$, we have $\mathbf{r}(t) = (2-t)\mathbf{i} + \sqrt{2-t}\mathbf{j}, 1 \leq t \leq 2$.

Here, $x = 2 - t, dx = -dt, y = \sqrt{2-t}, dy = \frac{-1}{2\sqrt{2-t}} dt$.

So, we have $\int_{C_2} y^2 dx + x^2 dy = \int_1^2 (t-2) dt + (2-t)^2 \left(\frac{-1}{2\sqrt{2-t}} \right) dt$.

Evaluating this integral, you obtain $-\frac{7}{10}$. Finally, $\int_C y^2 dx + x^2 dy = \frac{2}{3} - \frac{7}{10} = -\frac{1}{30}$.

Next, we calculate the double integral:

$$\iint_R \left(\frac{\partial N}{\partial x} - \frac{\partial M}{\partial y} \right) dA = \int_0^1 \int_x^{\sqrt{x}} (2x - 2y) \, dy \, dx$$

$$= \int_0^1 \left[2xy - y^2 \right]_x^{\sqrt{x}} = \int_0^1 \left(2x^{3/2} - x - x^2 \right) dx$$

$$= \left[\frac{4}{5} x^{5/2} - \frac{x^2}{2} - \frac{x^3}{3} \right]_0^1 = \frac{4}{5} - \frac{1}{2} - \frac{1}{3} = -\frac{1}{30}.$$

2. Notice that $\frac{\partial N}{\partial x} - \frac{\partial M}{\partial y} = 2 - 1 = 1$. Hence, $\int_C (y - x) dx + (2x - y) dy = \iint_R 1 \, dA$.

This is the area between the two semicircles, $\frac{1}{2} \pi (25 - 9) = 8\pi$.

3. Notice that $\frac{\partial N}{\partial x} - \frac{\partial M}{\partial y} = 2 - 1 = 1$. Hence, $\int_C (y - x) dx + (2x - y) dy = \iint_R 1 \, dA$.

This is the area of the ellipse having $a = 2, b = 1$. So, the answer is $\pi ab = 2\pi$.

4. We have $\frac{\partial M}{\partial y} = -2e^x \sin 2y = \frac{\partial N}{\partial x}$. Hence, $\iint_R \left(\frac{\partial N}{\partial x} - \frac{\partial M}{\partial y} \right) dA = 0$.

5. By Green's theorem, we have the following:

$$W = \int_C xy\,dx + (x + y\,dy) = \iint_R \left(\frac{\partial N}{\partial x} - \frac{\partial M}{\partial y} \right) dA = \iint_R (1 - x)\,dA$$

$$= \int_0^{2\pi} \int_0^1 (1 - r\cos\theta)r\,dr\,d\theta = \int_0^{2\pi} \left[\frac{r^2}{2} - \frac{r^3}{3}\cos\theta \right]_0^1 d\theta$$

$$= \int_0^{2\pi} \left(\frac{1}{2} - \frac{1}{3}\cos\theta \right) d\theta = \left[\frac{1}{2}\theta - \frac{1}{3}\sin\theta \right]_0^{2\pi} = \pi.$$

6. By Green's theorem, we have the following:

$$W = \int_C \left(x^{3/2} - 3y \right) dx + \left(6x + 5\sqrt{y}\,dy \right) = \iint_R \left(\frac{\partial N}{\partial x} - \frac{\partial M}{\partial y} \right) dA = \iint_R (6 + 3)\,dA.$$

So, the work is 9 times the area of the triangle: $W = 9\frac{1}{2}(5)(5) = \frac{225}{2}$.

Lesson 32

1. $y = x^2 - 2x, dy = (2x - 2)\,dx$. So, the line integral becomes

$$\int_C (y - x)\,dx + (2x - y)\,dy = \int_0^3 (x^2 - 2x - x)\,dx + (2x - x^2 + 2x)(2x - 2)\,dx$$

$$= \int_0^3 (-2x^3 + 11x^2 - 11x)\,dx$$

$$= \left[-\frac{x^4}{2} + 11\frac{x^3}{3} - 11\frac{x^2}{2} \right]_0^3$$

$$= -\frac{81}{2} + 99 - \frac{99}{2} = 9.$$

2. Let the circle be $x = a\cos t, y = a\sin t, 0 \le t \le 2\pi$. Then, the area is

$$A = \frac{1}{2}\int_C x\,dy - y\,dx = \frac{1}{2}\int_0^{2\pi} [a\cos t(a\cos t) - a\sin t(-a\sin t)]\,dt = \frac{1}{2}\int_0^{2\pi} a^2\,dt = \pi a^2.$$

3. $y = x^2 + 1, dy = 2x\,dx$; $y = 5x - 3, dy = 5\,dx$. The area is therefore

$$A = \frac{1}{2}\int_1^4 \left[x(2x) - (x^2 + 1) \right] dx + \frac{1}{2}\int_4^1 \left[x(5) - (5x - 3) \right] dx$$

$$= \frac{1}{2}\left[\frac{x^3}{3} - x \right]_1^4 + \frac{1}{2}[3x]_4^1 = \frac{1}{2}(18) + \frac{1}{2}(-9) = \frac{9}{2}.$$

4. The vector field $\mathbf{F}(x, y) = \dfrac{y}{x^2 + y^2}\mathbf{i} - \dfrac{x}{x^2 + y^2}\mathbf{j}$ is conservative because $\dfrac{\partial N}{\partial x} = \dfrac{x^2 - y^2}{\left(x^2 + y^2\right)^2} = \dfrac{\partial M}{\partial y}$.

By Green's theorem, the line integral is zero because $\displaystyle\int_C \frac{y\,dx - x\,dy}{x^2 + y^2} = \iint_R \left(\frac{\partial N}{\partial x} - \frac{\partial M}{\partial y}\right) dA = 0$.

5. The line joining the points is $y = \dfrac{y_2 - y_1}{x_2 - x_1}(x - x_1) + y_1$. So, $dy = \dfrac{y_2 - y_1}{x_2 - x_1}\,dx$.

$$\int_C -y\,dx + x\,dy = \int_{x_1}^{x_2}\left[-\frac{y_2 - y_1}{x_2 - x_1}(x - x_1) - y_1 + x\left(\frac{y_2 - y_1}{x_2 - x_1}\right)\right]dx$$

$$= \int_{x_1}^{x_2}\left[x_1\left(\frac{y_2 - y_1}{x_2 - x_1}\right) - y_1\right]dx = \left[\left[x_1\left(\frac{y_2 - y_1}{x_2 - x_1}\right) - y_1\right]x\right]_{x_1}^{x_2}$$

$$= \left[x_1\left(\frac{y_2 - y_1}{x_2 - x_1}\right) - y_1\right](x_2 - x_1) = x_1(y_2 - y_1) - y_1(x_2 - x_1)$$

$$= x_1 y_2 - x_2 y_1.$$

6. We have $A = \dfrac{1}{2}\Big[(0 - 0) + (4 - 0) + (12 - 4) + (6 - 0) + (0 + 3) + (0 - 0)\Big] = \dfrac{21}{2}$.

7. $\displaystyle\int_C f(x)\,dx + g(y)\,dy = \iint_R\left[\frac{\partial}{\partial x}g(y) - \frac{\partial}{\partial y}f(x)\right]dA = \iint_R[0 - 0]\,dA = 0$.

Lesson 33

1. This is the plane $y = x + z$.

2. Because $x^2 + y^2 = (u\cos v)^2 + (u\sin v)^2 = u^2$, this is the cone $x^2 + y^2 = z^2$.

3. $\mathbf{r}_u(u, v) = \mathbf{i} + \mathbf{j}, \mathbf{r}_v(u, v) = \mathbf{i} - \mathbf{j} + \mathbf{k}$.

At the point $(1, -1, 1)$, $u = 0$ and $v = 1$. $\mathbf{r}_u(0, 1) = \mathbf{i} + \mathbf{j}, \mathbf{r}_v(0, 1) = \mathbf{i} - \mathbf{j} + \mathbf{k}$.

The normal vector is the cross product, $\mathbf{N} = \mathbf{r}_u \times \mathbf{r}_v = \mathbf{i} - \mathbf{j} - 2\mathbf{k}$. Note that the surface is the plane $x - y = 2z$.

4. $\mathbf{r}_u(u, v) = 2\cos v\mathbf{i} + 3\sin v\mathbf{j} + 2u\mathbf{k}$, $\mathbf{r}_v(u, v) = -2u\sin v\mathbf{i} + 3u\cos v\mathbf{j}$.

At the point $(0, 6, 4)$, $u = 2$ and $v = \dfrac{\pi}{2}$. $\mathbf{r}_u\left(2, \dfrac{\pi}{2}\right) = 3\mathbf{j} + 4\mathbf{k}$, $\mathbf{r}_v\left(2, \dfrac{\pi}{2}\right) = -4\mathbf{i}$.

The normal vector is the cross product, $\mathbf{N} = \mathbf{r}_u \times \mathbf{r}_v = -16\mathbf{j} + 12\mathbf{k}$.

5. We know the point and the normal vector.

So, the tangent plane is $(x - 1) - (y + 1) - 2(z - 1) = 0 \Rightarrow x - y - 2z = 0$. This is the original plane.

6. We know the point and the normal vector.

So, the tangent plane is $-16(y - 6) + 12(z - 4) = 0 \Rightarrow 4y - 3z = 12$.

7. $\mathbf{r}_u(u, v) = 4\mathbf{i}$, $\mathbf{r}_v(u, v) = -\mathbf{j} + \mathbf{k}$. The cross product is $\mathbf{r}_u \times \mathbf{r}_v = -4\mathbf{j} - 4\mathbf{k}$.

The magnitude of the cross product is $\|\mathbf{r}_u \times \mathbf{r}_v\| = \sqrt{16 + 16} = 4\sqrt{2}$.

Finally, the area is $A = \displaystyle\int_0^1 \int_0^2 \|\mathbf{r}_u \times \mathbf{r}_v\| \, dA = \int_0^1 \int_0^2 4\sqrt{2} \, du \, dv = 4\sqrt{2}(2)(1) = 8\sqrt{2}$.

8. $\mathbf{r}_u(u, v) = -2\sin u\mathbf{i} + 2\cos u\mathbf{j}$, $\mathbf{r}_v = \mathbf{k}$.

We have $\mathbf{r}_u \times \mathbf{r}_v = 2\cos u\mathbf{i} + 2\sin u\mathbf{j}$ and $\|\mathbf{r}_u \times \mathbf{r}_v\| = 2$.

Finally, $A = \displaystyle\int_0^3 \int_0^{2\pi} \|\mathbf{r}_u \times \mathbf{r}_v\| \, dA = \int_0^3 \int_0^{2\pi} 2 \, du \, dv = 2(2\pi)(3) = 12\pi$.

9. We will show that $x^2 + y^2 + z^2 = 1$.

$$\begin{aligned}
x^2 + y^2 + z^2 &= \left(\sin u \cos v\right)^2 + \left(\sin u \sin v\right)^2 + \left(\cos u\right)^2 \\
&= \sin^2 u \cos^2 v + \sin^2 u \sin^2 v + \cos^2 u \\
&= \sin^2 u \left(\cos^2 v + \sin^2 v\right) + \cos^2 u \\
&= \sin^2 u + \cos^2 u = 1.
\end{aligned}$$

10. We first calculate the cross product:

$$\mathbf{r}_u \times \mathbf{r}_v = \begin{vmatrix} \mathbf{i} & \mathbf{j} & \mathbf{k} \\ \cos u \cos v & \cos u \sin v & -\sin u \\ -\sin u \sin v & \sin u \cos v & 0 \end{vmatrix}$$

$$= \sin^2 u \cos v \mathbf{i} + \sin^2 u \sin v \mathbf{j} + (\cos u \sin u \cos^2 v + \cos u \sin u \sin^2 v)\mathbf{k}$$

$$= \sin^2 u \cos v \mathbf{i} + \sin^2 u \sin v \mathbf{j} + \cos u \sin u \mathbf{k}.$$

The magnitude of the cross product is

$$\|\mathbf{r}_u \times \mathbf{r}_v\| = \sqrt{\left(\sin^2 u \cos v\right)^2 + \left(\sin^2 u \sin v\right)^2 + \left(\sin u \cos u\right)^2}$$

$$= \sqrt{\sin^4 u \left(\cos^2 v + \sin^2 v\right) + \sin^2 u \cos^2 u}$$

$$= \sqrt{\sin^4 u + \sin^2 u \cos^2 u}$$

$$= \sqrt{\sin^2 u \left(\sin^2 u + \cos^2 u\right)}$$

$$= \sqrt{\sin^2 u} = \sin u.$$

Lesson 34

1. $\dfrac{\partial z}{\partial x} = -1, \dfrac{\partial z}{\partial y} = 0.$ $dS = \sqrt{1 + (-1)^2 + 0}\, dA = \sqrt{2}\, dA.$ So, we have the following.

$$\iint_S (x - 2y + z)\, dS = \int_0^4 \int_0^3 (x - 2y + (4 - x))\sqrt{2}\, dy\, dx$$

$$= \sqrt{2} \int_0^4 \int_0^3 (4 - 2y)\, dy\, dx$$

$$= \sqrt{2} \int_0^4 \left[4y - y^2\right]_0^3 dx$$

$$= \sqrt{2} \int_0^4 3\, dx = 12\sqrt{2}.$$

2. $\dfrac{\partial z}{\partial x} = \dfrac{\partial z}{\partial y} = 0.$ $dS = \sqrt{1 + 0 + 0}\, dA = dA.$ So, we have the following.

$$\iint_S xy\, dS = \int_0^2 \int_0^{\sqrt{4 - x^2}} xy\, dy\, dx = \frac{1}{2} \int_0^2 x(4 - x^2)\, dx = \frac{1}{2}\left[2x^2 - \frac{x^4}{4}\right]_0^2 = 2.$$

3. We have the following.

$$3\int_0^3 \int_0^{2(3-x)} y(3-x)\,dy\,dx = 3\int_0^3 \left[\frac{y^2}{2}(3-x)\right]_0^{2(3-x)} dx$$

$$= 3(2)\int_0^3 (3-x)^3\,dx$$

$$= \left[-6\frac{(3-x)^4}{4}\right]_0^3 = \frac{243}{2}.$$

4. $\mathbf{r}_u(u, v) = \mathbf{i},\ \mathbf{r}_v(u, v) = \mathbf{j} + 2\mathbf{k}.\ \ \mathbf{r}_u \times \mathbf{r}_v = -2\mathbf{j} + \mathbf{k},\ \|\mathbf{r}_u \times \mathbf{r}_v\| = \sqrt{5}.$

Hence, $\displaystyle\iint_S (y+5)\,dS = \int_0^2 \int_0^1 (v+5)\sqrt{5}\,du\,dv = \sqrt{5}\int_0^2 (v+5)\,dv = \sqrt{5}\left[\frac{v^2}{2} + 5v\right]_0^2 = 12\sqrt{5}.$

5. $dS = \sqrt{(2x)^2 + (2y)^2 + 1}\,dA.$ So, we have

$$\iint_S \frac{xy}{z}\,dS = \iint_S \frac{xy}{x^2+y^2}\sqrt{1+4x^2+4y^2}\,dy\,dx$$

$$= \int_0^{2\pi} \int_2^4 \frac{r^2\cos\theta\sin\theta}{r^2}\sqrt{1+4r^2}\,r\,dr\,d\theta$$

$$= \int_0^{2\pi} \int_2^4 r\sqrt{1+4r^2}\,\cos\theta\sin\theta\,dr\,d\theta.$$

6. $G(x, y, z) = x + y + z - 1,\ \nabla G = \mathbf{i} + \mathbf{j} + \mathbf{k}.$ So, we have

$$\iint_S \mathbf{F} \cdot \mathbf{N}\,dS = \iint_R \mathbf{F} \cdot \nabla G\,dA$$

$$= \int_0^1 \int_0^{1-x} (3z - 4 + y)\,dy\,dx$$

$$= \int_0^1 \int_0^{1-x} (3(1-x-y) - 4 + y)\,dy\,dx$$

$$= \int_0^1 \int_0^{1-x} (-1 - 3x - 2y)\,dy\,dx.$$

7. $G(x, y, z) = z - \sqrt{36 - x^2 - y^2}$, $\nabla G = \dfrac{x}{\sqrt{36 - x^2 - y^2}}\mathbf{i} + \dfrac{y}{\sqrt{36 - x^2 - y^2}}\mathbf{j} + \mathbf{k}$.

$$\mathbf{F} \cdot \nabla G = \frac{x^2}{\sqrt{36 - x^2 - y^2}} + \frac{y^2}{\sqrt{36 - x^2 - y^2}} + z = \frac{x^2 + y^2}{\sqrt{36 - x^2 - y^2}} + \sqrt{36 - x^2 - y^2} = \frac{36}{\sqrt{36 - x^2 - y^2}}.$$

So, we have the following.

$$\iint\limits_{S} \mathbf{F} \cdot \mathbf{N}\, dS = \iint\limits_{R} \mathbf{F} \cdot \nabla G\, dA = \iint\limits_{R} \frac{36}{\sqrt{36 - x^2 - y^2}}\, dA = \int_{0}^{\pi/2} \int_{0}^{6} \frac{36}{\sqrt{36 - r^2}}\, r\, dr\, d\theta.$$

Lesson 35

1. There are six surfaces to the cube, each with $dS = \sqrt{1}\, dA$.

$z = 0, \mathbf{N} = -\mathbf{k}, \mathbf{F} \cdot \mathbf{N} = -z^2, \iint_S 0\, dA = 0$

$z = 2, \mathbf{N} = \mathbf{k}, \mathbf{F} \cdot \mathbf{N} = z^2, \iint_S 4\, dA = \int_0^2 \int_0^2 4\, dx\, dy = 16$

$x = 0, \mathbf{N} = -\mathbf{i}, \mathbf{F} \cdot \mathbf{N} = -2x, \iint_S 0\, dA = 0$

$x = 2, \mathbf{N} = \mathbf{i}, \mathbf{F} \cdot \mathbf{N} = 2x, \iint_S 4\, dA = \int_0^2 \int_0^2 4\, dx\, dy = 16$

$y = 0, \mathbf{N} = -\mathbf{j}, \mathbf{F} \cdot \mathbf{N} = 2y, \iint_S 0\, dA = 0$

$y = 2, \mathbf{N} = \mathbf{j}, \mathbf{F} \cdot \mathbf{N} = -2y, \iint_S (-4)\, dA = \int_0^2 \int_0^2 (-4)\, dx\, dy = -16.$

Adding these up, $\iint\limits_{S} \mathbf{F} \cdot \mathbf{N}\, dS = 16 + 16 - 16 = 16$. The divergence of F is $\operatorname{div} \mathbf{F} = 2 - 2 + 2z = 2z$.

So, we have the same result: $\iiint\limits_{Q} \operatorname{div} \mathbf{F} = \int_0^2 \int_0^2 \int_0^2 2z\, dz\, dy\, dx = \int_0^2 \int_0^2 4\, dy\, dx = 4(2)(2) = 16.$

2. There are two surfaces.

For the bottom, $z = 0, \mathbf{N} = -\mathbf{k}, \mathbf{F} \cdot \mathbf{N} = -2z^2$. So, $\iint\limits_{S} \mathbf{F} \cdot \mathbf{N}\, dS = \iint\limits_{R} -2z^2\, dA = \iint\limits_{R} 0\, dA = 0.$

For the side, the outward unit normal is

$$\mathbf{N} = \frac{2x\mathbf{i} + 2y\mathbf{j} + \mathbf{k}}{\sqrt{4x^2 + 4y^2 + 1}} \quad \text{and} \quad \mathbf{F} \cdot \mathbf{N} = \frac{1}{\sqrt{4x^2 + 4y^2 + 1}} \left[2x^2 z + 2y^2 z + 2z^2 \right].$$

So, we have

$$\iint_S \mathbf{F} \cdot \mathbf{N}\, dS = \iint_R \left[2\left(x^2 + y^2\right)z + 2z^2 \right] dA$$

$$= \int_0^{2\pi} \int_0^1 \left[2r^2\left(1 - r^2\right) + 2\left(1 - r^2\right)^2 \right] r\, dr\, d\theta$$

$$= \int_0^{2\pi} \int_0^1 \left[2r - 2r^3 \right] dr\, d\theta$$

$$= \int_0^{2\pi} \frac{1}{2}\, d\theta = \pi.$$

The divergence of F is $\operatorname{div}\mathbf{F} = z + z + 4z = 6z.$ The triple integral of the divergence is

$$\iiint_Q \operatorname{div}\mathbf{F} = \int_0^{2\pi} \int_0^1 \int_0^{1-r^2} 6z\, r\, dz\, dr\, d\theta$$

$$= \int_0^{2\pi} \int_0^1 \left(3 - 6r^2 + 3r^4\right) r\, dr\, d\theta$$

$$= \int_0^{2\pi} \left[3\frac{r^2}{2} - 6\frac{r^4}{4} + 3\frac{r^6}{6} \right]_0^1 d\theta$$

$$= \int_0^{2\pi} \left[\frac{3}{2} - \frac{3}{2} + \frac{1}{2} \right] d\theta = \pi.$$

3. We have the following.

$$\int_{-2}^{2} \int_{-\sqrt{4-y^2}}^{\sqrt{4-y^2}} \left(4xz + 2xy + y^2\right) dx\, dy = \int_{-2}^{2} \int_{-\sqrt{4-y^2}}^{\sqrt{4-y^2}} \left(4x\left(4 - x^2 - y^2\right) + 2xy + y^2\right) dx\, dy$$

$$= \int_{-2}^{2} \int_{-\sqrt{4-y^2}}^{\sqrt{4-y^2}} \left(16x - 4x^3 - 4xy^2 + 2xy + y^2\right) dx\, dy$$

$$= \int_{-2}^{2} \left[8x^2 - x^4 - 2x^2 y^2 + x^2 y + xy^2 \right]_{-\sqrt{4-y^2}}^{\sqrt{4-y^2}} dy$$

$$= \int_{-2}^{2} 2y^2 \sqrt{4 - y^2}\, dy.$$

Using a graphing utility, or a table of integrals, you obtain 4π.

4. The divergence is $\operatorname{div}\mathbf{F} = 2x + 2y + 2z.$ So, we have

$$\iiint_Q \operatorname{div}\mathbf{F} = \int_0^1 \int_0^1 \int_0^1 \left(2x + 2y + 2z\right) dz\, dy\, dx$$

$$= \int_0^1 \int_0^1 \left(2x + 2y + 1\right) dy\, dx$$

$$= \int_0^1 \left(2x + 2\right) dx = 1 + 2 = 3.$$

5. The divergence is $\operatorname{div} \mathbf{F} = 1 + 2y - 1 = 2y$. So, we have

$$\iiint_Q \operatorname{div} \mathbf{F} = \int_0^7 \int_{-5}^5 \int_{-\sqrt{25-y^2}}^{\sqrt{25-y^2}} 2y \, dx \, dy \, dz$$

$$= \int_0^7 \int_{-5}^5 4y\sqrt{25-y^2} \, dy \, dz$$

$$= \int_0^7 \left[-\frac{4}{3}\left(25-y^2\right)^{3/2} \right]_{-5}^5 dz = 0.$$

6. If $\mathbf{F}(x, y, z) = a\mathbf{i} + b\mathbf{j} + c\mathbf{k}$, then $\operatorname{div} \mathbf{F} = 0$. So, by the divergence theorem, $\iint_S \mathbf{F} \cdot \mathbf{N} \, dS = \iiint_Q \operatorname{div} \mathbf{F} = 0$.

Lesson 36

1. We first calculate the line integral. Let $x = 3\cos t$, $dx = -3\sin t \, dt$ and $y = 3\sin t$, $dy = 3\cos t \, dt$. Because $z = 0$, $\int_C \mathbf{F} \cdot d\mathbf{r} = \int_C -y \, dx + x \, dy$. So, we have

$$\int_C \mathbf{F} \cdot d\mathbf{r} = \int_C -y \, dx + x \, dy = \int_0^{2\pi} \left[(-3\sin t)(-3\sin t) + (3\cos t)(3\cos t) \right] dt = \int_0^{2\pi} 9 \, dt = 18\pi.$$

For the double integral, let $G(x, y, z) = z - (9 - x^2 - y^2), \nabla G = 2x\mathbf{i} + 2y\mathbf{j} + \mathbf{k}$ and $\mathbf{N} \, dS = (2x\mathbf{i} + 2y\mathbf{j} + \mathbf{k}) dA$. The curl of F is

$$\operatorname{curl} \mathbf{F} = \begin{vmatrix} \mathbf{i} & \mathbf{j} & \mathbf{k} \\ \dfrac{\partial}{\partial x} & \dfrac{\partial}{\partial y} & \dfrac{\partial}{\partial z} \\ -y+z & x-z & x-y \end{vmatrix} = 2\mathbf{k}.$$

So, $\operatorname{curl} \mathbf{F} \cdot \mathbf{N} dS = 2 \, dA$. Hence, $\iint_S (\operatorname{curl} \mathbf{F}) \cdot \mathbf{N} \, dS = \iint_R 2 \, dA = 2(\text{area of circle}) = 18\pi.$

2. Let $\mathbf{u} = \mathbf{i} + \mathbf{j} + \mathbf{k}$ and $\mathbf{v} = 2\mathbf{k}$ be the vectors forming the triangle.

Their cross product is $\mathbf{u} \times \mathbf{v} = \begin{vmatrix} \mathbf{i} & \mathbf{j} & \mathbf{k} \\ 1 & 1 & 1 \\ 0 & 0 & 2 \end{vmatrix} = 2\mathbf{i} - 2\mathbf{j}$. The surface is the plane is $G = 2x - 2y = 0$.

$\nabla G = 2\mathbf{i} - 2\mathbf{j}$ and $\mathbf{N} \, dS = (2\mathbf{i} - 2\mathbf{j}) dA$.

Next, we calculate the curl of F:

$$\operatorname{curl} \mathbf{F} = \begin{vmatrix} \mathbf{i} & \mathbf{j} & \mathbf{k} \\ \dfrac{\partial}{\partial x} & \dfrac{\partial}{\partial y} & \dfrac{\partial}{\partial z} \\ \arctan\dfrac{x}{y} & \ln\sqrt{x^2+y^2} & 1 \end{vmatrix} = \dfrac{2x}{x^2+y^2}\mathbf{k}.$$

Because the curl is orthogonal to $\mathbf{N}\,dS = (2\mathbf{i}-2\mathbf{j})\,dA$, the line integral equals zero:

$$\int_C \mathbf{F}\cdot d\mathbf{r} = \iint_S (\operatorname{curl}\mathbf{F})\cdot\mathbf{N}\,dS = 0.$$

3. The curl is $\operatorname{curl}\mathbf{F} = \begin{vmatrix} \mathbf{i} & \mathbf{j} & \mathbf{k} \\ \dfrac{\partial}{\partial x} & \dfrac{\partial}{\partial y} & \dfrac{\partial}{\partial z} \\ xyz & y & z \end{vmatrix} = xy\mathbf{j} - xz\mathbf{k}.$

Let $G(x,y,z) = x^2 - z,\ \nabla G = 2x\mathbf{i} - \mathbf{k},\ \mathbf{N}\,dS = (2x\mathbf{i}-\mathbf{k})\,dA.$

Then, we have

$$\int_C \mathbf{F}\cdot d\mathbf{r} = \iint_S (\operatorname{curl}\mathbf{F})\cdot\mathbf{N}\,dS = \iint_R (xy\mathbf{j} - xz\mathbf{k})\cdot(2x\mathbf{i}-\mathbf{k})\,dA = \iint_R xz\,dA$$

$$= \int_0^3\int_0^3 x(x^2)\,dy\,dx = \int_0^3 3x^3\,dx = \left[3\dfrac{x^4}{4}\right]_0^3 = \dfrac{243}{4}.$$

4. $\operatorname{curl}\mathbf{F} = \begin{vmatrix} \mathbf{i} & \mathbf{j} & \mathbf{k} \\ \dfrac{\partial}{\partial x} & \dfrac{\partial}{\partial y} & \dfrac{\partial}{\partial z} \\ 1 & 1 & -2 \end{vmatrix} = 0.$

So, the double integral is also zero. (There is basically no circular motion to the liquid.)

5. $\operatorname{curl} \mathbf{F} = \begin{vmatrix} \mathbf{i} & \mathbf{j} & \mathbf{k} \\ \dfrac{\partial}{\partial x} & \dfrac{\partial}{\partial y} & \dfrac{\partial}{\partial z} \\ -y\sqrt{x^2+y^2} & x\sqrt{x^2+y^2} & 0 \end{vmatrix} = 3\sqrt{x^2+y^2}\,\mathbf{k}.$

Letting N = k,

$$\iint\limits_{S}(\operatorname{curl}\mathbf{F})\cdot\mathbf{N}\,dS = \iint\limits_{R}3\sqrt{x^2+y^2}\,dA = \int_0^{2\pi}\int_0^2 (3r)\,r\,dr\,d\theta = \int_0^{2\pi}\left[r^3\right]_0^2 d\theta = \int_0^{2\pi} 8\,d\theta = 16\pi.$$

(There is circular motion.)

Glossary

Note: The number in parentheses indicates the lesson in which the concept or term is introduced.

Some concepts from beginning calculus, and even precalculus, have also been included that were introduced in *Understanding Calculus: Problems, Solutions, and Tips* (*Calculus*) or in *Understanding Calculus II: Problems, Solutions, and Tips* (*Calculus II*).

absolute value function: The absolute value function is defined by

$$f(x) = |x| = \begin{cases} x, x \geq 0 \\ -x, x < 0 \end{cases}.$$

It is continuous, but not differentiable, at $x = 0$. Its graph appears in the shape of the letter V. Reviewed in *Calculus*, Lesson 1.

acceleration (13): In calculus, acceleration is the rate of change of velocity and has two components: the rate of change in speed and the rate of change in direction. See **particle motion**. Introduced for two dimensions in *Calculus*, Lessons 34–35.

arc length (13): In three dimensions, arc length is

$$s = \int_a^b \sqrt{\left[x'(t)\right]^2 + \left[y'(t)\right]^2 + \left[z'(t)\right]^2}\, dt = \int_a^b \|\mathbf{r}'(t)\|\, dt.$$

The **differential of arc length** in three dimensions is

$$ds = \sqrt{\left[x'(t)\right]^2 + \left[y'(t)\right]^2 + \left[z'(t)\right]^2} = \|\mathbf{r}'(t)\|\, dt.$$

For arc length in two dimensions, see *Calculus II*, Lesson 8.

area of a region in the plane: Let f be continuous and nonnegative on the interval $[a, b]$. Partition the interval into n equal subintervals of length

$$\Delta x = \frac{b-a}{n},\ x_0 = a,\ x_1,\ x_2,\ldots,\ x_{n-1},\ x_n = b.$$

The area of the region bounded by f, the x-axis, and the vertical lines $x = a$ and $x = b$ is

$$A = \lim_{n \to \infty} \sum_{i=1}^{n} f\left(c_i\right) \Delta x, \ x_{i-1} \leq c_i \leq x_i,$$

provided that this limit exists. See *Calculus II*, Lesson 7.

axis of revolution: If a region in the plane is revolved about a line, the resulting solid is a solid of revolution, and the line is called the axis of revolution. See *Calculus II*, Lesson 30.

cardioid: Polar equations of the form $r = a\left(1 + \cos\theta\right)$ and $r = a\left(1 + \sin\theta\right)$ are called cardioids. See *Calculus II*, Lesson 29.

center of mass: Calculated by dividing moment about the origin by the total mass, either

$$\left(\bar{x}, \bar{y}\right) = \left(\frac{M_y}{m}, \frac{M_x}{m}\right) \ \text{or} \ \bar{x} = \frac{M_0}{m},$$

where $m = m_1 + m_2 + \cdots + m_n$ and the **moment about the origin** is given by $M_0 = m_1 x_1 + \ldots + m_n x_n$. For a region of uniform density (covered in *Calculus II*, Lesson 9), the center of mass is often called the centroid of the region. See **moment**.

centroid: The geometric center of a planar lamina or higher-dimensional object. When mass is uniformly distributed, the centroid is equivalent to the center of mass. See *Calculus II*, Lesson 9.

chain rule (5): Unlike in elementary calculus, multivariable calculus has a variety of chain rules. The one covered in this course is

$$\frac{dw}{dt} = \frac{\partial w}{\partial x} \frac{dx}{dt} + \frac{\partial w}{\partial y} \frac{dy}{dt},$$

where some of the derivatives are ordinary derivatives while others are partial derivatives.

compound interest formula: Let P be the amount of a deposit at an annual interest rate of r (as a decimal) compounded n times per year. The amount after t years is

$$A = P\left(1 + \frac{r}{n}\right)^{nt}.$$

If the interest is compounded continuously, the amount is $A = Pe^{rt}$. See *Calculus*, Lesson 27.

concavity: Let f be differentiable on an open interval I. The graph of f is concave upward on I if f' is increasing on I and concave downward on I if f' is decreasing on I. A graph is concave upward if the graph is above its tangent lines and concave downward if the graph is below its tangent lines. See *Calculus II*, Lesson 2.

conservative vector field (27, 30): A vector field $\mathbf{F}$ that can be represented as the gradient of a differentiable function f, known as the **potential function**: in short, a vector field for which $\mathbf{F} = \nabla f$. Gravitational fields and electric force fields are conservative. In a conservative vector field, the value of a line integral over a closed curve is zero.

continuous function (3): In elementary calculus, a function f is continuous at c if the following three conditions are met:

$$f(c) \text{ is defined, } \lim_{x \to c} f(x) \text{ exists, and } \lim_{x \to c} f(x) = f(c).$$

In multivariable calculus, a function of two variables is continuous at a point if 1) the function is defined at the point, 2) the limit exists at the point, and 3) the function value equals the limit.

Coulomb's law (27): The force exerted on a particle with electric charge q_1 located at (x, y, z) by a particle of charge q_2 located at $(0, 0, 0)$ is

$$\mathbf{F}(x, y, z) = \frac{c\, q_1\, q_2}{\|\mathbf{r}\|^2} \mathbf{u}.$$

critical point (6): For a function f defined on an open region R containing (x_0, y_0), the point (x_0, y_0) is a critical point if the partial derivatives of the function at that point $f_x(x_0, y_0)$ and $f_y(x_0, y_0)$ are both equal to zero, or one of them does not exist. These critical points are the candidates for **relative extrema**.

cross product (10, 13): The cross product of two vectors (also known as the vector product) allows you to find a third vector in space that is orthogonal to two given nonzero vectors. The cross product is a vector and is not commutative: Instead, $\mathbf{u} \times \mathbf{v} = -(\mathbf{v} \times \mathbf{u})$. The cross product equals zero for identical or parallel vectors. We calculate using a **determinant** formula: $\mathbf{u} = u_1\mathbf{i} + u_2\mathbf{j} + u_3\mathbf{k} = \langle u_1, u_2, u_3 \rangle$ and $\mathbf{v} = v_1\mathbf{i} + v_2\mathbf{j} + v_3\mathbf{k} = \langle v_1, v_2, v_3 \rangle$ is

$$\mathbf{u} \times \mathbf{v} = \begin{vmatrix} \mathbf{i} & \mathbf{j} & \mathbf{k} \\ u_1 & u_2 & u_3 \\ v_1 & v_2 & v_3 \end{vmatrix} = (u_2 v_3 - u_3 v_2)\mathbf{i} - (u_1 v_3 - u_3 v_1)\mathbf{j} + (u_1 v_2 - u_2 v_1)\mathbf{k}.$$

The magnitude of the cross product is a scalar, which equals $\|\mathbf{u} \times \mathbf{v}\| = \|\mathbf{u}\|\|\mathbf{v}\|\sin\theta$.

The derivative of the cross product is $\dfrac{d}{dt}[\mathbf{r} \times \mathbf{u}] = \mathbf{r} \times \mathbf{u}' + \mathbf{r}' \times \mathbf{u}$.

curl of a vector field (28): A vector field that measures another vector field's tendency to rotate (when curl = 0, a field is **irrotational**). Used as a test for conservative vector fields. Calculated using a cross product of the differential operator with the vector field: $\operatorname{curl}\mathbf{F} = \nabla \times \mathbf{F}$. For the vector field $\mathbf{F}(x, y, z)$,

$$\operatorname{curl}\mathbf{F}(x, y, z) = \left(\frac{\partial P}{\partial y} - \frac{\partial N}{\partial z}\right)\mathbf{i} - \left(\frac{\partial P}{\partial x} - \frac{\partial M}{\partial z}\right)\mathbf{j} + \left(\frac{\partial N}{\partial x} - \frac{\partial M}{\partial y}\right)\mathbf{k}$$

$$= \nabla \times \mathbf{F}(x, y, z) = \begin{vmatrix} \mathbf{i} & \mathbf{j} & \mathbf{k} \\ \dfrac{\partial}{\partial x} & \dfrac{\partial}{\partial y} & \dfrac{\partial}{\partial z} \\ M & N & P \end{vmatrix}.$$

curvature: A measure of how much a curve bends,

$$K = \frac{\|\mathbf{T}'(t)\|}{\|\mathbf{r}'(t)\|}.$$

The curvature of $y = f(x)$ is

$$K = \frac{|y''|}{\left[1 + (y')^2\right]^{3/2}}.$$

See *Calculus II*, Lesson 36.

curve (31): A planar curve is defined by the functions $x = f(t)$, $y = g(t)$, and $z = h(t)$. A curve is called **simple** if it does not cross itself.

cylinder (12): In elementary geometry, a cylinder results when lines perpendicular to a circle generate a tube shape, but in higher mathematics, a cylinder (or cylindrical surface) can refer to any surface created when any generating curve in a plane (not just a circle) is extended into a third dimension by lines intersecting that curve and orthogonal to its plane.

cylindrical coordinates (25): The three-dimensional generalization of **polar coordinates**: $x = r\cos t$, $y = r\sin t$, $z = z$.

cycloid: The curve traced out by a point on the circumference of a circle rolling along a line. See *Calculus II*, Lesson 28.

definite integral: Let f be defined on the interval $[a, b]$. Partition the interval into n equal subintervals of length $\Delta x = \dfrac{b-a}{n}$, $x_0 = a, x_1, x_2, \ldots, x_{n-1}, x_n = b$.

Assume that the following limit exists: $\displaystyle\lim_{n\to\infty}\sum_{i=1}^{n} f(c_i)\Delta x$, where $x_{i-1} \le c_i \le x_i$.

Then, this limit is the definite integral of f from a to b and is denoted $\displaystyle\int_a^b f(x)\,dx$. See *Calculus II*, Lesson 3.

del (15, 28): See **differential operator**.

delta x (Δx) (2, 7): The symbol Δx is read "delta x" and denotes a (small) change in x. Some textbooks use h instead of Δx.

density (22): Usually mass per unit volume, but for planar laminas, density is mass per unit of surface area.

derivative: In elementary calculus, the derivative of f at x is given by the following limit, if it exists:

$$f'(x) = \lim_{\Delta x\to 0} \frac{f(x+\Delta x)-f(x)}{\Delta x}.$$

Notations for the derivative of $y = f(x)$:

$$f'(x), \frac{dy}{dx}, y', \frac{d}{dx}\big[f(x)\big], D[y].$$

The definitions of slope and the derivative are based on the difference quotient for slope:

$$\text{slope} = \frac{\text{change in } y}{\text{change in } x} = \frac{\Delta y}{\Delta x}.$$

In multivariable calculus, the functions are of two (or more) variables, and we use partial derivatives:

$$f_x(x, y) = \lim_{\Delta x\to 0} \frac{f(x+\Delta x,\, y)-f(x, y)}{\Delta x}, \quad f_y(x, y) = \lim_{\Delta y\to 0} \frac{f(x,\, y+\Delta y)-f(x, y)}{\Delta y}.$$

determinant notation (10): In this course, we use a 3 × 3 determinant form only to help us remember and calculate the **cross product** of two vectors. Technically, a determinant is a single real number obtained by using determinant notation, but in that sense, this course has no determinants—which are a topic covered in linear algebra. See **cross product**.

differentiable (5): In multivariable calculus, a function $z = f(x, y)$ is differentiable at the point (x_0, y_0) if Δz can be written in the form $\Delta z = f_x(x_0, y_0)\Delta x + f_y(x_0, y_0)\Delta y + \varepsilon_1\Delta x + \varepsilon_2\Delta y$, where ε_1 and ε_2 tend to zero as $(\Delta x, \Delta y) \rightarrow (0, 0)$. Differentiability at a point on a surface implies that the surface can be approximated by a tangent plane at that point.

differential: In elementary calculus, we let $y = f(x)$ be a differentiable function. Then, $dx = \Delta x$ is called the differential of x. The differential of y is $dy = f'(x)dx$. For multivariable calculus, see **total differential**. See *Calculus II*, Lesson 2.

differential equation: A differential equation in x and y is an equation that involves x, y, and derivatives of y. The order of a differential equation is determined by the highest-order derivative in the equation. A first-order linear differential equation can be written in the standard form $\dfrac{dy}{dx} + P(x)y = Q(x)$. See *Calculus II*, Lessons 4–6.

differential operator (del) (∇) (15, 28): $\nabla = \dfrac{\partial}{\partial x}$, $\nabla = \dfrac{\partial}{\partial y}$, or $\nabla = \dfrac{\partial}{\partial z}$. Used in curl, divergence. Pronounced "del," or "grad," or "nabla."

directional derivative (15): A generalization of the concept of partial derivative that can be used to find the slope away from a point in any given direction.

direction numbers (9): Component numbers in a direction vector.

disk (3): Two-dimensional analog for intervals along the x-axis in beginning calculus. An open disk that is the interior of a circle. Compare with **planar lamina**.

divergence of a vector field (28, 35): A scalar that measures outward flux per unit volume, the tendency of a vector field to diverge from a given point. Positive divergence is a **source**, negative divergence is a **sink**, and divergence = 0 is **divergence free** or **incompressible**. Calculated using a dot product of the differential operator with the vector field: $\mathrm{div}\,\mathbf{F} = \nabla\cdot\mathbf{F}$.

divergence theorem (35): A generalization of **Green's theorem** that relates a **flux integral** over the boundary of a solid with a triple integral over the entire solid:

$$\iint_S \mathbf{F} \cdot \mathbf{N} \, dS = \iiint_Q \mathrm{div} \mathbf{F} \, dV = \iiint_Q \nabla \cdot \mathbf{F} \, dV.$$

dot product (9): The dot product of two vectors, $\mathbf{u} = \langle u_1, u_2, u_3 \rangle$ and $\mathbf{v} = \langle v_1, v_2, v_3 \rangle$, is $\mathbf{u} \cdot \mathbf{v} = u_1 v_1 + u_2 v_2 + u_3 v_3$. The dot product of two vectors is a real number, not a vector, and provides a method for determining the angle between two nonzero vectors; when the dot product equals zero, the two vectors are perpendicular to each other. For vectors in two dimensions, see *Calculus II*, Lesson 32.

double integral (20): If f is defined on a closed and bounded region in R in the xy-plane, then the double integral of f over R is

$$\iint_R f(x, y) \, dA = \lim_{\|\Delta\| \to 0} \sum_{i=1}^{n} f(x_i, y_i) \, \Delta A_i.$$

To solve, rewrite as an iterated integral. Can be used to solve for area, volume, mass, surface area, etc.

error analysis (5): Using the **total differential** to approximate function values.

extreme value theorem (6): If $z = f(x, y)$ is continuous on the closed and bounded region R in the plane, then there is at least one point in R at which f takes on a minimum value and at least one point in R at which f takes on a maximum value.

exponential function: The inverse of the natural logarithmic function $y = \ln x$ is the exponential function $y = e^x$. The exponential function is equal to its derivative, $\frac{d}{dx}\left[e^x\right] = e^x$. The exponential function to base a, $a > 0$, is defined by $a^x = e^{(\ln a)x}$. See *Calculus*, Lesson 1.

first derivative test: In elementary calculus, we let c be a critical number of f. If f' changes from positive to negative at c, then f has a relative maximum at $(c, f(c))$. If f' changes from negative to positive at c, then f has a relative minimum at $(c, f(c))$. See **second derivative test**. See *Calculus II*, Lesson 2.

flux integral (34): A surface integral that is used to model the flow of a liquid through a two-sided surface—an **orientable** surface. Flux integrals are not defined for surfaces that are not orientable.

function of two variables (2): A function with two independent variables (often x and y) and one dependent variable (often z or t). Let D (the domain) be a set of ordered pairs of real numbers. If to each ordered pair (x, y) in D there corresponds a unique real number $f(x, y)$, then f is a function of x and y.

fundamental theorem of calculus (1, 36): If f is a continuous function on the closed interval $[a, b]$ and F is an antiderivative of f, then

$$\int_a^b f(x)\,dx = F(b) - F(a).$$

This theorem and the second fundamental theorem of calculus show how integration and differentiation are basically inverse operations. If f is continuous on an open interval I containing a, the **second fundamental theorem of calculus** says that for any x in the interval,

$$\frac{d}{dx}\left[\int_a^x f(t)\,dt \right] = f(x).$$

fundamental theorem of line integrals (30): States that the line integral for any two points in a conservative vector field is simply the difference in the values of the **potential function** at those two points.

Gauss's law (35): Relates the flux out of a surface to the total charge inside the surface. In particular, if E is an electric field, then

$$\iint_S \mathbf{E} \cdot \mathbf{N}\,dS = \frac{Q}{\varepsilon_0}.$$

Here, Q is the electric charge inside a sphere and ε_0 is the permittivity of space, or the electric constant. Generalized to become the first of Maxwell's laws of electromagnetism.

gradient (15): A vector that points in the direction of maximum increase or steepest ascent; is orthogonal to level curves (for functions of two variables) and level surfaces (for functions of three variables). The gradient of a function of two (or more) variables is a vector-valued function; for a function of two variables, the gradient is $\mathbf{grad}\, f(x, y) = \nabla f(x, y) = f_x(x, y)\mathbf{i} + f_y(x, y)\mathbf{j}$. The dot product of the gradient with the unit vector gives the **directional derivative**.

Green's theorem (31): A theorem about points in the plane that relates a line integral around the boundary of a region with a double integral over the entire region:

$$\int_C M\,dx + N\,dy = \iint_R \left(\frac{\partial N}{\partial x} - \frac{\partial M}{\partial y} \right) dA.$$

Here, M and N are the components of a vector-valued function $\mathbf{F}$. This theorem generalizes to space, in two different ways, with the **divergence theorem** and **Stokes's theorem**.

growth and decay model (4): The solution to the growth and decay model $\frac{dy}{dt} = ky$ is $y = Ce^{kt}$. Introduced in *Calculus II*, Lesson 5.

half-angle formulas: $\sin^2 x = \dfrac{1 - \cos 2x}{2}$; $\cos^2 x = \dfrac{1 + \cos 2x}{2}$.

Used when exponents m and n are both even in the integral $\int \sin^m x \cos^n x\,dx$. Reviewed in *Calculus II*, Lesson 11.

harmonic function (4): A function that satisfies Laplace's partial differential equation for the steady-state distribution of the temperature in plates or solids.

horizontal asymptote: The line $y = L$ is a horizontal asymptote of the graph of f if $\lim_{x \to \infty} f(x) = L$ or $\lim_{x \to -\infty} f(x) = L$. See *Calculus II*, Lesson 5.

implicit differentiation: A technique used when it is difficult to express y as a function of x explicitly. The steps are as follows: Differentiate both sides with respect to x, collect all terms involving dy/dx on the left side of the equation and move all other terms to the right side, factor dy/dx out of the left side, and solve for dy/dx. See *Calculus II*, Lesson 2.

improper integral: An integral where one of the limits of integration is ∞ or $-\infty$, of the form

$$\int_a^{\infty} f(x)\,dx = \lim_{b \to \infty} \int_a^b f(x)\,dx,$$

or those that are not continuous on the closed interval $[a, b]$. See *Calculus II*, Lesson 15.

integrating factor: For a linear differential equation, the integrating factor is $u = e^{\int P(x)\,dx}$. See *Calculus II*, Lesson 6.

integration by partial fractions: An algebraic technique for splitting up complicated algebraic expressions—in particular, rational functions—into a sum of simpler functions, which can then be integrated easily using other techniques. See *Calculus II*, Lesson 13.

integration by parts: $\int u\,dv = uv - \int v\,du$. See *Calculus II*, Lesson 10.

integration by substitution: Let F be an antiderivative of f. If $u = g(x)$, then $du = g'(x)\,dx$, so we have

$$\int f\big(g(x)\big)g'(x)\,dx \;=\; F\big(g(x)\big) + C \text{ because } \int f(u)\,du \;=\; F(u) + C.$$

See *Calculus II*, Lesson 3.

iterated integrals (19): Repeated simple integrals, such as double integrals and triple integrals. The inside limits of integration can be variable with respect to the outer variable of integration, but the outside limits of integration must be constant with respect to both outside limits of integration.

inverse functions: Those whose graphs are symmetric across the line $y = x$.

A function g is the inverse function of the function f if $f(g(x)) = x$ for all x in the domain of g and $g(f(x)) = x$ for all x in the domain of f. The inverse of f is denoted f^{-1}. Reviewed in *Calculus II*, Lesson 1.

inverse square fields (27): Fields where the force decreases in proportion with the square of distance. Given $\mathbf{r} = x\mathbf{i} + y\mathbf{j} + z\mathbf{k}$, the vector field $\mathbf{F}$ is an inverse square field if $\mathbf{F}(x, y, z) = \dfrac{k}{\|\mathbf{r}\|^2}\mathbf{u}$.

inverse trigonometric functions: These inverse functions are defined by restricting the domain of the original function, as follows.

$$y = \arcsin x = \sin^{-1} x \Leftrightarrow \sin y = x, \text{ for } -1 \le x \le 1 \text{ and } -\frac{\pi}{2} \le y \le \frac{\pi}{2}.$$

$$y = \arccos x = \cos^{-1} x \Leftrightarrow \cos y = x, \text{ for } -1 \le x \le 1 \text{ and } 0 \le y \le \pi.$$

$$y = \arctan x = \tan^{-1} x \Leftrightarrow \tan y = x, \text{ for } -\infty < x < \infty \text{ and } -\frac{\pi}{2} < y < \frac{\pi}{2}.$$

$$y = \text{arcsec } x = \sec^{-1} x \Leftrightarrow \sec y = x, \text{ for } |x| \geq 1, \ 0 \leq y \leq \pi, \text{ and } y \neq \frac{\pi}{2}.$$

Reviewed in *Calculus II*, Lesson1.

Kepler's laws (14): 1) The orbit of each planet is an ellipse, with the Sun at one of the two foci; 2) a line joining a planet and the Sun sweeps out equal areas during equal intervals of time; 3) the square of the orbital period of a planet is directly proportional to the cube of the semimajor axis of the orbit.

Lagrange multiplier (17): A scalar, λ, used in a powerful technique given by Lagrange's theorem for solving optimization problems that have constraints.

lamina (22): A thin, flat plate of material, usually of uniform density.

Laplace's partial differential equation (4): Describes the steady-state temperature distribution in plates or solids. $\frac{\partial^2 z}{\partial x^2} + \frac{\partial^2 z}{\partial y^2} = 0$. A function that satisfies this equation is said to be **harmonic**.

law of conservation of energy (30): In a conservative force field, the sum of potential and kinetic energies of an object remain constant from point to point.

least squares regression line (8): Used to fit a line to a set of points in the plane. Works best when the data is nearly linear. Derived by minimizing the sum of the squares of the differences between the data and the line. If $f(x) = ax + b$, then the values of a and b are given by

$$a = \frac{n\sum_{i=1}^{n} x_i y_i - \sum_{i=1}^{n} x_i \sum_{i=1}^{n} y_i}{n\sum_{i=1}^{n} x_i^2 - \left(\sum_{i=1}^{n} x_i\right)^2}, \ b = \frac{1}{n}\left(\sum_{i=1}^{n} y_i - a\sum_{i=1}^{n} x_i\right).$$

level curve (2): Also known as a **contour line**, the set of all points in the plane satisfying $f(x, y) = c$, when $z = f(x, y)$ and c is a constant. Contrast with **trace**, which is the intersection of a surface with a plane.

level surface (2): Although a function in three variables $f(x, y, z)$ cannot itself be graphed, it is possible to graph a level surface, the set of all points in space where that function equals a constant, $f(x, y, z) = c$.

L'Hôpital's rule: A technique for evaluating indeterminate forms for limits such as $\dfrac{0}{0}$ or $\dfrac{\infty}{\infty}$, where no guaranteed limit exists. See *Calculus II*, Lesson 14.

limit: Defined informally, if $f(x)$ becomes arbitrarily close to a single number L as x approaches c from either side, we say that the limit of $f(x)$ as x approaches c is L, which we write as $\lim\limits_{x \to c} f(x) = L$.

Also, the equation $\lim\limits_{x \to c} f(x) = \infty$ means that $f(x)$ increases without bound as x approaches c.

More formally: Let f be a function defined on an open interval containing c (except possibly at c), and let L be a real number. The statement $\lim\limits_{x \to c} f(x) = L$ means that for each $\varepsilon > 0$, there exists a $\delta > 0$ such that if $0 < |x - c| < \delta$, then $|f(x) - L| < \varepsilon$.

See *Calculus II*, Lesson 1.

The definition for a limit in multivariable calculus is similar to that in elementary calculus, except that we use open disks (and approach from any direction) instead of using open intervals (approaching from only two directions). We say that $\lim\limits_{(x, y) \to (x_0, y_0)} f(x, y) = L$ if for each $\varepsilon > 0$, there exists $\delta > 0$ such that

$$|f(x, y) - L| < \varepsilon \text{ whenever } 0 < \sqrt{(x - x_0)^2 + (y - y_0)^2} < \delta.$$

linear model (8): Given a set of data, a linear model is a function $y = ax + b$ that closely fits the data.

line integral (28, 29): Integration over a **piecewise smooth curve**, which can be used to calculate the mass of a thin wire (where the value of the integral does not depend on the orientation of the curve) or work by a force field (where the orientation of the path does matter and determines the sign of the answer). **Green's theorem** implies that the line integral around any closed curve within a conservative vector field is zero. See **fundamental theorem of line integrals**.

lines in space (9): Defined using a point and a direction vector, these are quite different from lines in the plane (defined using slope and y-intercept). See **planes in space** and **parametric equations**.

log rule for integration: $\int \frac{1}{x} dx = \ln|x| + C$.

For a logarithmic function to base a, when $a > 0$ and $a \neq 1$, $\log_a x = \frac{1}{\ln a} \ln x$. See *Calculus*, Lesson 27. See *Calculus II*, Lesson 3.

mass (22): The double integral of the density function.

Maxwell's equations (36): Four partial differential equations, and their integral forms, describing the interaction of electric and magnetic fields. Their differential forms are as follows.

1. For an electric field $\mathbf{E}$ and a surface S enclosing a charge Q, $\nabla \cdot \mathbf{E} = \frac{\rho}{\varepsilon_0}$, where ρ is the charge density.

2. If $\mathbf{B}$ is a magnetic field, $\nabla \cdot \mathbf{B} = 0$.

3. If $\mathbf{E}$ is an electric field and $\mathbf{B}$ is a magnetic field, $\nabla \times \mathbf{E} + \frac{\partial \mathbf{B}}{\partial t} = 0$ (also known as Faraday's law).

4. If $\mathbf{E}$ is an electric field, $\mathbf{B}$ is a magnetic field, and $\mathbf{J}$ is the current density, $\nabla \times \mathbf{B} = \frac{\partial \mathbf{E}}{\partial t} + \mathbf{J}$.

Möbius strip (12, 33): A surface with only one side.

moment (22): Related to the turning force of a mass around a pivot or fulcrum. More precisely, if a mass m is concentrated at a point and if x is the distance between the mass and another point P, then the **moment** of m about P is mx. Formulas for the moments with respect to the axes are much simpler than the corresponding formulas in elementary calculus: $M_x = \iint_R y\rho(x, y)\,dA$, $M_y = \iint_R x\rho(x, y)\,dA$. Covered in *Calculus II*, Lesson 9.

multivariable calculus (1): Calculus of more than one variable. That is, the calculus of functions of two or more independent variables, and their graphs in space.

natural logarithmic function: The natural logarithmic function is defined by the definite integral $\ln x = \int_1^x \frac{1}{t} dt$, $x > 0$. See *Calculus II*, Lesson 3.

normal: Perpendicular or orthogonal. A vector is normal to a surface at a point if it is perpendicular to the surface at the point. Also, the normal component of acceleration is the direction of the acceleration and is given by $a_N = \|\mathbf{v}\|\|\mathbf{T}'\| = \mathbf{a} \cdot \mathbf{N} = \sqrt{\|\mathbf{a}\|^2 - a_T^2}$, where the normal vector is written $\mathbf{N}$ or $\mathbf{n}$. See *Calculus II*, Lesson 35.

one-sided limits: The limit from the right means that x approaches c from values greater than c. The elementary notation is $\lim\limits_{x \to c^+} f(x) = L$.

Similarly, the limit from the left means that x approaches c from values less than c, notated $\lim\limits_{x \to c^-} f(x) = L$. See *Calculus*, Lesson 5.

optimization (7, 17): Finding maximum and minimum values (extrema) of a function. The candidates for extrema are the **critical points**.

orientable (34): A surface is orientable when its unit normal vector $\mathbf{N}$ can be defined at every nonboundary point on a surface S such that the normal vectors vary continuously over the surface.

orthogonal (9): Two vectors are orthogonal (perpendicular) if their dot product is zero. The orthogonal trajectories of a given family of curves are another family of curves, each of which is orthogonal (perpendicular) to every curve in the given family. See **normal** and **dot product**.

parallelepiped (10): A three-dimensional object whose faces are all parallelograms.

parameter (13): Used to defined a vector-valued function, a parameter is an independent variable.

parametric equation (9): By equating corresponding components of a direction vector $\langle x - x_1, y - y_1, z - z_1 \rangle$ with three **direction numbers** (a, b, c), we can define a line in space in terms of three parametric equations, $\overline{PQ} = \langle x - x_1, y - y_1, z - z_1 \rangle = t \langle a, b, c \rangle$:

$x = x_1 + at$

$y = y_1 + bt$

$z = z_1 + ct.$

In the special case where a, b, and c are all nonzero, the parameter t can also be omitted in favor of so-called symmetric equations that omit t of the form $(x-x_1)/a = (y-y_1)/b = (z-z_1)/c$. More generally, for any parametric curve, we consider x, y, and z as functions of a fourth variable ("parameter") t. The curve traced out by the parametric equations $x = f(t), y = g(t), z = h(t)$ induces an orientation to the curve as the parameter t increases. See *Calculus II*, Lesson 28.

parametric surface (33): A generalization of a parametric curve, given by a vector-valued function having two parameters. As the parameters u and v vary over their domains, the function traces out a surface in space: $\mathbf{r}(u, v) = x(u, v)\mathbf{i} + y(u, v)\mathbf{j} + z(u, v)\mathbf{k}$. For example, the paraboloid $z = x^2 + y^2$ can be described as a parametric surface $\mathbf{r}(u,v) = u\mathbf{i} + v\mathbf{j} + (u^2 + v^2)\mathbf{k}$.

partial derivatives (3, 4): The generalization of derivatives from elementary calculus, defined as

$$\frac{\partial f}{\partial x} = f_x(x, y) = \lim_{\Delta x \to 0} \frac{f(x + \Delta x, y) - f(x, y)}{\Delta x} \; ; \; \frac{\partial f}{\partial y} = f_y(x, y) = \lim_{\Delta y \to 0} \frac{f(x, y + \Delta y) - f(x, y)}{\Delta y}.$$

There are four second-order partial derivatives:

$$\frac{\partial}{\partial x}\left(\frac{\partial f}{\partial x}\right) = \frac{\partial^2 x}{\partial x^2} = f_{xx}; \quad \frac{\partial}{\partial y}\left(\frac{\partial f}{\partial y}\right) = \frac{\partial^2 y}{\partial y^2} = f_{yy}$$

$$\frac{\partial}{\partial y}\left(\frac{\partial f}{\partial x}\right) = \frac{\partial^2 f}{\partial y \partial x} = f_{xy}; \quad \frac{\partial}{\partial x}\left(\frac{\partial f}{\partial y}\right) = \frac{\partial^2 f}{\partial x \partial y} = f_{yx}.$$

partial differential equation (4): An equation containing partial derivatives. See **Laplace's partial differential equation**.

particle motion (13): The position, velocity, and acceleration are all vectors; the speed is a scalar.

Position: $\mathbf{r}(t) = x(t)\mathbf{i} + y(t)\mathbf{j} + z(t)\mathbf{k}$.

Velocity: $\mathbf{v}(t) = \mathbf{r}'(t) = x'(t)\mathbf{i} + y'(t)\mathbf{j} + z'(t)\mathbf{k}$.

Acceleration: $\mathbf{a}(t) = \mathbf{r}''(t) = x''(t)\mathbf{i} + y''(t)\mathbf{j} + z''(t)\mathbf{k}$.

Speed: $\|\mathbf{v}(t)\| = \|\mathbf{r}'(t)\| = \sqrt{[x'(t)]^2 + [y'(t)]^2 + [z'(t)]^2}$.

piecewise smooth curve (28, 30): A curve for which the interval of the curve can be partitioned into a finite number of smooth subintervals. The lower-dimensional counterpart of a **simply connected region**.

planar lamina (22): A flat plate of uniform density. See *Calculus II*, Lesson 9.

plane in space (11): A plane in space is determined by a point on the plane and a vector normal to the plane. The standard equation of a plane in space is $a(x - x_1) + b(y - y_1) + c(z - z_1) = 0$. The general form of a plane is $ax + by + cz + d = 0$, where a, b, and c are components of the normal vector to the plane.

polar coordinates (21): An alternative to rectangular (Cartesian) coordinates of $P = (x, y)$, with each point instead given by (r, θ), where r is the distance from P to the origin and θ is the angle the segment $\overline{OP}$ makes with the positive x-axis. Useful for solving double integrals involving circles, cardioids, rose curves, and anything involving $x^2 + y^2$. See *Calculus II*, Lesson 29.

planimeter (32): An engineering device, based on **Green's theorem**, for calculating the area of a region by tracing out its boundary.

potential function (27): The differentiable function whose gradient can represent a particular conservative vector field $\mathbf{F}$ as follows: $\mathbf{F} = \nabla f$. Finding a potential function is comparable to antidifferentiation: sometimes easy to see at a glance, but sometimes difficult or impossible to find.

projection (11): When a vector $\mathbf{u}$ is projected onto a vector $\mathbf{v}$, the result is a multiple of $\mathbf{v}$, written

$$\text{proj}_{\mathbf{v}}\, \mathbf{u} = \left(\frac{\mathbf{u} \cdot \mathbf{v}}{\|\mathbf{v}\|^2} \right) \mathbf{v}.$$

The projection is used to find the distance between a plane and a point not in that plane.

quadric surface (12): A family of three-dimensional surfaces analogous to conic sections, consisting of paraboloids, ellipsoids (of which the sphere is a special case), elliptic cones, elliptic paraboloids, hyperboloids (of one or two sheets), and hyperbolic paraboloids. The general equation of a **quadric surface** is

$$Ax^2 + By^2 + Cz^2 + Dxy + Exz + Fyz + Gx + Hy + Iz + J = 0.$$

radian: Calculus uses radian measure. If a problem is stated in degree measure, you must convert to radians: $360°$ is 2π radians; $180°$ is π radians. See *Calculus II*, Lesson 1.

relative extrema (6): A relative maximum or relative minimum.

second derivative test: Let $f'(c) = 0$ (c is a critical number of f). If $f''(c) > 0$, then f has a relative minimum at c. If $f''(c) < 0$, then f has a relative maximum at c. See *Calculus II*, Lesson 2.

second partials test (6): Similar to the second derivative test in elementary calculus, used to determine whether critical points are relative extrema or not. Let (a, b) be a critical point of f. Define the quantity $d = f_{xx}(a, b) f_{yy}(a, b) - \left[f_{xy}(a, b)\right]^2$. Then, we have the following.

1. $d > 0, f_{xx}(a, b) > 0 \Rightarrow$ relative minimum.

2. $d > 0, f_{xx}(a, b) < 0 \Rightarrow$ relative maximum.

3. $d < 0 \Rightarrow$ saddle point.

4. $d = 0$: Test is inconclusive.

simply connected region (30): A region that is connected (in one piece), and every simple closed curve in the region encloses only points that lie in the region. A higher-dimensional analog of the **piecewise smooth curve**.

Snell's law of refraction (18): When light waves traveling in a transparent medium strike the surface of a second transparent medium, they tend to "bend" (undergo refraction) in order to follow the path of minimum time.

solid of revolution: If a region in the plane is revolved about a line, the resulting solid is a solid of revolution, and the line is called the axis of revolution. When the plane is a circle, the resulting solid is a **torus**. See **theorem of Pappus**. See *Calculus II*, Lesson 7.

solution curves: The general solution of a first-order differential equation represents a family of curves known as solution curves, one for each value of the arbitrary constant. See *Calculus*, Lesson 35, and *Calculus II*, Lesson 5.

spherical coordinates (26): Similar to longitude and latitude coordinates on Earth, but the first coordinate ρ is a distance, while the other two are angles. The distance ρ is from a point in space P to the origin O, θ is the same angle as used in **cylindrical coordinates**, and φ is the angle between the positive z-axis and the line segment $\overline{OP}$, $0 \le \varphi \le \pi$. Especially useful for like spheres that have a center of symmetry.

Stokes's theorem (36): A higher-dimension analog of **Green's theorem** that relates a **line integral** around a closed curve C to a **surface integral** of a closed, oriented surface S for which C is the boundary. Letting the unit normal to that surface be $\mathbf{N}$ and $\mathbf{F}(x, y, z)$ be a vector field whose component functions have continuous first partial derivatives, then **Stokes's theorem** states that $\int_C \mathbf{F} \cdot d\mathbf{r} = \iint_S (\operatorname{curl} \mathbf{F}) \cdot \mathbf{N} \, dS$.

summation formulas:

$$\sum_{i=1}^{n} c = c + c + \cdots + c = cn.$$

$$\sum_{i=1}^{n} i = \frac{n(n+1)}{2}.$$

$$\sum_{i=1}^{n} i^2 = \frac{n(n+1)(2n+1)}{6}.$$

surface (31): Surfaces are graphs in space, such as **quadric surfaces** and **surfaces of revolution**. A surface is **simply connected** if every simple closed curve in the region encloses only points that are inside that region.

surface area (23): In space, surface area equals the double integral of the differential of surface area. If $z = f(x, y)$ is defined over a region R in the xy-plane, the **surface area** is

$$S = \iint_R \sqrt{1 + \left[f_x(x, y) \right]^2 + \left[f_y(x, y) \right]^2} \, dA.$$

surface integral (34): A generalization of line integrals, which instead of being defined on a curve in space are defined on a surface in space. Let the surface S be given by $z = g(x, y)$, let $f(x, y, z)$ be defined at all points on S, and let R be the projection of S onto the xy-plane. With suitable hypotheses on f and g, the **surface integral** is

$$\iint_S f(x, y, z) \, dS = \iint_R f(x, y, g(x, y)) \sqrt{1 + (g_x)^2 + (g_y)^2} \, dA.$$

theorem of Pappus: If a region is rotated about the y-axis, then the volume of the resulting solid of revolution is $V = 2\pi \bar{x}A$. See *Calculus II*, Lesson 9.

torus: A surface or solid shaped like a tire or doughnut and formed by revolving the region bounded by the circle $x^2 + y^2 = r^2$ about the line $x = R$ $(r < R)$. See *Calculus II*, Lesson 31.

total differential $(5, 16)$: Similar to the tangent line approximation to a curve in elementary calculus, the total differential is a tangent plane approximation to a surface. The total differential of z is the expression

$$dz = \frac{\partial z}{\partial x} dx + \frac{\partial z}{\partial y} dy = f_x(x, y) dx + f_y(x, y) dy.$$

trace (2): The intersection of a surface with a plane—for example, the intersection with one of the three coordinate planes. The trace of a surface is a curve in space, unlike a **level curve**, which is a curve only in the xy-plane.

trigonometric functions: The right triangle definition of the trigonometric functions uses the following right triangle.

$\sin \theta = \dfrac{a}{c}.$

$\cos \theta = \dfrac{b}{c}.$

$\tan \theta = \dfrac{\sin \theta}{\cos \theta} = \dfrac{a}{b}.$

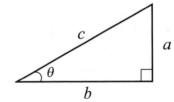

For a point (x, y) on the unit circle $x^2 + y^2 = 1$, the unit circle definition of the trigonometric functions is

$\sin \theta = y, \cos \theta = x, \tan \theta = \dfrac{\sin \theta}{\cos \theta} = \dfrac{y}{x}$

$\csc \theta = \dfrac{1}{\sin \theta}, \sec \theta = \dfrac{1}{\cos \theta}, \cot \theta = \dfrac{1}{\tan \theta} = \dfrac{x}{y}.$

These are reviewed in *Calculus II*, Lesson 1.

trigonometric identities: Trigonometric identities are trigonometric equations that are valid for all values of the variable (typically x or θ) and offer an important technique for simplifying differentiation and integration problems. These are presented in *Calculus II*, Lesson 2. In addition to those described under **trigonometric functions**, some of the most useful are as follows.

$$sin^2 x + cos^2 x = 1.$$

$$\tan^2 x + \sec^2 x = 1.$$

$$\cos 2x = \cos^2 x - \sin^2 x.$$

$$\sin 2x = 2\sin x \cos x.$$

$$\cos^2 x = \frac{1 + \cos 2x}{2}.$$

$$\sin^2 x = \frac{1 - \cos 2x}{2}.$$

trigonometric substitution: A technique for converting integrands to trigonometric integrals. See *Calculus II*, Lesson 12.

triple integral (24): The definition is similar to the definition of double integral:

$$\iiint\limits_Q f(x, y, z)\, dV = \lim_{\|\Delta\| \to 0} \sum_{i=1}^{n} f(x_i, y_i, z_i)\, \Delta V_i.$$

There are six orders of integration for triple integrals in Cartesian coordinates:

dz dy dx, dz dx dy, dy dz dx, dy dx dz, dx dy dz, dx dz dy.

triple scalar product (10): Using three vectors, we take the dot product of one vector with the cross product of two other vectors. Can be used to find the volume of a parallelepiped defined by three vectors that do not lie in the same plane.

$$\mathbf{u} \cdot (\mathbf{v} \times \mathbf{w}) = \begin{vmatrix} u_1 & u_2 & u_3 \\ v_1 & v_2 & v_3 \\ w_1 & w_2 & w_3 \end{vmatrix}.$$

unit tangent vector (13): A unit vector pointing in the direction of motion is $\mathbf{T}(t) = \dfrac{\mathbf{r}'(t)}{\|\mathbf{r}'(t)\|}$, where $\mathbf{r}$ is a vector-valued function (position vector).

vector (9, 13, 31): For quantities that have both magnitude and direction, such as velocity, acceleration, and force. Contrasted with scalars, which have only magnitude, such as speed, mass, volume, and time. Usually appear in lowercase, bold letters.

vector field (27): A vector field assigns a vector to each point in space. A vector field is **conservative** if there exists a differentiable function f (called the **potential**) such that $\mathbf{F} = \nabla f$. The gradient of a function is a vector field. A **rotation vector field** is of the form $\mathbf{F}(x, y) = -y\mathbf{i} + x\mathbf{j}$; a **radial vector field** is of the form $\mathbf{F}(x, y) = x\mathbf{i} + y\mathbf{j}$.

vector-valued functions (13): Functions that input a scalar to get a vector. More precisely, functions that use vectors, instead of algebraic variables, to define their outputs, usually of the form $\mathbf{r}(t) = f(t)\mathbf{i} + g(t)\mathbf{j} + h(t)\mathbf{k}$, or the more compact form, $\mathbf{r}(t) = \langle f(t), g(t), h(t) \rangle$, where f and g and h are the **component functions** and t is the input **parameter**. See *Calculus II*, Lessons 33.

velocity (13): The derivative of the position function. The velocity vector is tangent to the path of a particle and points in the direction of motion. The magnitude of the velocity (a scalar) is the speed. See **particle motion**. See *Calculus II*, Lessons 34.

volume (20): The double integral of a nonnegative function defined on a closed and bounded region in the plane.

work (29): Force times distance: $W = F \cdot D$. In one dimension, if the force is variable, given by $f(x)$, then the **work** W done by moving the object from $x = a$ to $x = b$ is $W = \int_a^b F(x)\,dx$. In multivariable calculus, $W = \int_C \mathbf{F} \cdot d\mathbf{r}$. See *Calculus II*, Lessons 8.

Summary of Differentiation Formulas

1. Constant multiple rule: $\dfrac{d}{dx}[cu] = cu'$.

2. Sum or difference rule: $\dfrac{d}{dx}[u \pm v] = u' \pm v'$.

3. Product rule: $\dfrac{d}{dx}[uv] = uv' + vu'$.

4. Quotient rule: $\dfrac{d}{dx}\left[\dfrac{u}{v}\right] = \dfrac{vu' - uv'}{v^2}$.

5. Constant rule: $\dfrac{d}{dx}[c] = 0$.

6. Chain rule: $\dfrac{d}{dx}[f(u)] = f'(u)u'$, one generalization of which is $\dfrac{dw}{dt} = \dfrac{\partial w}{\partial x}\dfrac{dx}{dt} + \dfrac{\partial w}{\partial y}\dfrac{dy}{dt}$.

7. General power rule: $\dfrac{d}{dx}[u^n] = nu^{n-1}u$.

8. $\dfrac{d}{dx}[x] = 1$.

9. $\dfrac{d}{dx}[e^x] = e^x$.

10. $\dfrac{d}{dx}[e^x] = e^x$.

11. $\dfrac{d}{dx}[\log_a x] = \dfrac{1}{(\ln a)x}$.

12. $\dfrac{d}{dx}[a^x] = (\ln a)a^x$.

13. $\dfrac{d}{dx}[\sin x] = \cos x$.

14. $\dfrac{d}{dx}\big[\cos x\big] = -\sin x.$

15. $\dfrac{d}{dx}\big[\tan x\big] = \sec^2 x.$

16. $\dfrac{d}{dx}\big[\cot x\big] = -\csc^2 x.$

17. $\dfrac{d}{dx}\big[\sec x\big] = \sec x \tan x.$

18. $\dfrac{d}{dx}\big[\csc x\big] = -\csc x \cot x.$

19. $\dfrac{d}{dx}\big[\arcsin x\big] = \dfrac{1}{\sqrt{1-x^2}}.$

20. $\dfrac{d}{dx}\big[\arctan x\big] = \dfrac{1}{1+x^2}.$

21. $\dfrac{d}{dx}\big[\operatorname{arc\,sec} x\big] = \dfrac{1}{|x|\sqrt{x^2-1}}.$

22. Derivative of the cross product: $\dfrac{d}{dt}\big[\mathbf{r}\times\mathbf{u}\big] = \mathbf{r}\times\mathbf{u}' + \mathbf{r}'\times\mathbf{u}.$

Summary of Integration Formulas

1. $\int kf(x)\,dx = k\int f(x)\,dx.$

2. $\int \left[f(x) \pm g(x) \right]dx = \int f(x)\,dx \pm \int g(x)\,dx.$

3. $\int d(x) = x + C.$

4. Power rule for integration: $\int x^n\,dx = \dfrac{x^{n+1}}{n+1} + C,$ for $n \neq -1.$

5. Log rule for integration: $\int e^x\,dx = e^x + C.$

6. $\int e^x\,dx = e^x + C.$

7. $\int a^x\,dx = \left(\dfrac{1}{\ln a} \right)a^x + C.$

8. $\int \sin x\,dx = -\cos x + C.$

9. $\int \cos x\,dx = \sin x + C.$

10. $\int \tan x\,dx = -\ln|\cos x| + C.$

11. $\int \cot x\,dx = \ln|\sin x| + C.$

12. $\int \sec x\,dx = \ln|\sec x + \tan x| + C.$

13. $\int \csc x\,dx = -\ln|\csc x + \cot x| + C.$

14. $\int \sec^2 x\, dx = \tan x + C.$

15. $\int \csc^2 x\, dx = -\cot x + C.$

16. $\int \sec x \tan x\, dx = \sec x + C.$

17. $\int \csc x \cot x\, dx = -\csc x + C.$

18. $\int \dfrac{dx}{\sqrt{a^2 - x^2}} = \arcsin \dfrac{x}{a} + C.$

19. $\int \dfrac{dx}{a^2 + x^2} = \dfrac{1}{a}\arctan \dfrac{x}{a} + C.$

20. $\int \dfrac{dx}{x\sqrt{x^2 - a^2}} = \dfrac{1}{a}\operatorname{arc\,sec} \dfrac{|x|}{a} + C.$

Quadric Surfaces

Quadric surfaces (discussed in Lesson 12) are the three-dimensional analogs of conic sections (circle, ellipse, parabola, hyperbola). Their general equation is $Ax^2 + By^2 + Cz^2 + Dxy + Exz + Fyz + Gx + Hy + Iz + J = 0$.

Notice that the squared terms determine the overall shape for each quadric surface. Any cross-multiplied terms (such as xy, xz, or yz), as well as linear terms and constants, merely tilt or shift the position of the overall shape.

ellipsoid: $\dfrac{x^2}{a^2} + \dfrac{y^2}{b^2} + \dfrac{z^2}{c^2} = 1$.

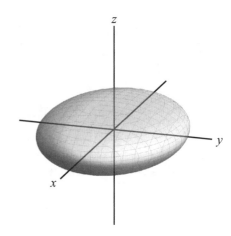

    All three squared terms are positive.

    Is a sphere when $a = b = c$.

    Traces are all ellipses.

hyperboloid of one sheet: $\dfrac{x^2}{a^2} + \dfrac{y^2}{b^2} - \dfrac{z^2}{c^2} = 1$.

    Only one of the three squared terms is negative.

    Traces parallel to the two positive terms (xy) are ellipses; traces parallel to the plane of the negative term (xz and yz) are hyperbolas.

    Other orientations are

$$\frac{x^2}{a^2} - \frac{y^2}{b^2} + \frac{z^2}{c^2} = 1$$

    and

$$-\frac{x^2}{a^2} + \frac{y^2}{b^2} + \frac{z^2}{c^2} = 1.$$

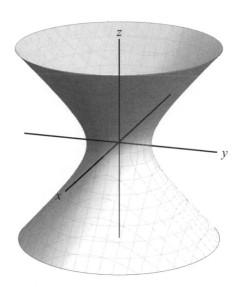

hyperboloid of two sheets: $-\dfrac{x^2}{a^2} - \dfrac{y^2}{b^2} + \dfrac{z^2}{c^2} = 1 = \dfrac{z^2}{c^2} - \dfrac{x^2}{a^2} - \dfrac{y^2}{b^2}$.

Two of the three squared terms are negative.

Traces parallel to the plane of one negative term (xz or yz) are hyperbolas; for the plain with both squared terms negative, there is no trace plane.

Other orientations are

$$\dfrac{x^2}{a^2} - \dfrac{y^2}{b^2} - \dfrac{z^2}{c^2} = 1$$

and

$$-\dfrac{x^2}{a^2} + \dfrac{y^2}{b^2} - \dfrac{z^2}{c^2} = 1.$$

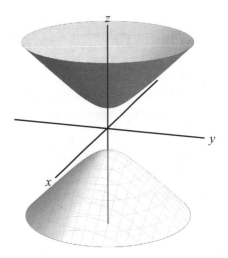

elliptic cone: $\dfrac{x^2}{a^2} + \dfrac{y^2}{b^2} - \dfrac{z^2}{c^2} = 0$.

A double cone, similar to hyperboloid of one sheet, except the two elliptic cones touch only at a single point.

Only one of the three squared terms is negative.

Traces parallel to the plane of the two positive terms are ellipses; others are hyperbolas.

Other orientations are

$$\dfrac{x^2}{a^2} - \dfrac{y^2}{b^2} + \dfrac{z^2}{c^2} = 0$$

and

$$-\dfrac{x^2}{a^2} + \dfrac{y^2}{b^2} + \dfrac{z^2}{c^2} = 0.$$

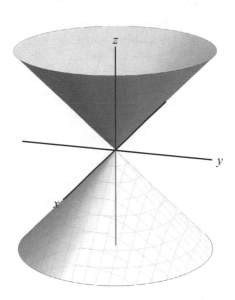

elliptic paraboloid: $\dfrac{x^2}{a^2} + \dfrac{y^2}{b^2} = z$.

Two positive squared terms set equal to a linear third term.

A cylinder created by rotating a parabola when $a = b = 1$.

Traces are ellipses in planes parallel to the squared terms (x^2, y^2); traces are parabolas in planes parallel to the plane of the term that is not squared (z).

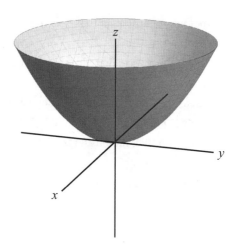

hyperbolic paraboloid: $\dfrac{x^2}{a^2} - \dfrac{y^2}{b^2} = z$.

Symmetrical saddle shape when $a = b = 1$.

One positive squared term and one negative squared term set equal to a linear third term.

Traces are parabolas in the plane parallel to the squared terms (x^2, y^2); traces are hyperbolas in planes parallel to the plane of the term that is not squared (z).

An alternative orientation is

$$\frac{y^2}{b^2} - \frac{x^2}{a^2} = z.$$

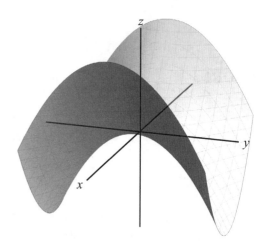

Bibliography

Fleisch, Daniel. *A Student's Guide to Maxwell's Equations*. Cambridge: Cambridge University Press, 2008. A clear and thorough discussion of the integral and differential forms of Maxwell's famous equations of electromagnetism—an interesting supplement at the conclusion of this course. Includes a few worked problems for each equation, plus a free website providing hints and solutions to several dozen more problems.

Larson, Ron, and Bruce H. Edwards. *Calculus*. 10th ed. Florence, KY: Brooks/Cole, 2014. This text covers an entire three-semester calculus sequence.

———. *Calculus: Early Transcendental Functions*. 6th ed. Florence, KY: Brooks/Cole, 2015. This text offers a different approach to the exponential and logarithmic functions, presenting them in the beginning of the textbook.

Larson, Ron, and Bruce H. Edwards. *Multivariable Calculus*. 10th ed. Florence, KY: Brooks/Cole, 2014. Contains the chapters about multivariable calculus (Chapters 10–14) from the full three-semester textbook by the same authors, *Calculus*, 10th edition.

———. *Precalculus Functions and Graphs: A Graphing Approach*. 5th ed. Boston: Houghton Mifflin, 2008. An excellent source for precalculus, algebra, and trigonometry.

Penrose, Roger. *The Road to Reality: A Complete Guide to the Laws of the Universe*. New York: Vintage, 2007. Someone completing this course with an interest in theoretical physics might enjoy reading Chapter 6 ("Real-Number Calculus") or Chapter 10 ("Surfaces") of this encyclopedic attempt to survey all mathematics of importance for contemporary physics.

Saxon, John H., Jr., and Frank Y. H. Wang. *Calculus with Trigonometry and Analytic Geometry*. 2nd ed. Edited by Bret L. Crock and James A. Sellers. Wilmington, MA: Saxon Publishers, 2002. This is another good choice among calculus texts and is edited by James A. Sellers, who produced *Algebra I*, *Algebra II*, and *Mastering the Fundamentals of Mathematics* with The Great Courses.

Simmons, George. *Calculus with Analytic Geometry*. 2nd ed. New York: McGraw-Hill, 1996. A somewhat different approach to the three-semester calculus sequence.

Internet Resource

Wolfram|Alpha. www.wolframalpha.com. From the makers of *Mathematica* (the software used to create many of the graphics found in the video lessons for this course), this free website can solve many questions that might arise during this course. The website gives the derivative, integral, and graph for a wide variety of functions.

Notes